PARASITIC DISEASES

PARASITIC DISEASES

Volume 1. The Immunology

Other Volumes in Preparation

PARASITIC DISEASES

Volume 1
THE IMMUNOLOGY

Edited by John M. Mansfield
School of Medicine
University of Louisville
Louisville, Kentucky

MARCEL DEKKER, INC.   New York and Basel

Library of Congress Cataloging in Publication Data

Main entry under title:

Parasitic diseases.

Includes index.
Contents: v. 1. The immunology.
1. Parasitic diseases. 2. Veterinary parasitology.
I. Mansfield, John M. [date]. [DNLM: 1. Parasitic
diseases. WC 695 P2235]
RC119.P347   616.9'6   81-9741
ISBN 0-8247-1409-1 (v. 1)   AACR2

MARCEL DEKKER, INC.
270 Madison Avenue, New York, New York 10016

Current printing (last digit):
10 9 8 7 6 5 4 3 2 1

PRINTED IN THE UNITED STATES OF AMERICA

Preface

Parasitic Diseases has been conceived in order to promote the recent developments in studies of the major parasitic diseases. The diseases represented in each volume will primarily be those of humans and their domestic animals targeted by the World Health Organization for intensive study: African trypanosomiasis, Chagas' disease, filariasis, leishmaniasis, malaria, and schistosomiasis. Each volume will be internally consistent in its focus on a common theme. Volume 1 covers recent developments in the immunology of these diseases. The authors have not only reviewed and discussed specific aspects of clinical and experimental immunology but have also suggested the direction of future studies to be performed in these areas. Readers are expected to be conversant with parasitological aspects of each disease (e.g., life cycle, host, vectors) and with immunological dogma. For this reason, each chapter will devote little space to aspects of parasite biology or the basics of clinical or experimental immunology. Reference texts are available elsewhere for these topics.

Volumes 2 and 3 of *Parasitic Diseases,* which are now being written, will focus on recent developments in the chemotherapy and genetics of parasitic diseases and, like Volume 1, will be authored by experts with established records in their fields. It is my hope that this series will be of value in opening up these areas of study to new and concerned health science professionals who have an interest in the control or cure of the major parasitic diseases.

John M. Mansfield

Contributors

Daniel G. Colley   Research and Development Section, Veterans Administration Medical Center, and Department of Microbiology, Vanderbilt University School of Medicine, Nashville, Tennessee

Anil N. Jayawardena   Laboratory of Epidemiology and Public Health and Department of Pathology (Immunology), Yale University School of Medicine, New Haven, Connecticut

Raymond E. Kuhn   Department of Biology, Wake Forest University, Winston-Salem, North Carolina

Charles D. Mackenzie   Department of Medical Helminthology, London School of Hygiene and Tropical Medicine, London, England

John M. Mansfield   Department of Microbiology and Immunology, School of Medicine, University of Louisville, Louisville, Kentucky

Bridget M. Ogilvie* Department of Parasitology, National Institute for Medical Research, London, England

Steven G. Reed† Division of Medical Sciences, National Research Institute of the Amazon, Manaus, Amazonas, Brazil

Present affiliation

*Department of Tropical Medicine, The Wellcome Trust, London, England
† Department of Medicine, Division of International Medicine, Cornell University Medical College, New York, New York

Contents

PREFACE   iii

CONTRIBUTORS   v

Chapter 1   IMMUNE RESPONSES AND IMMUNOREGULATION IN
EXPERIMENTAL AND CLINICAL SCHISTOSOMIASIS   1
Daniel G. Colley

Chapter 2   IMMUNE RESPONSES IN MALARIA   85
Anil N. Jayawardena

Chapter 3   IMMUNOLOGY OF *TRYPANOSOMA CRUZI* INFECTIONS   137
Raymond E. Kuhn

Chapter 4   IMMUNOLOGY AND IMMUNOPATHOLOGY OF
AFRICAN TRYPANOSOMIASIS   167
John M. Mansfield

Chapter 5   IMMUNOLOGY AND IMMUNOPATHOLOGY OF
INFECTIONS CAUSED BY FILARIAL NEMATODES   227
Bridget M. Ogilvie and Charles D. Mackenzie

Chapter 6   IMMUNOLOGY OF *LEISHMANIA* INFECTIONS   291
Steven G. Reed

INDEX   315

PARASITIC DISEASES

1

Immune Responses and Immunoregulation in Experimental and Clinical Schistosomiasis

DANIEL G. COLLEY Veterans Administration Medical Center and Vanderbilt University School of Medicine, Nashville, Tennessee

I.	Introduction	2
II.	Cercariae	2
	A. Antigenic Preparations	2
	B. Host Responses	3
	C. Regulation of Responsiveness	5
	D. Consequences and Conjecture	7
III.	Schistosomules	8
	A. Antigens	9
	B. Host Responses	9
	C. Regulation of Responsiveness	18
	D. Consequences and Conjecture	23
IV.	Adult Worms	24
	A. Antigens	25
	B. Host Responses	27
	C. Regulation of Responses	33
	D. Consequences and Conjecture	36
V.	Eggs	37
	A. Antigens	38
	B. Host Responses	39
	C. Regulation of Responsiveness	46
	D. Consequences and Conjecture	50
VI.	Summary	52
	References	52

I. INTRODUCTION

The immunological aspects of the host-parasite relationship established during infections with the three major species of schistosomes which mature within humans (*Schistosoma mansoni, Schistosoma japonicum,* and *Schistosoma haematobium*) have received a considerable amount of attention. The overtly observed relationship is, in reality, one of multiple, sequential, and concomitant responses and regulations initiated by the different life-cycle stages, each presenting a repertoire of potentially antigenic moieties. Conventionally, analyses of this rabbit warren-like complex have begun by considering either acquired immunity or immunopathology and are based on investigations of the effector mechanisms which deal with the worm or egg stages, respectively. This chapter will reverse this approach by first considering the positive and negative immune responses which involve each life-cycle stage. The parasite forms dealt with are the cercariae, schistosomules, adult worms, and eggs. The functional results of these various interactions, in terms of the disease process or prevention of it, may emanate from these more basic considerations. The chosen framework and intent of this chapter are not to provide a compendium of the vast sum of work on the immunology of schistosomiasis. The literature discussed will thus be selective rather than all-inclusive. For other reviews regarding either wider or more sharply defined immunological aspects of schistosomiasis, the reader is referred to Warren [1,2], Lewert [3], Smithers [4], World Health Organization [5], Smithers and Terry [6], Colley [7], Phillips and Colley [8], Butterworth [9], and Kagan and Pellegrino [10].

II. CERCARIAE

It is debatable whether one should consider cercariae to be a life-cycle stage encountered by the mammalian host. The cercaria is the free-living, water-adapted, infectious schistosome stage which is shed from the infected intermediate snail host. Immediately upon penetration of the mammalian host, the cercaria begins a transformation which soon qualifies it as a schistosomule. Stirewalt has recently reviewed the structural and physiological alterations which attend this fascinating differentiation [11]. Thus, once within the mammalian host, the parasite is no longer considered a cercaria but is now defined as a schistosomule. However, because the process of penetration exposes the host to various cercarial products and components, and since the transition represents a continuum, there has been considerable interest in mammalian host responses against cercariae or cercaria-derived products.

A. Antigenic Preparations

Intact cercariae and numerous preparations derived from cercariae have been observed to react with a wide variety of immune reactants which can be induced by either artificial exposure or active infection [12-17]. Serologic reactions against whole cercariae can be detected either as the Cercarien hüllen Reaktion (CHR) [18] or by fluorescent antibody techniques [19]. The CHR formation occurs within the framework of the cercarial mucoid glycocalyx [18,20], but whether the antigens involved are part of this coat or only trapped within it when reacted with antibody remains unclear. There are several antigens involved in the CHR reaction; some are shared by the snail intermediate host, the cercaria, and the adult worm, while others are shared between either snail and cercaria or cercaria and adult [21]. The molecular complexity of crude cercarial extracts has been described [22-24], and using rabbit antisera raised against such saline extracts, most of the reactive components are localized in the mucoid filamentous coat and in the pre- and postacetabular glands of the cercariae [25]. The heterogeneity of the cercarial extracts commonly used to detect serologic responses during schistosomiasis is matched by the multitude of antibody responses detectable by using these preparations [12,13,26] in an array of serologic assays.

B. Host Responses

1. In Vivo

Based on the preceding discussion concerning cercarial-schistosomular transformation upon penetration, there is no naturally occurring opportunity to observe in vivo anticercarial immune responses. In this sense the term *cercarial dermatitis* (schistosome dermatitis) is a misnomer in regard to homologous schistosome infections within permissive definitive hosts. A semantic argument could occur when considering the cercarial dermatitis which follows the penetration of cercariae of a heterologous source into a nonpermissive host (such as cercariae of a duck schistosome into human skin), or following penetration by irradiated cercariae. In these instances the cercarial-schistosomular transformation is abortive and yields dying cercariae rather than schistosomules. In either case, various immune responses have been observed to be major contributors to the reactions [27-34].

Based on histologic analysis and passive transfer experiments, these reactions include the participation of cell-mediated phenomena [27-30], immediate hypersensitivity [27-29,31-34], cutaneous basophil hypersensitivity [31], and antibody-mediated Arthus reactions [30]. However, in some instances primary cercarial exposure may lead to dermal reactions, and this may be attributable to the complement-activating capacity of cercarial extracts [35,36] and their direct chemotactic, eosinophil-activating activity [37].

Other considerations of in vivo responses mounted against cercarial materials can be drawn from the extensive literature pertaining to the use of cercaria-derived materials as skin test antigens in experimental and human studies [14,16, 30,38-44]. As observed with dermatitis-inducing systems, cercarial extract-elicited delayed-type hypersensitivity [14,16,40,43,44] and immediate, reagin-like mediated hypersensitivity [38,39,41-44] occur frequently following active infection or sensitization. However, it is important to point out that these anti-cercarial antigen responses commonly do not arise prior to similar responses against adult worm extracts [45]. This has often been interpreted as indicating that many reactions detected as anticercarial may actually be induced by immunogens shared by adult worms and cercariae.

2. In Vitro

The in vitro detection of immune reactivity against intact cercariae is best demonstrated by the CHR assay [18] and immunofluorescence [19]. It appears that a variety of antigens participate with specific antibodies in the formation of these pericercarial envelopes of reaction material [21]. The specific antibodies which yield positive indirect immunofluorescence, using intact cercariae as the target, appeared to arise sooner in more heavily infected mice and rhesus monkeys, but not prior to adult worm maturation [19].

A wide variety of in vitro serologic assays have been developed based on various cercarial extracts and test procedures. These systems have been primarily employed in epidemiologic and survey studies [42,43,46,47]. In general these assays neither are sensitive enough nor display sufficient specificity to be used dependably as the sole diagnostic criterion to indicate the presence or absence of infection, or the intensity of infection. However, an enzyme-linked immunosorbent assay (ELISA) using antigens from cercariae, adult worms, or eggs has been successfully applied in differentiating acute and chronic sera [48]. In testing the sera of 21 well-defined acute or chronic *S. mansoni*-infected patients and nine *Cercopithecus* sp. monkeys (from the initiation of infection to 28 months after infection), it was seen that 2 months after infection acute sera contained significantly more anticercarial activity than anti-worm activity [48]. A progression to less relative quantities of anticercarial antibodies occurred during continued infection.

In vitro assays of cell-mediated immune capabilities induced by cercarial antigenic preparations have been reported using direct and indirect macrophage migration inhibition tests with guinea pigs [40,49], and by lymphocyte blastogenesis using guinea pig [49], mouse [15,37,50], or human [17,51] lymphocytes. Lymphocyte responsiveness to cercarial extracts during *S. mansoni* infections of guinea pigs paralleled their responsiveness to both adult worm and egg antigenic materials, peaking between 4 and 8 weeks after infection for migration inhibition factor (MIF) production and after 8 weeks of infection for blastogenesis assays [49]. In mice, optimal sensitization for lymphocyte responsiveness to a cercarial antigenic preparation (CAP) required multiple weekly infections or exposure to CAP in complete Freund's adjuvant (CFA) [15]. A single exposure of mice to 500 heavily irradiated cercariae required 6 weeks before the detection of substantial CAP-induced lymphocyte blastogenesis [37]. In this model the irradiated cercariae do not develop past the schistosomular phase and subsequently die. Human peripheral blood mononuclear cells (PBMN) obtained from *S. mansoni*-infected patients respond to cercarial extracts in a dose-dependent manner [17,51]. Their degree of responsiveness does not bear any overt relationship to the intensity of the patients' infection [17].

C. Regulation of Responsiveness

It is difficult to evaluate the actual degree of cercarial exposure encountered by persons in various endemic areas. Although the sociological influences which may result in the continued exposure of adults have been questioned [52], it seems clear that in many endemic areas children are at risk of repeated cercarial penetration (see Ref. 52). Thus, childhood in an endemic area may involve multiple sensitizations by cercaria-associated antigens. Furthermore, the antigens shared by cercariae with other life-cycle states would be encountered continually. It might, therefore, be reasonable to anticipate that the host may need to regulate its responsiveness to these antigens.

There is little in vivo evidence to indicate whether anticercarial responses, either humoral or cellular, are regulated during active infection. While comparing ELISA values using a cercarial antigenic preparation, it was seen that sera obtained from chronic (4 year) human infections had less antibody as compared with cercariae than did sera from early (4 month) infections [48]. The sera of two *Cercopithecus* sp. monkeys once infected displayed this same decreasing trend of anticercarial antibody during infection. Perhaps more significantly, the same pattern was observed for a monkey which was repeatedly infected (7 times in 28 months), so that in the face of repeated known antigenic exposures the response decreased [48].

Upon analysis of the in vitro responsiveness of lymphocytes obtained from patients chronically infected with *S. mansoni*, it has become clear that several immunoregulatory mechanisms are initiated during the course of the infection [51,53-57]. Ottesen et al. [51] have reported that the extent of lymphocyte blastogenesis induced by a cercarial extract was highest when testing lymphocytes from acute, early *S. mansoni*-infected patients, and progressively declined to the levels of uninfected controls as infections became chronic. These data appeared in apparent conflict with those published by Colley et al. [17] which demonstrated increases in the levels of responsiveness, and the dependability of responsiveness, against CAP as infection continued. However, the former group [51] exclusively utilized autologous (the patient's own) serum as the medium supplement for their lymphocyte cultures, whereas the latter group [17,53] employed sera obtained from uninfected persons (normal human serum [NHS]) in their culture medium. The dichotomy of results was resolved when Colley et al. [53] also utilized sera from chronically infected patients in their system, and similarly, when Ottesen and Poindexter [57] compared NHS with sera from infected patients. Thus, in parallel cultures it was seen that either a chronic patient's own serum, or that of an unrelated chronic patient, almost inevitably significantly decreased the response to CAP. Neither the phytohemagglutinin (PHA), *Candida albicans* extract-induced [53], pokeweed mitogen (PWM), streptokinase-streptodornase (SKSD), nor tetanus toxoic responses [57] were affected by the serum source. Similarly, the sera from infected patients did not decrease the non-schistosome responsiveness of lymphocytes from uninfected subjects [57]. Continued analysis of this phenomenon of schistosome antigen-specific serosuppression indicates that its expression may also depend on the status of the cells [58]; that is, a few patients (5-10%) appear to have sera which can suppress other patient's cells, and yet their own cellular response to CAP is unaffected by their own sera or by the suppressive sera from a third individual [59].

Another regulatory system directed against CAP-induced responsiveness, which is expressed by almost all (96%) of the chronic *S. mansoni* patients tested involved adherent and/or phagocytic (A/P) peripheral blood mononuclear cells [54]. Removal of such cells by adherence to plastic and phagocytosis of carbonyl iron led to significantly increased responses to CAP. This was true whether the response was measured by the incorporation of tritiated thymidine or measured morphologically by increased numbers of blastoid lymphocytes. Removal of A/P cells did not alter responses induced by PHA or *C. albicans* extract, and the serosuppression described above could act in concert with this A/P cell suppression. This would indicate that the situation which would be presumed to occur in vivo in the chronically infected patient (unseparated cells containing A/P suppressors and autologous suppressive serum) would lead to the minimal degree of responsiveness when the patient's lymphocytes encountered cercarial antigenic materials. Nylon wool columns will also remove an adherent suppressor cell from patients' PBMN cells, and this also results in elevated CAP-induced responses [56]. This effect was also seen to work in concert with serosuppression and generally lowered the responses of patients' cells to non-schistosome antigens or mitogens while raising their responses to CAP [56]. In the only two chronic patients studied it was seen that the addition of indomethacin (an inhibitor of prostaglandin synthetase) to PBMN cell cultures exposed to CAP greatly increased the responses to this antigenic preparation [58]. It is possible that this effect is operative through control of the A/P cells described above.

Another system which affects lymphocyte responsiveness involves a non-specific suppression by the cercarial extract CAP [55]. It has been reported that in vitro lymphocyte responses induced by PHA were substantially diminished when the PHA was presented in the presence of CAP. This suppressive effect was dependent upon the concentration of CAP (supraoptimal concentrations being most dependably effective) and occurred whether the tested lymphocytes were obtained from *S. mansoni* patients or even from uninfected control subjects [55].

D. Consequences and Conjecture

It seems clear that the dermal responses observed during schistosome dermatitis are largely based upon antobody and cell-mediated reactions against invading cercariae [27-34]. These responses are often most intense when they involve the suicidal penetration of cercariae into nonpermissive hosts, as opposed to human schistosome cercariae involved in human percutaneous penetration [34]. The nonpermissive situation is perhaps mimicked in the artificial system involving penetration of resistant hosts by highly irradiated cercariae which are destined to develop no further [60]. It has been suggested that the ability of rhesus monkeys to deal effectively with such cercariae is a correlate of their immune status against *S. japonicum* challenge [60]. Immunization schemes using irradiated cercariae have been shown to be capable of inducing substantial protection against subsequent challenge by infectious cercariae [33,61-67]. It is interesting to also consider the situation involved in another rather effective approach to immunization which utilized heterologous infections [65,68-70]. Although various species restrictions exist, and induced protection is usually partial, this methodology has also taken advantage of systems (usually cercariae of *Schistosoma mattheei, Schistosome bovis* or *Schistosoma rodhani*) in which postcercarial development is minimal. Although totally speculative, it might be concluded that abortive cercarial penetration results in the presentation to the host of an effective immunogen for the induction of at least partial immunity. The nature of an immunogenic change brought about either by irradiation or during the host's handling and removal of materials through dermal responses to particulate cercarial remnants might be worthy of further consideration.

Conventional immunization regimens using dead cercariae or cercarial preparations have been generally ineffective in the induction of resistance against subsequent challenge [5,8,26,37]. A moderate degree of protection was afforded rats exposed to a cercarial membrane preparation [66], but mice fully sensitized with either CAP [37] or cercarial secretion material [26] to express humoral and cell-mediated reactivity have, in some studies, failed to exhibit even a modicum of protection upon subsequent challenge. Similarly, rhesus monkeys sensitized to express high titer CHR antibody showed no sign of resistance to challenge cercariae [71].

Yet even lacking a correlation between immune responses active against cercarial antigens and protective capabilities, it is perhaps important to remember that this does not rule out the possible participation of such responses in resistance. It may only mean that they are not, of themselves, sufficient for its expression. The possibility must also be considered that responses observed in vitro may not be fully expressed in vivo. This is emphasized by the various immunoregulatory events cited above which involve CAP-induced responses. The usual situation, even in "protected" hosts, is partial immunity where not all the challenge cercariae are resisted and where those which persist are not inhibited in their subsequent oviposition. It is possible that this condition rests on a balance of effector and regulatory mechanisms. Thus far, studies on resistance mechanisms have only emphasized trying to perfect and understand the effector side of the coin. It can be anticipated that CAP-response regulating serosuppression and A/P suppressor cells [53,54,56-58] occur within chronic *S. mansoni* patients. Whether they are effective regulators of anticercarial reactions within the first 24 hr following dermal penetration by cercariae can currently be only a matter of speculation. Another system cited above which might conceivably contribute to a nonspecific reduced responsiveness within the microenvironment of dermal penetration could be the CAP suppression of general (PHA) induced responses observed to affect normal or patient lymphocytes [55]. This suppression was dependent upon a sufficient concentration of CAP, and it might be theorized to cause unresponsiveness only within a given area of localized cercarial activity. Host genetics is another aspect to be considered in regard to the development of resistance. Information is beginning to accumulate that even within the realm of mouse "immunoschistosomology" there are considerable differences regarding resistance between different inbred strains [72]. It appears that, following low-level active chronic infection, some inbred strains do not develop dependable protection (CBA/J, C57BL/6J, BALB/c) whereas others do (NIH/Nmri CV, A/J, C57BL/KsJ) [72]. Furthermore, the same strains do not always fall in the same groups (high or low protection) when immunization is induced by irradiated cercarial exposure. Under these conditions C57BL/6K mice become highly protected whereas A/J mice do not [73]. Although these fascinating studies are as yet not fully understood, they provide a potential immunogenetic background against which many intriguing future investigations may be mounted (also see Section VI).

III. SCHISTOSOMULES

Schistosomules are the postpenetration, immature larval worms which result from the cercarial transformation initiated by skin penetration or artificial in vitro means [11]. The schistosomule is a transitional form which migrates from the skin to the lungs and then continues on to the portal system within the liver. The pathway followed to the lungs is apparently primarily by the blood vascular system [74,75], and conflicting evidence indicates that the lung-to-liver journey may occur by either, or both, the vasculature or the pleural space-diaphragm-liver route [76-78]. During this migration the schistosomule undergoes a great many changes pertinent to its feeding and metabolism, size, shape and mobility, and membrane characteristics. All the facets of its nature, many of which are poorly understood, undoubtedly play major roles in establishing the host-parasite interface which follows initial or challenge infections by cercariae. An understanding of this interface is considered essential in attempts to better control resistance phenomena because it is this stage (the early schistosomule) which is proposed as the target for effective anti-schistosome protective responses [79].

A. Antigens

Until recently, the inability to obtain the schistosomular stage artificially has effectively prevented in-depth attempts to analyze the antigenic components of schistosomules. Because of the vicissitudes of life-cycle maintenance, problems concerning the collection of satisfactory quantities of schistosomules still hamper such efforts. However, there are currently several methods published which can artificially provide this larval stage in vitro (reviewed in Ref. 11) [80,81]. Thus, studies are now beginning to appear in which target schistosomular antigens are being investigated [82-85]. Yet these investigations use schistosomules as the targets for various antibodies induced by exposure to either irradiated cercariae or active infection, and the characterization is based solely on inhibition of binding to schistosomules by membrane antigen fractions from adult worms [82,84].

It should be cautioned that not all schistosomules are created equal, or maintained equally, and the comparisons made among the data from various systems must always be considered in the context of the method of preparation, medium or maintenance, duration of culture, etc. The mention of such variables actually leads to a more fundamental aspect of schistosomular characterization: early schistosomules rapidly (within hours) alter themselves such that they express or take on different surface antigens and different membrane characteristics [79,85]. These alterations, which often depend upon the milieu in which the organisms are maintained, will be discussed in greater detail in Sections III.C and IV.C.

B. Host Responses

1. In Vivo

The majority of evidence that schistosome hosts develop responses against schistosomules involves demonstrations of intradermal or pulmonary immune reactions against them in immunized hosts. Intradermal lesions centered around schistosomules have been observed to be extremely complex immunologic reactions [86]. In immunized mice they involve eosinophil-enriched infiltrates [87], but the efficacy of this response alone is in doubt [34,87-89]. Pulmonary lesions or "tuftlike foci" have been extensively described as surrounding a schistosomule challenge in rhesus monkeys [90] and in mice [91,92]. In mice this concept has been modified to allow testing for resistance by intravenous (tail vein) injections of in vitro-prepared schistosomules [92]. These organisms will lodge in the pulmonary vasculature and thus allow analysis of both the method of their handling by the host's defenses and the effect of manipulations of the organisms themselves. Furthermore, more precise timings of the reactions against schistosomules can be evaluated. Cellular infiltrates in nonimmune mice, upon intrapulmonary challenge with schistosomules, begin within 30 min with the arrival of neutrophils. Approximately 80% of the organisms are eliminated by 6 days. Mice immune because of chronic *S. mansoni* infection exhibit an augmented, accelerated response which involves eosinophilia and results in the destruction of virtually all challenge organisms [92]. This system has proven useful in analyzing the immune effector mechanisms which are mounted against schistosomules in immunized hosts [88]. A role for T lymphocytes has been implicated by the lack of significant pulmonary responses in athymic, nude (nu/nu) mice, while nu/+ heterozygotes responded well and were protected. However, further passive transfer studies [88] indicate that the defect seems to be humoral (T-dependent antibody production?) since sera from immunized nu/+ provide an effector mechanism to nu/nu litermates. Eosinophils were not lacking in the tuftlike foci formed in appropriately serum-transferred nu/nu mice, indicating a humoral induction mechanism at work in this local eosinophilia (reviewed in Ref. 93). These or other radiation sensitive (650 R), bone marrow-derived, effector cells were also required to get immune, serum-mediated elimination of schistosomules [88]. Another line of evidence that the schistosomule is the target of the major resistance effector mechanisms comes from serum passive transfer studies. The IgG fraction of sera obtained from mice appropriately infected with *S. mansoni* for 12-15 weeks confers a degree of protection to recipient mice [94,95]. This effect was manifested when the sera were administered a day prior to challenge, but not if transfer was delayed until 5 days after challenge. This implies that the early schistosomule is the stage which is most susceptible to attack [94]. A recent study has indicated that immune serum and complement can effect schistosomular killing in the absence of accessory cell contact (in a millipore chamber) [96].

In addition to studies demonstrating that the schistosomule often acts as the in vivo target of immune reactants induced by adult worms (Section IV.B) there is evidence accumulating that they can also induce immune responses. Early attempts to demonstrate the induction of resistance by immunizing schemes which chemotherapeutically killed developing, early-stage schistosomules were ineffective [97]. Although innovative, such attempts may simply be subject to timing errors because other approaches indicate that some degree of significant protection can be shown to develop within 2-4 weeks after the initial immunizing infections of rats [98-100] or mice [101] with viable cercariae. Phillips et al. [100] have extensively analyzed this early period of resistance in rats by using passive transfers of either 3 ml of sera of 2×10^8 nonadherent peritoneal exudate cells from rats at different times after infection. Between 2 and 4 weeks of infection it was seen that protection was mediated by the cellular component (primarily T lymphocytes), and the resistance seen subsequent to that, between 7 to 10 weeks, was only transferable with immune serum.

Another newly developed procedure which implicates schistosomules as effective immunogens (as opposed to being only targets for cercaria- or adult worm-induced responses) utilizes cryopreserved schistosomules [102-1]5]. Active, viable schistosomules produced in vitro by the shear-pressure technique [11,106] can be recovered following stepwise cooling to -196°C [102,104]. The infectivity of such schistosomules derived from unirradiated cercariae is low (between 0-2.8%) upon intramuscular injection into mice [102,104]. Those derived from ^{60}Co-irradiated (50 krad) cercariae, which, following recovery from freezing, were introduced to the host as schistosomules, did not proceed past this point of development [104]. They were, however, effective immunogens in NIH/Nmri CV mice in that they resulted in the development of substantial protection against cercarial challenge [105]. Challenge infections were done 6-7 weeks after administration of the cryopreserved, irradiated schistosomules.

The studies described above which involved nude mice [88] and cellular passive transfer in rats [100] implicated a role for T lymphocytes in protection and more particularly in schistosomule-induced responses [100]. Direct demonstration that schistosomules can indeed act as stimulators of T helper cells has come from the use of an artificial system utilizing schistosomules as carriers for the hapten trinitrophenol (TNP) [107-109]. Following either infection or sensitization, mice or rats were injected intravenously with TNP-coupled schistosomules, and 4 days later their spleen cells were assayed for anti-TNP plaque-forming cells using TNP-sheep erythrocytes as targets. This allowed an evaluation of the degree of T-cell priming which had occurred against the surface antigens of the schistosomule during the first exposure [107-109]. Ramalho-Pinto and colleagues have demonstrated that following active infection (either bisexual or unisexual) there is a substantial generation of specific T helper cells. This response was detected between 7 and 10 days and did not occur in nude mice [107]. The same situation occurred following injection of 30 formalin-fixed schistosomules, and the carrier effect could be detected 6 months after sensitization [109]. High levels of carrier priming could also be induced by injections of 10 μg of crude adult worm tegumental membrane [108]. Less effective primings were obtained with various other life-cycle stages [108].

2. In Vitro

a. Lymphocyte Stimulation

The in vitro induction of primary immune responsiveness by schistosomules has not yet been analyzed. However, a recent investigation has demonstrated the immunogenicity of intact, viable schistosomules with regard to the
stimulation of sensitized lymphocytes [110]. Coculture of 20×10^6 spleen
cells obtained from mice infected with *S. mansoni* for 2-15 weeks with schistosomules (500-5000) in 2 ml culture medium stimulated the production of a
soluble material which was chemotactic for eosinophils and mononuclear cells.
Pretreatment of the spleen cells with anti-Thy-1 antisera and complement prevented the production of this lymphokine [110]. This material is thus far in-
distinguishable from the activity termed ESP/ECF-L [111].

b. Antischistosomular Effector Mechanisms

During the last decade a plethora of in vitro systems have been described
which share the end results of damaging or killing schistosomules but display
incredible variety in regard to the combinations of cells and sera which singly
or in combination produce the desired effect on the schistosomular target. An
attempt will be made to summarize each of the currently prominent systems,
but the reader must beware in that there is great variability in these systems.
It may be critical to consider differences in the host species, schistosomular preparations, terminal assays, culture conditions, purity of cellular preparations,
and as yet unimagined crucial conditions prior to any attempts at generalization
of this body of information.

Normal Serum It has been known for some time [35] that *S. mansoni*
cercariae activated complement in normal sera and resulted in anaphylactoid
activity. Furthermore, this conversion of C3 by cercariae in vitro proceeded via
the alternate complement pathway (ACP) and led to cercarial death [36]. Subsequently, decomplementation in vivo by cobra venom factor was seen to partially abrogate acquired resistance due to active infection [112]. Further studies
demonstrated that approximately 35% of artificially transformed schistosomules
were susceptible to the in vitro action of complement alone. This effect was
ACP mediated. Greater than 80% were killed in the presence of immune serum
and complement (see below) [112]. The activation of the ACP may be due in
some part to residual cercarial glycocalyx. If so, then differences in schistosomules could perhaps account for the fact that killing by normal serum is not
universally observed [113]. However, the activation of C3 by schistosomules
prepared by both in vitro rat skin penetration [114] and mechanical transformation [115] has also been observed. A recent study [116] confirms the normal serum killing of skin and mechanically obtained schistosomules and further

demonstrates that schistosomules obtained 4 days after infection (from the lungs) are no longer sensitive to this ACP-mediated destruction.

Lethal Antibody Sera obtained from a wide variety of infected hosts exhibit cytotoxicity for schistosomules in vitro in the presence of a source of complement [117-121]. This activity resides primarily in the IgG fraction [117,118] and can be absorbed out by an adult worm membrane fraction [82]. Immunoglobulin subclass analysis reveals that in the mouse this antibody is of the IgG_{2a} isotype [122]. Although rats could be sensitized with adult worm antigens to produce high titers of lethal antibody, they were not afforded protection by this regimen [82].

Eosinophils

Eosinophils and Specific Antibody: Fc-mediated Binding. One of the most common conditions with which eosinophils have traditionally been associated is infection with tissue-dwelling helminths. Schistosomiasis is a prime example of this situation [8]. Teleologically it would be comforting if this relationship had a functional basis. It is currently thought that eosinophils may participate in acquired host resistance phenomena in schistosomiasis [9]. The three experimental avenues which have led to this hypothesis are (1) the involvement of eosinophils in the inflammatory responses against schistosomules in resistant hosts (Section III.B.1), (2) the abrogation of resistance by administration of specific anti-eosinophil serum [123], and (3) in vitro observations of eosinophils effecting damage and killing isolated schistosomules (see below).

The in vitro antibody-mediated eosinophil-schistosomule interaction was originally observed by Butterworth [9] who, with his colleagues [124-133] and other groups [122,134-139], has subsequently considered several adaptations of the system. In the earlier human eosinophil ^{51}Cr release assay (^{51}Cr-labeled schistosomules were the targets) human antibody system it was shown that the antibody involved was an opsonic IgG [128] which could be removed by absorption with whole schistosomules. Release of ^{51}Cr (damage) from the schistosomules was seen only to be mediated by eosinophils based on abrogation by treatment with anti-eosinophil serum and complement [126] and based on purity of cell preparation [128]. Ultrastructural analysis confirmed that there was an interaction between the eosinophils and the schistosomular membrane [127]. The same system was defined in baboons [126], and a degree of correlation was observed between the level of the antibody which mediated this antibody-dependent cell-mediated cytotoxicity (ADCC) and the resistance status of the baboon [130]. There is evidence that the major basic protein (MBP) isolated from eosinophil granules (which makes up approximately 25% of the cell's total protein content) can effect damage of schistosomules. Furthermore, MBP is generated during this ADCC reaction and localized on the schistosomular membrane [132]. Using newly developed cell separation procedures [131] this group has now reexamined some of the earlier data concerning the cell types involved and the meaning of ^{51}Cr release. It is now confirmed that the ^{51}Cr release assay does not necessarily indicate schistosomular killing [131,140]. Currently, using high-yield, normal granulocytes, both neutrophils and eosinophils could be seen to cause the antibody-mediated release of ^{51}Cr, but only eosinophils yield morphologically damaged (killed) schistosomules [131]. It is hypothesized that neutrophil-mediated (antibody-dependent) damage is reversible, whereas eosinophil-mediated (antibody-dependent) damage continues on to ultimate lesion formation.

Based on this hypothesis Butterworth et al. are now examining the interactions of these two cell types with schistosomules to try to determine what differences might exist to explain this finding [133]. These studies concern differences in the adherence and damage mechanisms exhibited by neutrophils and eosinophils. Eosinophils appear to adhere better to antibody-coated schistosomules than do neutrophils (at any concentration of antibody or cells). Although eosinophils generally have fewer Fc receptors than neutrophils, it was seen that they differ qualitatively: expression of eosinophil Fc receptors requires incubation at 37°C, whereas neutrophils adhere best at 4°C [133]. Furthermore, although staphylococcal protein A (SPA) blocked the adherence of either cell in a concentration-dependent manner (again implicating IgG Fc-mediated binding), SPA could only reverse the established binding of neutrophils, not eosinophils. It appears that neutrophils "browse" on antibody-coated schistosomules, while eosinophils bind firmly and do not subsequently detach.

Another approach has been to artificially bind either neutrophils or eosinophils to naked schistosomules (not coated with antibody) via a concanavalin A (ConA) ligand-bridge [133]. Both types of cells did bind in this system, but neither killed the organisms, and both could be competitively inhibited away from the schistosomules with α-methylmannoside (i.e., in this setting both exhibited equally reversible binding). However, upon artificial degranulation of ConA-bound cells by the calcium ionophore A23187, bound eosinophils went on to irreversible binding (via degranulation) and killing of the organisms [133]. Such studies are beginning to approach the actual mechanisms involved in at least this single system. Note, however, that not all human eosinophil ADCC methodologies have provided the level of killing observed in the studies cited above [136].

Other groups have investigated eosinophil interactions with antibody-coated schistosomules with similar, but sometimes variant, results. Using rat antibody and eosinophils, Mackenzie et al. [134] noted that these cells mediated ^{51}Cr release and some cytoplasmic damage [134], but this effect was not observable at the ultrastructural level [140]. Inhibition of schistosomular damage was seen when adult worm surface membrane preparations were included in the assay system. Subsequent studies revealed morphologically identifiable tegumental damage induced by eosinophils attached via antibody, but it required high cell numbers and a longer time period [135]. Studies by others regarding this antibody-mediated, rat eosinophil system have identified the immunoglobulin participant as a member of the IgG_{2a} subclass [139], an IgG heat-stable anaphylactic antibody class in the rat. This antibody titer peaked between 30 and 42 days after infection. Upon ultrastructural evaluation of the eosinophil-schistosomular interactions, Capron and colleagues observed mast cells in their preparations [138,139]. After rigorous depletion of these mast cells, the remaining eosinophil preparations were decidedly less effective in killing antibody-coated schistosomules. Upon continued investigations the complexity of this two-cell synergism was thought to involve binding of the mast cell surface by the Fc portion of IgG_{2a}. This reaction led to the release of soluble mast cell-derived pharmacological mediators which were as effective as the cells themselves in assisting eosinophil-mediated destruction of schistosomules [138]. It is unknown whether this antibody-dependent, eosinophil-mediated, mast cell-assisted phenomenon could, in the presence of a source of complement, utilize the previously described C3 receptor binding of mast cells to schistosomules [114] to involved mast cells.

Eosinophil-mediated ADCC destruction of schistosomules has also been reported using mouse cells [122,137]. The in vitro observed destruction was assayed in parallel by subsequent in vivo injection of the schistosomules following in vitro treatments [137]. Although the percentage of recoverable adult schistosomes (infectivity) was low following 24 or more hours in vitro incubation (whether the conditions killed or not), there was a clear decrease in this infectivity after incubation in the presence of peritoneal exudate cells and immune sera [136]. Schistosomular killing occurred whether the cells were obtained from *Trichinella spiralis*- or *S. mansoni*-infected mice. Neutrophils were ineffective in this ADCC reaction, but monocytes did participate (see below). Sera from *T. spiralis*-infected mice were wholly ineffectual in mediating eosinophil ADCC against schistosomules. Both studies of this system agree that the antibody involved is of the IgG class [122,137], and it is further delineated as being of the IgG_1 subclass [122]. It was this subclass (IgG_1) which was earlier implicated in the passive transfer of resistance in mice [95].

Eosinophils and Complement: C3 Receptor Binding. Smithers and his colleagues at Mill Hill had established the eosinophil Fc-mediated ACDD antischistosomule system using rat immune components [134,135] but had also observed that rat eosinophils were bound to schistosomules in the presence of fresh normal rat serum as well [115,135]. This adherence was shown to be due to activation of the ACP on the schistosomular surface and subsequent binding of the eosinophils by their C3 receptors. It resulted in the death of the organism [115], and this effect was easily visualized at the ultrastructural level [135]. Chemotactic factors active on rat eosinophils were observed to be generated in this system [135], and under these normal rat serum, C3-mediated conditions the generation of the chemotactic agent proceeded by activation of the ACP [141].

Analysis of the interaction of human eosinophils and schistosomules in fresh serum also led to the activation of the ACP and was seen to provide for more efficient killing of the organisms than the classical ADCC eosinophil reaction [136]. Furthermore, under these conditions (fresh serum) eosinophils performed better than did human neutrophils [136].

Eosinophils, Specific Antibody, and Complement: Fc and C3 Receptor-Mediated Binding. Proceeding logically, those groups which had observed eosinophil killing of schistosomules in either the rat [141] or human systems [136], as mediated via both antibody and complement, have pursued this subject looking for, and finding, synergy between the two mechanisms. In the rat model, superior adherence and killing was observed when the system involved antibody and C3-coated schistosomules exposed to eosinophils [141]. The maximal killing was achieved sooner than previously observed in the separate systems, and it was demonstrated that eosinophil chemotactic factors were generated via both the classic and alternate complement pathways [141]. It should be remembered in the discussion below (Section III.C.4) that the speed of initiating schistosomular killing in vivo may be of some practical consequence. Maximal killing of schistosomules was also achieved in the human eosinophil-mediated studies [136] in the presence of both antibody and complement. Under this condition eosinophils acted in a preferential manner compared with neutrophils. The antibody in this system was of the IgG class.

Neutrophils. Studies investigating the schistosomicidal activities of neutrophils have been less popular than those involving eosinophils, but several investigators have described such systems [113,121,136]. Dean and his co-workers observed the killing of schistosomules in the presence of antibody and complement using both rat [113] and guinea pig [121] materials. Anwar et al. [136], examining the human system, found that neutrophils did exhibit some degree of killing in the presence of antibody alone, complement alone, or antibody and complement than with complement alone, and this was better than with antibody alone. Under the two conditions involving complement, neutrophils were distinctly inferior to eosinophils in their schistosomular killing [136]. In the ADCC system, Butterworth et al. [133] now observe ^{51}Cr release mediated by neutrophils, but not actual killing, and ascribe this to their less firm attachment to the organisms, which is in turn attributed to their inability to elaborate the same granular contents (notably MBP) as eosinophils [133].

Mononuclear Phagocytes

Mononuclear Phagocytes Alone. A newly described system has been observed which indicates that, when schistosomules are cultured in the presence of normal human peripheral blood monocytes and normal heat-inactivated human or fetal calf serum, a significant percentage (about 18%) of the organisms are killed. Cytotoxicity was based on morphologic evidence and in vivo infectivity rates [142,143]. Neither neutrophils nor nonadherent mononuclear cells inflicted damage under these conditions. The killing was maximal by 6 hr.

In an extension of the normal human monocyte killing system it was seen that peripheral blood adherent monocytes from tuberculosis patients were very effective in this killing [143]. In a possibly similar system involving nonspecific activation of murine macrophages, it has been shown that such cells can mediate in vitro killing of schistosomules [144]. Active cells were obtained after in vivo treatment with Bacillus Calmette-Guerin (BCG) or *Corynebacterium parvum.* Killing appeared due to soluble, released mediators, and neither proteose-peptone nor thioglycollate could induce this cellular activity [144].

Mononuclear Phagocytes and IgG Antibody. Peritoneal exudate cells from normal rats (rich in macrophages), when sensitized with sera from rats resistant to *S. mansoni,* have been observed to adhere to and kill schistosomules [145]. This occurred in the absence of complement, and heating at 56°C for 30 min did not interfere with this cytophilic antibody activity. The ability of the sera to mediate this killing correlated well with the degree of resistance of the donor rats [145].

Anwar et al. [136] examined the efficacy of normal human peripheral blood mononuclear cells (there was no attempt to use monocytes) obtained by Ficoll-Hypaque centrifugation to kill schistosomules in the presence of antibody, complement, or antibody and complement. A modicum of killing was obtained (means of 22, 31, and 37%, respectively). Mononuclear cells alone, in normal heat-inactivated serum, killed an average of 16% of the schistosomules. In contrast, Ellner and Mahmoud [142], using normal human monocytes obtained by adherence of mononuclear cell preparations, observed a twofold increase in schistosomular killing in the presence of heat-inactivated human sera from *S. mansoni*-infected patients [143].

Complement-independent, antibody (IgG) dependent, macrophage-mediated killing of schistosomules has been reported using the mouse system [137]. The macrophages could be obtained from normal, proteose-peptone-stimulated mice and, although adherence of the normal populations was less than that observed with exudates from *S. mansoni*-infected mice, the extent of killing of the target organisms was comparable [137].

Mononuclear Phagocytes and IgE Antibody or IgE Immune Complexes. Capron and colleagues have established the participation of a new antibody-effector cell combination, relevant to in vitro schistosomacidal activity, which involves specific IgE antibody and normal macrophages. This system was first reported with rat sera and cells [146,147] and has been extended to include human and baboon mononuclear phagocytes and their respective sera from infected subjects [148]. The system involves preincubation at 37°C of the macrophages with the IgE-containing serum. The schistosomules are then added to the culture, and the macrophages adhere strongly to the organisms within 3 hr. Absorption of the serum by *S. mansoni* soluble adult worm antigens reduced its efficacy [146] and ϵ-chain specific anti-rat IgE serum also removed the activity. Anti-rat IgG, IgM, and IgA did not affect the adherence. The reaction could be monitored by a ^{51}Cr release assay [147,148]. Absorption and ultracentrifugation analysis has shown that the IgE responsible is actually in the form of complexes of schistosome-specific IgE-soluble parasite antigens [147]. Aggregated IgE was also seen to bind to macrophages at $37°$C. IgE-immune-complex binding to macrophages elicits activation of the macrophages accompanied by increases in lysosomal enzymes and subsequent schistosomacidal activity [147]. The appearance of the responsible IgE closely correlated with the establishment of resistance in the rat. The reactivity was specific for *S. mansoni* in that it did not affect L$_3$ larvae of *Dipetalonema viteae* [147]. Ultrastructural analysis demonstrated the presence of IgE on the macrophage surface and the destructive nature of the interaction with schistosomules. The serum activity was always cytophilic and never opsonic in its relationship between the cells and the organism [146,148]. It is intriguing to consider this new (nonatopic) role for IgE in a condition where high-level production of IgE is the rule. An earlier in vivo failure to demonstrate a localized protective role for reaginic antibody in *S. mansoni*-challenged rats [149] may need to be reexamined with consideration as to the availability of suitable cellular components in the dermal reaction site.

Cytotoxic T Lymphocytes. There has been one report that indicates that murine cytotoxic T lymphocytes (CTL), generated against H-2 alloantigens, failed to effect damage on appropriate H-2-bearing schistosomules [150]. This appeared true despite adequate binding to these organisms. A note of caution, prior to totally disregarding future studies on antischistosomular CTL, might be a reminder that rat peritoneal exudate cells, which might be expected to be rich in CTL, were effective in passively transferring resistance to normal rats during a very tightly defined period of time [100]. Furthermore, bridging of CTL to schistosomules via H-2, anti-H-2 recognition may not allow localized CTL effects on some hypothetical crucial target parasite antigen.

C. Regulation of Responsiveness

Without adequate supplies of even crude schistosomular antigenic preparations it is difficult to assess how or whether responses induced by schistosomules are internally controlled. It is clear that, as it matures under certain circumstances, the parasite renders itself somewhat beyond the reach of previously effective immune responses, and this will be discussed below. However, there are several experimental studies which indicate that immunoregulatory events affecting responsiveness against this stage do occur.

1. Resistance and Passive Transfer

In an analysis of the development of resistance acquired due to active infection of the mouse, Sher et al. [151] determined the number of schistosomules recoverable from the lungs of challenged mice (about 5 days after challenge) and observed that a decreased lung recovery which occurred 3-4 weeks after primary infection did not actually correlate to significant permanent protection. This was explained on the basis of an induced delay in (not cessation of) schistotomular migration [151] and was found to be due to the early development of a species of antibody which did not kill schistosomules upon passive transfer but merely retarded their arrival in the lungs [94]. Subsequent analysis determined that the factor in 3-week serum which was responsible for delayed migration was IgG_2, while actual protective passive transfers were accomplished with the IgG_1-containing fractions of chronic mouse serum [95]. Whether or not the IgG_2 (delaying antibody) is still present in the efficacious, chronic sera is unknown. This situation may be one of immunoregulation which aids the host protective response by converting the IgG_2 response in favor of the subsequently predominating IgG_1 capability. This may have consequences for protection in mice, in that if the schistosomules are sufficiently delayed they may be afforded the opportunity to develop their own protective measures prior to encountering the effective mediators of host resistance.

The complex longitudinal interactions which accompany infection and the development of resistance in the rat were alluded to earlier [100] (Section B.1). Phillips and his colleagues [66,100,152,153] have analyzed in depth some of the cellular and humoral aspects of acquired resistance in Fischer rats during *S. mansoni* infection. At 2 and 3 weeks after infection, cellular (primarily T lymphocyte) components affectively transferred immunity, but this capability was subsequently lost, and if anything, late in infection cellular transfer somewhat elevated the number of surviving challenge worms [153]. Another pattern was observed upon serum transfers [152,153]. Sera from 2-3 week infected rats actually augmented challenge organism survival, and this "enhancing" capability was then lost in favor of a protective serum function which was maximal at 7-10 weeks after a single primary infection [153]. When passive transfers of cells and sera from 2-3 week infected rats were done in concert it was seen that the enhancing effect of the serum totally abrogated the protective cellular effect [152]. These alterations clearly appear to involve internal modulational changes in the immune responses which progress with infection. The 2-3-week sera can interfere with the efficacy of the lymphoid population's handling of schistosomules upon challenge, but given sufficient time (>4 weeks) the cellular element ceases to be effective in its own right. The serum components also must be under progressive controls for the augmenting capacity gives way to protective elements, which in turn fade without continued, or high-level initial, exposure

[66]. Protection was not maintained past 40 weeks of infection despite the continuance of stable, low-level worm burdens past this point [66].

2. Helper T Lymphocytes

Using TNP-schistosomule hapten-carrier conjugates, the ability of schistosomular surfaces to act as T helper cell stimulators has been established [107-109] in rats and mice. Active primary infection of mice led to the maximum development of schistosomule-specific T helper cells between 7 and 10 days after infection. Thereafter, there was a steady decline in the level of this specific activity while nonspecific helper response increased in actively infected mice [109]. The waning of specific helpers was seen in infected rats but was not accompanied by increases in background helper activity. Antibody of the IgG class, with specificity for schistosomular surfaces, was detected in 5-week infected mouse serum and reached high titers by 11 weeks. Passive transfer of such sera (8-11 weeks) was seen to interfere with the generation of specific helper cells in the usually optimal 8-10-day infected mice [109]. It is possible that such anti-carrier activity may operate by interfering with T-B-cell cooperation via blockage of carrier-specific antigens. The case of mice sensitized with formalin-fixed schistosomules provides an interesting adjunct to this system [109]. In this case, helper T cells develop (a bit more slowly) to the levels observed in actively infected mice, but they are then maintained at that level for more than 24 weeks (not modulated as seen in active infection by 4-6 weeks). No anti-schistosomular surface antibody developed in these formalin-fixed sensitized mice. Although Sher [88] has indicated the necessity for T-dependent antibody production to achieve protection, it is unclear how these particular schistosomule-carrier-specific T helpers are involved in protection. Their appearance is not well correlated with the occurrence of protection, and the mice exposed to formalin-fixed schistosomules, in spite of continued high levels of functional helpers, were not protected against challenge infections. Nonetheless, the complexity of interactions is well documented and may shed considerable light on the internal regulations occurring during the development and expression of resistance.

3. Human Monocyte Effector Systems

Ellner et al. [142,143] have recently reported the efficacy of normal human monocytes to kill schistosomules in vitro. This effect could be manifested in normal human serum-supplemented medium, but was augmented twofold in the presence of sera from actively infected patients [142]. These researchers have also examined the capability of monocytes from schistosomiasis patients to participate in schistosomular killing [143]. Monocytes from patients with moderate (< 400 eggs per gram of stool) infections with S. mansoni behaved similarly to those from normal, uninfected donors, except that in their own sera they were more effective than the normal donor's cells in their own sera. However, cells from heavily infected patients (> 1200 eggs per gram) exhibited greatly decreased effectiveness and neither autologous sera, normal sera, nor sera pooled from moderately infected patients made any difference [143]. Thus, the monocytes themselves appeared defective in this capacity. Monocytes from patients with tuberculosis were seen to be very effective in killing schistosomules in the presence of any serum source. This is reminiscent of the activated macrophage work of Mahmoud et al. [144] in the mouse system. Thus, there appears to be some regulatory aspect involved in the monocyte defect in heavily infected *S. mansoni* patients.

4. Schistosomular Acquisition of Refractoriness to Immune Attack

There is a large body of information which hypothesizes that one of the major methods by which adult schistosomes evade the immune effector mechanisms of the host is by acquiring a "protective overcoat" of host antigens on their tegumental surfaces, thereby, in effect, masquerading as the host itself, [5,6,8, 154-156]. The evidence involving the presence of host antigens on adult worms will be dealt with later (Section IV.C.1), but the topic of the acquisition of certain of these properties during the schistosomular stage bears considerable impact on the concepts of the immunogenicity and antigenicity of schistosomules and will be discussed here.

The development by schistosomules of insusceptibility to the in vitro action of ACP-mediated complement killing in several normal sera [116] or lethal antibody and complement [157] was seen to occur in vivo by 4 days. This insensitivity to lethal antibody was shown to parallel the presence on the schistosomular surface of mouse erythrocyte antigens [157]. The lethal antibodies were seen not only to be ineffective in killing 4-day-old schistosomules which had mouse erythrocyte antigens on their surfaces, they also did not bind to these organisms. Continued work along this line led to the demonstration that when schistosomules, collected by in vitro passage through mouse skin, were cultured in vitro in the presence of human blood of various blood group specificities, they acquired the appropriate A, B, H, and Lewis[b+] antigens on their surfaces. It was concluded that the antigens were passively acquired in their glycolipid or megaloglycolipid forms [158].

The schistosomule-protecting effect of culture in the presence of mouse erythrocytes has also been reported in connection with subsequent intravenous challenge using such schistosomules [92]. In this system, organisms cultured for 24 or 44 hr in medium containing erythrocytes elicited less cellular reactivity and survived in the lungs of immune hosts more than did freshly derived schistosomules [92]. Furthermore, fresh schistosomules, or those cultured for 4 days in an erythrocyte-free medium, allowed equal attachment of murine peritoneal exudate cells, and both types were susceptible to ADCC cytotoxic effects [137], albeit the general viability of the culture larvae was decreased. However, 4-day incubation in the presence of erythrocytes decreased the binding of eosinophils and macrophages and prevented effective ADCC reactions.

In apparent contrast to such evidence that concomitant development of refractoriness is predicated solely on the acquisition of host antigen are several studies which indicate that it is the inherent nature of schistosomules to develop such an insensitivity without the aid of host components in the medium [85] if they are metabolically active. Dean [85] studied *S. mansoni* early phase schistosomules derived by in vitro penetration of rat skin and cultured in defined media. Their susceptibility to binding and killing by guinea pig lethal antibody was monitored during culture in the presence or absence of several metabolic inhibitors. They were compared with the antibody action on schistosomules derived in vivo after 2 or 6 days of infection. If allowed to maintain their metabolic activity, fresh schistosomules became refractory even when cultured in defined media [85]. Tavares et al. [159] have extended these observations using schistosomules prepared in vitro by mechanical means. They demonstrated that the addition of serum to the defined medium increased the rate of acquisition of refractoriness to antibody cytotoxicity. The hypothesis that this augmentation in rate, induced by serum, may rest on the stimulation of some metabolic capability of the larvae has been pursued [160]. It was seen that the incorporation of labeled amino acids into schistosomular tegumental proteins and the development of protection of the organism in vitro were simultaneously stimulated by the addition of serum to the cultures, and both processes were inhibited by inclusion of puromycin in the medium [160]. Most labeling occurred within 3 hr, and no newly developed proteins were identified. In contrast to the system studied by McLaren et al. [157], these investigators observed that schistosomules that developed insensitivity to the action of antibody were still as capable of binding the antibody to an equivalent degree as when they were sensitive to it. This continued expression of the target antigens had been reported by others [161,162]. Gazzinelli has further shown the defined medium plus serum system allows (stimulates) the development of schistosomular resistance to attack by human granulocytes mediated by specific antibody with or without complement, and the acquisition of this resistance is prevented by puromycin inhibition [163].

These data appear to indicate that normal physiological alterations in newly transformed schistosomules may account, at least in part, for the development of their observed refractoriness to subsequent immune injury. In some respects this interpretation fits well with the observations which have been made regarding schistosomular membrane changes [79]. The transformation from cercaria to schistosomule is accompanied by the change from a conventional trilaminate plasma membrane to one which exhibits seven layers [164,165]. The latter structure is actually two closely opposed bilipid membranes. This structure forms within 1-3 hr by a process of intact multilaminate-membrane-bound vesicle insertion. Schistosomules obtained by either skin penetration or mechanical in vitro methods [11,80,81] undergo the same processes in the same general time frame. It was further demonstrated that the outer set of membranes (membranocalyx) were continually being replaced by this fusion process [166, 167]. Thus, it is feasible that this process is one of the methods by which the developing schistosomule becomes relatively impervious to potentially damaging reactants. It does not support the hypothesis that acquired host antigens act to protect schistosomules, but neither can it be used to refute that host antigen acquisition occurs and may hypothetically alter membrane level interactions in favor of the organism. The evidence for, and nature of, some of the host antigens thus far investigated will be elaborated below (Section IV.C.1).

D. Consequences and Conjecture

Schistosomules are fascinating from purely a biological point of view and are pivotal in regard to gaining the further immunological understanding of schistosomiasis needed to attack the question of immunization from either the pragmatic or theoretical point of view. We are faced with an organism which is induced, through poorly understood trigger mechanisms, to rapidly undergo substantial morphologic, metabolic, and physiologic differentiation. Neither the processes nor the controls of the processes governing this transformation are known. During this period the schistosomule presents the host immune system with its best chance to effect parasite destruction, but only briefly. Furthermore, during this short time the schistosomules themselves may transiently induce a degree of responsiveness capable of reacting with the early phase of the next schistosomule to come along. This type of simplistic overview belies the fact that not all resistance mechanisms produce elimination by the lung stage [168, 169]. However, it is generally agreed that the death of many challenge organisms occurs early on. Also, there is no information on whether even later observed decreases in adult worm recoveries based on predictions obtained at the lung stage might or might not represent the later consequences of lesions inflicted earlier in their development.

There seems to be no good reason to think that schistosomules do not take part in at least some of the induction process of immune responsiveness. They do, even if briefly, present potentially immunogenic components to the host. Furthermore, we know that in some cases even this transient, short-term presentation does result in responses which can then be elicited by this stage [107-110]. The timing of the development of both the T helper cells with carrier specificity for schistosomular surfaces [107-109], and the early T-cell involvement in schistosomule-induced lymphokine production [110] , make this clear. Of course it is not yet so clear that these, or comparably induced responses, are involved in the protective response to challenge infections. It is intriguing to consider the possibility that the data from studies on abortive infections (with either heterologous schistosomes or irradiated organisms) are trying to tell us something about the dermal-pulmonary immunogenicity of dying schistosomules. Studies of the physicochemical nature of irradiated schistosomules, as well as their anatomical distribution and interactions in the host during the *induction* phase of resistance, merit considerable attention.

The extensive list compiled of demonstrated in vitro means of killing schistosomules, involving an array of effector cells and mediators in various combinations, makes the point that this stage of the research effort is in a proliferative phase. Obviously there should eventually be a consolidation phase during which it can be hoped that some of the current systems will fall into perspective. But clearly, we are not yet there, and the meaning of all the subsystems remains unclear. Reassembly of the pieces and assessment of their relative contributions within the immune host are simply not yet feasible, or advisable. Evaluation of the systems in comparable terms, analyses considering the nature and potential contributions of the known receptors on participating cells, and an assessment of the likelihood of finding such reactants in the locations of confrontation are all useful exercises. However, we should be mindful that the precise location of killing is not fully known. Also, at least two of the most potentially rewarding cell systems now being considered would not be under evaluation if only "reasonable" effector systems from other branches of immunological experience were allowed consideration. These "bonus discoveries," involving various roles for eosinophils and the IgE-immune complex-mediated macrophage participation, now exist due to a breadth of thinking and approach. This openness to the unusual represents the best of what may come from the basic side of these investigations into very practical problems involving schistosomiasis.

IV. ADULT WORMS

The adult worms of the three human schistosomes mature within 3-6 weeks after cercarial penetration and primarily reside in the venules draining the intestines or bladder. Schistosomes are digenetic and spend most of their time *en copula,* producing an estimated average of 150-3000 fertilized eggs per day per worm pair, dependent upon the species in question. These living, macroscopic (0.25-2.00 X 7-28 mm) worms maintain themselves within the vasculature of the host under conditions which would be more than sufficient to discourage continued residence by an allogeneic transplant. Mean worm life spans in humans are considered to be in the 5-10 year range [170] , but longevity records for worms in individual patients are approximately 30 years. During this time they not only live in equilibrium with the host immune responses, they do not even induce coagulation events. Their ability to escape the triggering of the clotting mechanisms may be explained in part by the existence of a recently reported coagulation factor XIIa inhibitor (bilharzin) obtained from these adult worms [171, 172]. However, their evasion of the very immune responses which they evoke, and which are effective against schistosomules, is unlikely to be even theoretically attributable to one or two characteristics. The term which has been applied to their ability to stimulate resistance mechanisms, which are expressed against challenge infections, while they themselves exist in the same milieu is concomitant immunity [79,155]. This terminology has been borrowed from tumor immunology where it was used to express essentially the same phenomenon of continued existence in the face of a stimulated immune reactivity which effectively prevents the development of challenge exposures [173]. This situation will be expanded upon below.

A. Antigens

Extracts of adult schistosomes contain over 60 components which, when presented to a host, can induce separate antibody responses. Because adult worms can be obtained from experimental infections in reasonable quantities, this stage has provided some of the major antigenic preparations used in serologic and skin test studies. This has resulted in extensive information concerning worm antigen-induced responses, but to a large extent the data do not tell us very much about the antigens themselves because of the heterogeneity and the lack of standardization of such efforts. Some progress has been made by systematically or selectively examining antigenic worm materials and comparing them as to specificity, physicochemical characterization, and localization in or on the parasite.

Whole worm extracts have been very useful in attempts to evaluate immune responses in schistosome infections, but they have proved to be extremely complex [12,13,174-176]. Attempts at reducing their heterogeneity to allow manipulations of a few components have been extensive in some cases [177] and rested on extensive physicochemical separation methodologies. More recently, affinity chromatography has been used to isolate purified adult worm malate dehydrogenase isoenzymes [178,179]. This activity, a major contributing antigen in crude extracts (antigen 4 [178]), is seen to be one of the malate dehydrogenase isoenzymes which is specific for the genus *Schistosoma* [178, 179]. It is highly immunogenic and can be localized in situ in the cellular layer of the worm cecum. A statistical but low-grade (27%) level of protection was induced in mice by exposure to this homogeneous material [178]. It is anticipated that continued exploitation of affinity chromatography for enzyme-active antigens, the unique use of schistosomidical drugs as certain specific ligands [180], and immunoaffinity will aid in the purification of individual anti-genic moieties. Another approach which may assist antigen preparation in re-gard to available quantities has been employed by Hillyer and colleagues [181, 182]. This approach has taken advantage of the cross-reactive or shared anti-gens noted to occur between *S. mansoni* and *Fasciola hepatica*. *F. hepatica* is a larger, more abundantly available source of antigenic material, and thus allows preparation on a large scale of an adult antigen which is an effective immunogen in mice. Substantial protection is achieved by its utilization in mice and ham-sters [182], reflecting the protection afforded by *F. hepatica* infection [183].

Another source of schistosome antigens has been the use of "excretion and secretion," or E-S antigens. These materials are not obtained by disruption of the adult parasites, but rather by in vitro culture of the worms in a suitable medium and then collection of that medium. It was seen early that such fluids did indeed contain antigenic moieties [12,13], and that they were somewhat less complex than extracts. Yet their yield is low, and as analyzed by Murrell et al. [184], they still contain some 15 protein components separable on disc gel electrophoresis. No distinct advantage was noted for these expensive and laborious-to-produce preparations over other manipulations [189]. However, it might be mentioned that these are presumably the materials to which the host is systemically exposed. While the adult worms eat and copulate in the venules, they are likely to be releasing their excess or spent materials and excre-ment into the circulation for clearage in the portal systems or export through-out the body. We currently know little about these materials either immuno-logically or physiologically, and less about their systemic and localized effects on the host. One such form of excreta for which there is some information is the so-called schistosome pigment. This material is a product of partial diges-tion of erythrocytes by the worms. It is chemically composed of a porphyrin ring and a large proteinaceous molecule [185]. In both mice and humans [185, 186] this material is initially deposited in the endothelial and subendothelial portal areas and is often seen in phagolysosomes. Subsequently, in a residual form it is found in periportal and subcapsular areas and in granulomas. Eventu-ally it is at least partially eliminated. This substance, easily identified by micros-copy, is apparently inert and induces no inflammation or fibrogenesis [186]. This is not to say that it might not be involved in the intense reticuloendothelial hyperplasia seen in chronic schistosomiasis [2].

Another set of antigens, probably represented in the E-S materials [184, 185], is made up of membrane turnover products and those moieties which com-prise the external tegumental surface of the adult worms. Isotopic labeling pro-cedures have led to estimates that when adult worms are cultured in vitro the antigens derived from the tegument and shed into the medium are released by two processes: one due to a low-level membrane turnover rate and the other based on a more rapid secretory process [188]. Many of the antigens shed were in particulate membrane form [187]. Further studies have confirmed the particulate nature of much of the released material [189]. Localization of these reactions demonstrated that the tegument contributed the bulk of the exportable protein, while the gut epithelium was responsible for most of the released polysaccharide [189]. The majority of worm secretions were calculated to have a rapid turnover with a half-life of a few hours [189] which was consistent with the rapid secretory process detected previously [188]. Characterization of surface antigens from adult worms is hindered by the need to apply appropriate methodologies of labeling and isolation, but recent attempts are beginning to yield results [190,191].

The chronic intravascular nature of schistosomiasis has led some to suspect that quantifiable amounts of worm-derived material may occur in the circulation and that some of it might be antigenic. The fruitfulness of the resultant studies [192-194] justified the hypothesis, and has led to the quest for more "circulating antigens." Often these antigens may actually be in the form of circulating immune complexes which are quite frequently observed in the sera from both patients and experimentally infected animals [195-202]. The most completely characterized of the circulating antigens has been studied by Nash and his colleagues [203-205]. This material is a negatively charged, large-molecular-weight polysaccharide composed mainly of N-acetylgalactosamine, D-glucuronic acid, and minor amino acid constituents, classifying it as a proteoglycan [203,204]. The parasite source of this antigen has been identified within the gut epithelial cells and the cecum [205-209], and it has been termed gut-associated proteoglycan (GASP) [205]. There are obvious parallels between these studies and those concerning the polysaccharide secretion by gut epithelium [189]. A relatively complete approach can begin to be realized in relationship to at least this one parasite antigen. Parasite antigens can also be found in other host body fluids. One such antigen, termed antigen M, has been reported in the urine [209] and breast milk [210] of *S. mansoni* patients. The extensive involvement of circulating parasite antigens and immune complexes during schistosomiasis may be useful immunodiagnostically [202], and of potential danger immunopathologically, but it also may have very fundamental importance in regard to the immunobiology of this host-parasite relationship.

B. Host Responses

1. In Vivo

When considering active schistosome infections there is an unavoidable difficulty in ascribing any given in vivo phenomenon to a response induced or elicited by adult schistosomes. The problem is that upon full development of mature worms these organisms immediately begin to produce large quantities of eggs. Thus, it is sometimes hard to judge the guilty party for any given response observed. Fortunately, although there are shared and cross-reactive antigens common to these two stages, there are also sufficient differences between the components of eggs and worms to usually allow for differential responsiveness, even using crude antigenic preparations. The use of unisexual infections or only egg exposure may also help. Nonetheless, in certain situations it remains confusing as to which stage may be responsible for a particular reaction. However, it is abundantly clear that the host does develop a vast multiplicity of immune responses against adult worm components during infection. These have been most commonly examined in vivo in the form of skin test reactions against worm-derived antigens [14,16,43,177,211,212].

a. Acute Schistosomiasis

Acute or toxemic clinical schistosomiasis is a syndrome which has been most commonly reported during S. japonicum infection [213-217], but which can also occur upon infections with S. mansoni [218-220]. It is usually, but not always, associated with initial infections of substantial intensity. The average incubation period is between 30 and 50 days from the time of exposure. The onset of disease is usually acute, beginning with chills and fever, headache, anorexia, liver tenderness, cough, and often arthralgia, urticaria, lymphadenopathy, and eosinophilia. Because of these manifestations and the coincidence with worm maturation, egg production, and considerable systemic antigenic release, this syndrome has been generally thought to involve toxic products and antigen-excess, serum sickness-type, immune complex disease [1,2,5,7,8]. There is no question that this estimate was justified on circumstantial grounds, but until recently there had been no clinical or experimental studies of acute schistosomiasis which measured immunologic parameters. Lawley et al. [202] have now measured circulating immune complexes by a radiolabeled $C1_q$ binding assay in the sera of acute S. mansoni patients (6-15 weeks after exposure) and have compared their results with uninfected subjects and patients with documented infections of more than 3 years duration. Elevated $C1_q$ binding activity was found in the sera of 93% of the 15 acute patients, 18% of the 11 chronic patients, and none of the normal subjects. $C1_q$ precipitates were positive for moderate amounts of IgM and IgG, but small amounts of IgA, IgE, or C3. Anti-adult schistosome antibody titers were significantly elevated in the sera of acute patients when compared with the titers in chronic sera. It is clear that the presence of circulating immune complexes (CIC) indeed paralleled the occurrence of clinical acute schistosomiasis symptomatology. The early high levels of CIC and subsequent waning has also been reported in heavily infected mice [197]. In this setting, dramatic levels were observed between 7 and 12 weeks of infection, after which they decreased. Another murine study did not note as prominent a decrease [201].

Several studies have noted that circulating, precipitating, and fluorescent antibody titers against adult worm antigen, including GASP [207], diminish after being elevated in early human infections [221-223].

An aspect of acute disease which is observed pathologically involves a higher incidence of miliary, egg-focused, necrotic lesions [215, 218-220] in the liver and intestinal wall. It is feasible that these lesions could also be immune complex mediated. This, however, would be in a localized setting, emanating from a centrally located, antigen-producing egg lodged in the tissues [224]. Toxic reactions to released egg enzymes would be yet another possible explanation [225].

b. Chronic Schistosomiasis

The vast majority of the more than 200 million people who have schistosomiasis proceed to chronic, relatively asymptomatic infections. Of these, some progress to serious disease involving bladder calcification and urogenital tract disorders in schistosomiasis haemotobium, and with either *S. mansoni* or *S. japonicum,* intestinal disease and portal fibrosis with resultant portal hypertension and collateral circulation [1,2,5]. There is currently no evidence available that adult worms are directly involved in the etiology of any of these conditions except as the etiologic agents of the infection and producers of the eggs. This does not mean that they or their products (other than eggs) are not involved in some aspects of disease etiology, but if they are we do not yet know it. When a worm dies within the vasculature (either of natural, i.e., unknown, causes or prompted by effective chemotherapy) is usually swept to the liver and impacted there. Under this condition worms most certainly cause lesion formation, and if in sufficient numbers, they could result in a mild Jarisch-Herxheimer reaction. Although debated, such transient events do not appear to result in permanent damage [226]. The role of eggs in the process of severe schistosomiasis will be dealt with later (Section V.B).

Another aspect concerning chronic schistosomiasis in which worm antigens may play a role is that of immune complex-mediated glomerular lesions [5,7,8]. Various nephropathies have been reported in association with experimental [201, 227-235] and clinical hepatosplenic [235-246] schistosomiasis. Membranoproliferative lesions appear to be most commonly reported. In one experimental study in chimpanzees infected with *S. japonicum,* glomerulonephropathy was seen to be independent of portal fibrosis [231]. However, portal hypertension and liver damage may play a role in murine glomerular lesions [201,233]. Adult worm antigens were localized in thickenings of the basement membranes in *S. japonicum*-infected *Macaca* monkeys and were associated with deposits of IgG, IgM, IgA, IgE, and B_1C [232]. Similar lesions were reported in heavily infected mice [233], and schistosome adult antigens were again observed, but this first required elution of the immunoglobulins. Within the 12 weeks that infections were followed, single sex infections exhibited considerably fewer glomerular alterations [233]. Adult worm and soluble egg antigens were detected, often with IgM, IgG, and C3, in most severe and some mild glomerular lesions in *S. mansoni*-infected baboons [234]. The possibility of autoimmune damage has been discussed in relationship to circulating DNA and anti-DNA in hamsters and humans infected with *S. mansoni* [235]. Clinical studies have also provided evidence of immune reactants in the glomerular lesions. In one study adult worm antigen (probably GASP) was detected in lesions from 2 of 12 *S. mansoni* patients studies, while eluates from two patients contained serologic activity primarily for worm gut epithelium but also for miracidia [244]. Acid eluates from two of five *S. mansoni* patients in a different study exhibited specificity for gut and tegument of adult worms, but none for cercariae, eggs, or mouse liver tissue (the worms tested were obtained from mice) [246]. Pretreatment with antiserum against GASP inhibited the anti-gut specific reaction. The clinical significance of schistosomal-associated nephropathies may be considerable in hospital-based patients, but remains unconfirmed in epidemiologic field settings. In one postmortem study on 246 consecutive autopsies in Cairo, Egypt, it was seen that the renal alterations observed were not related to either the presence of or intensity of *S. haematobium* or *S. mansoni* infection [247].

c.   Resistance

The underlying theory behind "concomitant immunity" in schistosomiasis is that the adult worms induce protective immune responses but are not affected by them, whereas the immature, schistosomular stage is susceptible. Having discussed the vulnerability of early schistosomules and having listed evidence that they themselves can induce immunity under certain circumstances, the ability of adult worms to induce resistance needs to be examined.

If the rhesus monkey survives acute disease, it tolerates schistosome infections well (due to elimination of most adult worms) and develops good protection. Using this species as a model system, several investigators have observed protection following single sex infections [71]. Furthermore, the use of eggs alone as an immunization scheme was ineffective [71]. It was then shown that active, percutaneous infection with cercariae was not necessary; complete protection was achieved by surgically implanting 7-8-week-old adult worms from other hosts [248]. Similarly, intraperitoneal injection of schistosomules and adult *S. japonicum* or *S. mansoni* worms induced immunity in rhesus monkeys [249]. A variety of anti-worm antigen responses can be observed as skin test reactions in infected rhesus monkeys [211]. Further analysis of the rhesus model has led to several unique immunization schemes utilizing transfer factor from normal monkeys plus immune serum, or BCG plus immune serum [211,

250]. These two regimens statistically reduced challenge worm burdens (mean reduction = 33%). BCG alone did not induce resistance in these studies, nor did adjuvant and a worm membrane preparation. A group which received *Corynebacterium parvum* and antigen developed lymphocyte responsiveness to adult worm antigen prior to challenge, and this group and the transfer factor plus serum group responded strongly after challenge in in vitro lymphocyte studies to adult antigen. The responses were transient, lasting about 3 weeks. A variety of serologic tests demonstrated the development of antibodies to adult, egg, and cercarial antigens, but there was no correlation of antibody titers and protection levels. It seems that stimulation of both cellular and humoral arms of the immune response must be present and activated to express protection in this system. Use of another primate for resistance studies, the baboon, has led to the observation that protective immunity against either *S. haematobium* or *S. mansoni* in this species requires long-term, active infections [251,252]. This would imply that the early stage is not an important inducer, but the use of trickle (multiple low-dose exposures) infections to immunize may cloud this point.

Resistance studies with rats, another species which develops strong protection upon infection [99,100] and eliminates most of its initial worm load, have come the closest to showing positive protection with extracts or fractions of adult schistosomes [253]. Even in these experiments using whole worm homogenates, the level of significant protection was sometimes equaled by that in albumin-immunized controls. Phillips et al. [66] have compared soluble preparations from cercariae, adults, and eggs in their immunization capabilities in rats. Although the preparations may not have contained the appropriate adult worm immunogen, the data do not favor the role of the adult in stimulation of resistance. Their administration did not convey the level of protection which irradiated cercariae, and even the soluble preparation from cercariae, provided [66]. From many attempts to artificially immunize mice (other than by the use of irradiated organisms) only a very few have been successful [178,182]. Neither multiple infections followed by chemotherapy [226] nor intraperitoneal exposure of mice to living adult worms encased in diffusion chambers [254] led to the partial resistance which usually accompanies active infection. The induction of protection in mice by active infection has recently received renewed interest and has been examined in regard to a variety of conditions [101,169, 255-259]. There is now some agreement [163,255,256] that the resistance induced in mice by active infection requires bisexual (male and female) infection to achieve any substantial degree of dependable protection. This is in obvious contrast to the situation in the rhesus monkey [71]. Furthermore, although the actual role of the eggs in the induction of immunity in this active disease model is still under debate [255,257,260], it seems clear that they contribute to protection [257]. Because the route and timing of egg administration is crucial [255,257,260], they may not be needed in an immunogenically specific role. It may be that they, and the response to them, either cause mechanical obstruction within the lungs, perhaps acting in some local adjuvant role, or aid in the localization of needed specialized accessory cells such as eosinophils or activated macrophages (see Section V.D). It bears stating that under other conditions of immunization there is not an absolute requirement for pulmonary egg deposition to achieve protection in the mouse. This is obvious from the successes obtained using highly irradiated cercariae or schistosomules [32,33,60-70, 102,104] and passive transfer of partial resistance into normal mice using immune serum alone [89,94,95]. It appears inescapable that there is more than one set of specifically inducible mechanisms which can afford protection to mice. Analysis of these various systems is far from complete, and some surprises may be obtained. Whether or not it is related directly to the question of number of eggs, it has been observed that there is a dose-time relationship at play in the development of active disease-induced protection [101]. Using an early perfusion technique [169] to determine the degree of protection (comparing immature worm burdens with mature worm numbers in the same host) in relationship to number of harbored adult worms and time, Long et al. [101] and Colley and Freeman [449] concluded that the degree of protection is directly related to the adult worm burden harbored. The actual numbers of worms needed to induce significant protection decreases with increased time of chronic infection and may vary considerably with mouse strain. It has also been noted that the use of different pools or even clones of cercariae to establish the protecting infection can lead to a widely different degree of protection [258]. Furthermore, different clones of cercariae vary in their susceptibility to resistance mechanisms [258]. These observations clearly provide a basis for much of the variability encountered in this field. It is hypothesized [258] that the observed differences are predicated upon immunogenic and antigenic differences inherent in the separate clones. Although this is an entirely feasible explanation, in light of the data regarding the relationship of protection to adult worm burden, it might be critical to establish that the cercarial variation was not related to their inherent virulence, i.e., differences in a clone's physiological ability to establish adult infection. The commendable but low number of cercariae used to establish protection might be critical in this regard. Whether the explanation is physiologic, immunological, or some other consideration, it is crucial to realize the inherent variability brought to these systems by the parasite as well as the host.

2. In Vitro

In vitro demonstrations of anti-worm responses are beginning to accumulate in both experimental [49,250,261,262] and clinical schistosomiasis [17,51,53-58, 262-265]. Under certain conditions human lymphocyte responsiveness to adult extracts was observed early in infection and tended to be less with patients of longer duration infection [51,264]. The regulation of these events will be discussed below.

C. Regulation of Responses

1. In Vivo

The long-term in vivo survival of adult schistosomes is generally thought to depend on a combination of capabilities ascribed to the worms which allow them to effectively evade or prevent the responses which the host would normally mount against an intravascular foreign object [4-6,8]. Some of these capabilities primarily involve physiologic characteristics of these trematodes, whereas others may actually depend more upon the effect of the worm on the host's response systems.

a. The Parasite

It is by now quite clear that adult worms obtained from mice exhibit antigens of mouse specificity on their tegument. The presence of these acquired host antigens has been demonstrated primarily through the use of the passive transfer of intact adult worms from one species of host into the vasculature of a different host species. Most often, if the host which received the worms has been previously immunized against erythrocytes, or other tissues, of the donor species, the worms are rejected by the recipient [154,156,158,266-270]. Although this seems true of "mouse" worm transfers, some reports indicate that immunizations against rat or hamster tissues do not lead, upon transfer of "rat" or "hamster" worms, to the destruction of these adult schistosomes [267,271, 272]. In the case of the rat worms (a generally poor host for *S. mansoni*), the evidence that these organisms appear to exhibit only low quantities of rat host antigens may be interpreted as compatible with the hypothesis that acquisition of sufficient host antigens assists the worm in functionally avoiding the host immune response. Acquisition of sufficient host antigens might therefore correlate with their survival in a good host [267] (for example, in mice). The repertoire of host antigens acquired during early schistosomular development includes certain erythrocyte antigens [158], immunoglobulins of various antibody specificities [273,274], major histocompatibility complex (MHC) antigens [275], and Forssman-like antigen [276]. Interestingly, the immunoglobulins may be bound to the tegument via Fc receptors [273,277]. The fascinating possibility of a degree of stage specificity in regard to the acquisition of different host antigens has been demonstrated in the material called intercellular substance (ICS), the glycocalyx-like moieties of the squamous cells of the skin epidermis [278]. Schistosomules which penetrated mouse skin did not exhibit these ICS antigens

10 min after penetration, but those recovered 2 and 24 hr afterward displayed increasing amounts of ICS. These host antigens were lost after the organisms left the skin, for they were not found on lung (6 day), liver (3 week), or fully adult (7 week) schistosomes [278]. Presumably the maturing organism sheds (by membrane turnover) ICS acquired during its sojourn through the skin and, since it encounters no more of this substance on subsequent journeys, it does not continually reacquire it. As well as acquired host antigens, the phenomenon known as "antigen mimicry" [13,21,279] occurs wherein the parasite actually synthesizes host, or hostlike, materials. The most completely documented of these situations is the occurrence of mouse α_2-macroglobulin on *S. mansoni* adults obtained from mice or monkeys [280,281].

It is difficult to provide definitive proof that adult worms are protected from host responses by this array of host, or hostlike, antigens on their surfaces. The basis of the demonstration, in large part, rests on the destruction inflicted on worms by immunization against host antigens. This killing is associated with ultrastructurally observable lesion formation [155]. However, when monkey worms were transferred into monkeys rendered hyperimmune by virtue of a previous infection [282], a majority of the worms were seen to be alive and active although similar damage occurred. In fact, while extensive damage might be observed at one location on a worm, other areas were perfectly healthy. Thus, it could be interpreted that host mechanisms can attack worms in spite of host antigens, but either the nature of the organism's syncytial tegument, rapid turnover repair mechanisms or nondetrimental sloughing prevent permanent damage [156,187-189]. It remains possible that the degree of damage effected by host mechanisms might be more than could be repaired if the parasite surface did not have at least whatever partial protection might be provided by host antigens [267].

Nonspecific immunodepression of the anti-sheep erythrocyte (SRbc) plaque-forming cell capacity of mice infected with *S. mansoni* has been observed at the time of maturation of worms [283] and during chronic infection [284]. The suppression was associated with either bisexual or unisexual infection, was eliminated by chemotherapeutic cure, and could be mimicked in normal mice by injection of an adult worm membrane preparation [284]. Both humoral and cell-mediated anti-SRbc responses were suppressed by this treatment [285].

b. The Immune Responsiveness

Humoral immune responses against some adult worm antigens appear to decrease with the establishment of chronic schistosomiasis [202,208,221-223]. This has been observed in regard to both IgM and IgG specific anti-worm titers [208], and it occurs in the face of the high levels of total IgG observed in chronic patients [208]. Based on the continued intravascular existence of the adult worms, it must be assumed that this apparent decrease in the production of some anti-worm antibodies happens during a period of continuous exposure of the host to antigens of the worm. It therefore may well reflect specific worm regulatory control of the host's responsiveness.

2. In Vitro

a. Parasite

Active immunosuppressive activity has been ascribed to both adult *S. mansoni* membrane preparations in vivo [284] and low-molecular-weight (500-1000) products of adult worms in vitro [285]. In the latter system, mouse, rat, and human lymphocyte responsiveness was suppressed in regard to their responses to the mitogens ConA, PHA, or LPS and to allogeneic cells [285]. The sera from infected rats could also suppress these responses.

b. The Immune Responsiveness

Several in vitro studies of lymphocyte responses to worm antigens during *S. mansoni* infection have described various immunoregulatory mechanisms which occur in relationship to worm-induced responsiveness [51,53,54,56-58,286,287]. In one study, the peripheral blood mononuclear cells from approximately 40% of the chronic patients studied could be specifically induced by exposure to a worm preparation (SWAP) to express a nonspecific suppressor cell effect on autologous cells responding to PHA stimulation [286]. This worm antigen-induced suppressor system has also been observed to occur by 8 weeks after *S. mansoni* murine infection [287]. Sera from almost all chronic *S. mansoni* patients have been seen to contain a suppressive activity which effectively dampens SWAP-induced responsiveness [51,53,54,57,58]. It was further observed that, independent of this specific serosuppression, there existed in the PBMN cell population of over 80% of chronic patients tested (but not uninfected or transiently infected patients) adherent and/or phagocytic cells which decreased SWAP-induced responsiveness [54,56]. These suppressive A/P cells did not affect PHA- or *Candida albicans* extract-induced responses and could act in combination with serosuppression to almost eliminate SWAP-stimulated lymphocyte responses [54,56]. It has been preliminarily shown that the inclusion of indomethacin in SWAP-induced lymphocyte cultures greatly augments these responses [58]. This is circumstantial evidence for the involvement of regulatory "suppressor" macrophages acting via prostaglandin synthesis and release [288,289]. In a study using the whole blood culture lymphocyte blastogenesis assay, which might be expected to contain all of these suppressive agents, decreased responses to worm antigens were not observed in relationship to the duration of *S. japonicum* infection [264]. The recently reported lack of monocyte effector mechanisms using

cells of heavily infected patients [143] is as yet unexplained. It remains speculative whether the loss of responsiveness was caused by heavy infection or whether an inability to kill schistosomules predisposed these patients to heavy infection.

D. Consequences and Conjecture

It is easy by either skin test, serology, or in vitro culture to demonstrate immune
responses which occur against various worm antigens during schistosome infection.
The relatively stable maintenance of adult worm burdens once established indicates that living mature adult worms evade, prevent, utilize, or ignore most of
these responses which the host mounts against them. Although some degree of
resistance is generally considered to be expressed against maturing worms (between the lung and liver stage), in the natural situation there is little likelihood
that the adult serves as a functional target for acquired resistance mechanisms.
It remains unknown whether or not a thorough understanding of the means by
which this evasion is accomplished would allow a shift in this balance. However,
regardless of its direct practicality to schistosomiasis, the elucidation and unravel-
ing of the mechanisms involved may well aid in an overall understanding of immunoregulatory mechanisms at play in other chronic conditions such as neo-
plasias, allogeneic grafts, other spectral chronic infectious diseases, and the regulatory failures behind certain autoimmune states.

Several intriguing hypotheses have been discussed in relationship to the
ability of adult schistosomes to survive unhindered. The release of membrane
antigens [187] and the occurrence of circulating free antigens [192-194,203-
205] and immune complexes [195-202] suggest the possibility that these materials may have roles in the regulation of immune responsiveness. This situation
finds parallel support in the area of tumor immunology where circulating antibody, tumor antigens, and immune complexes have been involved in the concept
of immunological enhancement [290,291]. The modulatory effect of passive
serum transfer in rats, which is dependent upon the duration of infection [100],
might well fit this hypothesis. The evidence in the human that transition from
acute to chronic infection is accompanied by a decrease in circulating immune
complexes [202] may mitigate against their involvement in establishing the
chronic state, but may not reflect the total spectrum of immune complex production or localization. The regulatory mechanisms which might involve immune complexes could be either enhancement (possibly interfering with effector
mechanisms) or a more active process such as induction of suppression through
triggering of suppressor cells [292]. This could perhaps occur by their interact-
ing with suppressor T cells via IgG Fc receptors (Tγ cells) [293,294].

Closely tied to the concept of antibody-mediated enhancement are thoughts
regarding antiidiotypic regulation [295] during schistosomiasis. There is currently

no evidence that antidiotype, or antireceptor, regulation occurs in schistosome infection. However, specific idiotypic antibodies often occur upon prolonged immunization, presumably due to chronic stimulation by cells and antibodies of a given idiotype. This is certainly the case in schistosomiasis, and it seems that future investigation should consider that this fine-tuning mechanism may afford the type of regulation observed in schistosomiasis where other responses are generally well preserved.

Another train of thought concerning immunosuppression has been hypothesized by Hubbard [296]. As stated previously [280,281], schistosomes express mouse α_2-macroglobulin on their surface. This moiety has nonspecific immunosuppressive capabilities [296]. It is theorized that denatured α_2-macroglobulin (perhaps denatured by interactions with suitable proteinases with which it combines) may then decrease lymphocyte reactivity [296]. It seems possible that this immunosuppressive mechanism might occur in the localized area of the surface of this schistosome [281], thereby helping to prevent worm rejection.

V. EGGS

Adult pairs of schistosomes produce from several hundred to several thousand eggs per day. These eggs consist of an embryo (the miracidium) within a rigid shell of sclerotin. This material is a stable, cross-linked "quinone-tanned" protein [297]. The outer surface of the shell is covered with microspines [298-300], and superimposed over these is a fibrous network [300]. The shell is also fenestrated in some areas with micropores [298,299]. Within the shell the miracidium lies in a fluid medium enclosed in the vitelline membrane. The morphology of the eggs of the three main human schistosomes (*S. haematobium, S. mansoni,* and *S. japonicum*) is diagnostic for each species, i.e., they display either a terminal or lateral spine, or a sublateral nub of a spine, respectively. These eggs vary in size from 40-70 X 70-190 μm and mature during the several days after oviposition. Once mature, the embryo lives for approximately a fortnight. This stage does not multiply in the mammalian host, and if the life cycle is to be carried one, the embryonated eggs must reach a freshwater environment via either the urine or the feces prior to their death. Once in fresh water they hatch, releasing the free-swimming miracidia to find, penetrate, and multiply asexually within the specific intermediate molluscan host for each species.

However, many of the eggs (perhaps 20-65%) do not successfully bore through the vascular wall and the wall of the gut or the bladder to be excreted [301]. These then live for awhile and die within the host tissues. The bladder and intestinal walls, liver, and lungs are the final resting places for the majority of these eggs. A wide variety of ectopic sites of egg deposition have also been reported [2]. Various enzyme activities and phospholipids have been reported to be associated with the miracidia [302-304]. Some directly toxic effects of living eggs have been reported in an in vitro tissue culture system [225]. Surprisingly little is known concerning the metabolism of schistosome eggs. It is reported that they express active DNA, RNA, and protein synthesis. They are not glycolytically active, but they do metabolize acetate, catabolize amino acids, and utilize the Krebs cycle [305]. The per egg levels of activity appeared to be quite low.

A. Antigens

The existence of egg antigens is very simply demonstrated by using the serum of an infected patient or experimental animal to do a circumovum precipitin test (COPT) [10,306]. In this system lyophilized or living eggs are mixed with the serum tested, and a positive result appears as precipitating material forming as serpiginous columns stemming from several points on the egg. von Lichtenberg has also demonstrated by fluorescent antibody studies the seepage of antigens from eggs in vivo, and the subsequent sequestration of these materials within the induced granulomas [224]. Egg antigenic moieties have since been harvested in the supernatant fluid of a 100,000 X*g* centrifuged saline homogenate of *S. mansoni* eggs. These materials were shown to be capable of inducing strong cell-mediated sensitization [307]. Exposure to this preparation, called soluble egg antigens (SEA), sensitized mice to granuloma formation upon later exposure to *S. mansoni* eggs. Polyacrylamide gel electrophoresis of SEA revealed eight bands which stained with Coomassie blue [307]. Later electrophoretic analysis of this preparation using sodium dodecyl sulfate (SDS) polyacrylamide gel electrophoresis demonstrated at least 18-20 individual Coomassie blue-staining bands, and six bands which stained with periodic acid Schiff reagent (PAS). Four PAS bands stained faintly for Coomassie blue [308]. Upon double diffusion testing with infected sera, SEA exhibited from three to six immunoprecipitin bands [308].

There have now been several studies aimed at the purification of some of the antigens which comprise *S. mansoni* SEA [309-316]. Immunoaffinity procedures are now being successfully applied to isolating individual components of *S. japonicum* SEA [317]. It is likely that a distinct *S. mansoni* egg antigen has also been purified by a rigorous phenol extraction procedure which has yielded a high-molecular-weight (> 200,000) neutral polysaccharide antigen [318]. The results of these laborious, and largely analytical, studies are beginning to provide hope that purified antigens from eggs will soon be available in preparative quantities to allow investigations into the individual immune responses which together comprise the complex reactions against schistosome eggs [5,8,319-322].

B. Host Responses

1. In Vivo

a. Pathogenesis

The gross and microscopic observations of host responses to schistosome eggs, either artificially introduced or encountered during active infection, have been thoroughly described and analyzed. Many of these studies have been reviewed [1-3,5,7,8,321]. As opposed to host responses against the other schistosome stages which are generally either protective or have little detectable effect on the host, the reactions associated with egg deposition are clearly immunopathogenic. Therefore, most of the many studies conducted on the pathophysiology and pathogenesis of schistosomiasis in humans or experimental hosts have ultimately examined the host responses to eggs.

In most experimental hosts it is generally agreed that the host's granulomatous response against eggs deposited in the tissues (primarily the liver and intestinal wall) is the major pathogenic process contributing to disease [2,7,8,321-328]. The observations vary considerably in regard to the host chosen and the schistosome studied [329-332], but the overall conclusions are that egg-focused granulomatous lesions are pathologic, and in many cases they are ultimately responsible for the development of portal hypertension due to blockage of hepatic portal blood flow. In this situation collateral circulation develops with shunting of many of the eggs to the lungs, possibly leading to cor pulmonale.

In humans and higher primates such as the chimpanzee, it is still debated whether egg-induced granuloma formation is the direct precursor of periportal fibrosis, i.e., the forerunner of the development of Symmer's clay-pipe stem fibrosis [333-337]. Several new approaches are now being applied to some of these questions which concern the relationship between granulomas and fibrosis. Quantitative analysis of the collagen synthetic activity of slices of liver from 9-10 week *S. mansoni*-infected mice showed that these livers produced 16 times the amount of collagen as parallel control liver slices [338]. It was suggested that the immunological stimulus of anti-egg reactions led to this production. In other systems it has been shown that a lymphokine activity could stimulate collagen synthesis by cultured fibroblasts [339]. As a possible connecting link in schistosomiasis, it has been seen that culture supernatant fluids from isolated, intact granulomas contain a fibroblast-stimulating activity [340]. It is therefore possible that a portion of the granulomatous relationship to fibrosis is not only concerned with physical blockage of blood flow by coalescence but also by regulation of collagen deposition. Histopathologic and morphometric studies on human schistosomal liver tissues have raised the question of reticulin fiber depo-

sition in the perisinusoidal spaces, perhaps occurring secondarily to high intra-
luminal pressures due to compensated arterial flows [341]. The appearance of
myofibroblasts with classic fibroblasts within the protal spaces may further indicate the secondary effects of chronic inflammation due to egg-induced reactions
[342].

b. Description of the Granulomatous Response

Numerous publications have described the schistosome egg granuloma.
Two groups of investigators, von Lichtenberg and his colleagues [224,322,343]
and Warren and his co-workers [320,321,344,345], have been especially active
in this area. Two main approaches have been utilized. One is to describe granuloma formation as it occurs usually upon hepatic egg deposition during active
infection. The other is to analyze the response evoked upon artificial deposition
of isolated eggs into the pulmonary vasculature of an experimental host following
intravenous injection of the eggs via the tail vein. Some have investigated either
S. haematobium [322,345,346] or S. japonicum [320,322,346-348] egg-induced
lesions. Granuloma formation is supposed to vary somewhat depending on the
maturity of the egg in question, but this is not always observed [322]. In general, the response to S. mansoni and S. haematobium eggs advanced from minimal
reactions, to mixed inflammatory reaction (rich in eosinophils), to epithelioid
cell granulomas, and on to involuting and scarring gramulomas [322]. Schistosoma japonicum eggs elicit a somewhat different response pattern which involves
more of a psuedoabscess-histiogranulocytic granuloma progression [322]. These
lesions now appear to be full of eosinophils [320,348], although other reports
have claimed that these granulocytes are largely neutrophils [322,347]. One
basic difference among the three species is that S. mansoni eggs are primarily deposited as single eggs, whereas S. haematobium, and more so S. japonicum, eggs
are deposited in multiegg clusters [346]. The reactions to all the eggs, with some
notable differences in the case of S. japonicum, appear to be immunologically
mediated granulomatous responses to antigenic nidi. Upon further examination
of the prerequisites for this granuloma formation using S. mansoni eggs, it was
seen that isolated miracidia elicited a dramatically different, rapidly formed and
cleared neutrophilic response, while egg shells alone are singularly ignored by the
host response system [349]. Intact living or dead eggs evoked granuloma formation [349], but eggs depleted of their releasable antigenic materials induced
only foreign-body reactions [350].

Ultrastructural, hepatic S. mansoni egg-induced granulomas were seen to
contain numerous eosinophils, fibroblasts, and macrophages, as well as some
neutrophils, lymphocytes, plasma cells, and multinucleated giant cells [298,
351,352]. During later stages of infection, immunoblasts and plasma cells may
become more prominent [352]. Granulomas in the serosal-muscularis regions

of the small intestine were similarly comprised [353]. A quantitative study of
the cell types in isolated pulmonary *S. mansoni* granulomas demonstrated that,
initially, lymphocytes were the almost exclusive cell type found, but then eosinophils became predominant (above 70% at their peak) [354]. Granuloma volumes
in the lungs of mice treated with specific anti-eosinophil serum and injected with
S. mansoni eggs were one-tenth the volumes of those in normal-serum-treated
control mice [355]. Large mononuclear cells were usually 30% of the normal
granuloma population, and neutrophils were never more than 10% [354].

     Although the tissue-trapped eggs are a dead-end life-cycle stage, it is of
interest to know whether the dead eggs are destroyed or just remain. The rate
of destruction of *S. japonicum* eggs in murine lungs is more rapid than *S. haematobium* eggs, which were in turn more quickly destroyed than *S. mansoni* eggs
[356]. Preexposure to eggs increased their rate of destruction upon subsequent
egg deposition [356]. This anamnestic destructive rate has been confirmed in
mice [357] and extended to rhesus monkeys [358]. Furthermore, there was
host species variation in that the half-life of *S. mansoni* eggs in rhesus monkeys
was only 7 days as compared with 4 weeks in mice [357,358]. Eosinophils, and
to some extent macrophages, have been morphologically associated with in vivo
egg destruction within granulomas both morphologically [351,359] and by
eosinophil depletion experiments [360].

c. The Etiology of the Granulomatous Response to Eggs

     It has been established that accelerated schistosome egg-induced granulo-
matous responses are immunological sensitization phenomena [224]. Mature
eggs elaborate antigenic materials which are responsible for this sensitization and
elicitation [224,307,350], and the sequestration of these released materials is
largely due to the granulomatous response [224,361,362]. Furthermore, although antibody and antigen-antibody reactions are clearly a part of the normally
encountered granulomatous response, Warren and his colleagues have amply demonstrated that granuloma formation can occur in the absence of antibody production [363]. This has recently been confirmed in mice made B-cell deficient
by anti-μ injections in that they exhibited normal granulomatous responses
against eggs [364]. It is clear that granuloma formation to *S. mansoni* eggs is
primarily based upon a state of cell-mediated hypersensitivity [319]. This is a
stage-specific reaction [365] which does not develop upon exposure to irradiated cercariae or unisexual infections. Cross-sensitization studies using the eggs
of *S. japonicum*, *S. haematobium*, and *S. mansoni* indicate that *S. japonicum*
eggs are more antigenically distinct than those of the other two species [345].
A plethora of procedures which alter host cell-mediated immune capabilities
have been applied to the elucidation of the nature of the mechanisms responsible for egg-induced granuloma formation to *S. mansoni* eggs [366-375]. All

of these studies are consistent with an understanding of granuloma formation based on a cell-mediated immunological mechanism. Studies on the *S. japonicum* egg-induced lesions do not yet clearly define its etiology. Large mononuclear cells were predominant in such pulmonary lesions with eosinophils being the next most common cell [348]. Many of the aspects of *S. japonicum* sensitization and lesion formation make it likely that the underlying mechanism here is involved with antigen-antibody reactions. Some degree of T lymphocyte participation may be inferred by the ability of lentinan (a T-cell adjuvant) to augment these reactions [376]. *Schistosome haematobium* egg-focused lesions bear close resemblance to the situation with *S. mansoni* eggs [345].

d. Egg-Induced Granulomas in T-Depleted or Congenitally Athymic Mice

Several groups have investigated the outcome of active schistosomiasis mansoni in mice which were functionally deprived of their T-lymphocyte capabilities [377-385]. These studies have focused on alterations in host responsiveness to eggs and on other related pathophysiologic aspects of the disease. Artificial T depletion was seen to abolish such T-lymphocyte-mediated anti-egg immune responses as lymphocyte blastogenesis, delayed dermal reactivity, reaginic antibody production, and eosinophilia. A T-independent antibody function was still observed [377]. In this study the T-depleted *S. mansoni*-infected mice developed a more rapidly fatal disease than did intact parallel-infected mice, whereas the uninfected T-depleted controls remained healthy for months after the termination of the experiment [377,378]. The granulomatous lesions observed in depleted infected mice were largely liquefactive, necrotic lesions in both gut and liver sites. In contrast to typical *S. mansoni* egg lesion histopathology, there was severe, egg-related, parenchymal cell destruction [378]. Many of the T-depleted mice developed septicemia, presumably secondary to their necrotic gut lesions, which may also have contributed to the mortality rate [378]. More recently, similar methodology has again resulted in the same increased morbidity and mortality in T-depleted *S. mansoni*-infected mice [382, 383]. These studies further documented liver cell damage by increased enzyme levels. They also described an unexpected decrease in the number of eggs produced by worms in such mice [382] and an even greater decrease in the rate of excretion of the eggs produced in the mice [384]. The passive administration of serum from egg-sensitized or chronically infected, immunologically intact animals helped to reverse some of the liver damage associated with the hepatocellular toxicity described in the egg lesions by this study [383]. Furthermore, such passive transfers aided in increasing egg excretion rates and worm fecundity [384]. The serum-related observations are as yet unexplained but provide a fascinating area for speculation. Two other studies have been reported which observed deleterious results related to *S. mansoni* infections in congenitally athymic (nu/nu; nude) mice [381,385]. The egg lesions observed in these mice were primarily monocytic in nature, with few epithelioid cells and almost no eosinophils or giant cells. Although infected heterozygous (nu/+) mice provided the normally recorded picture, the nude lesions were described as resulting in zonal hepatocellular damage, which was not characteristic of latent hepatitis-virus-induced lesions [381]. Antigenic material from the eggs was observed diffusely throughout these lesions as opposed to its sequestration in the normal granulomas [224,381]. In contrast to heterozygotes, many infected nude mice died around week 8 of infection [385], and hepatic necrosis (not always egg associated) was noted at 7 and 8 weeks in the infection. These four studies, utilizing artificially and genetically T-lymphocyte-depleted mice, indicate that, although the normal granulomatous lesions are themselves pathogenic, being the direct contributors to hepatosplenic disease and the portal hypersensitive state [321,323], they also perform a host protective role in the walling off of tissue-deposited eggs.

Two studies in nude mice stand in apparent contradiction to these observations [379,380]. In these instances *S. mansoni* infections in nude mice did not lead to increased morbidity or mortality, but rather improved the usual disease-associated parameters found in murine schistosomiasis [380]. In these studies the egg lesions observed were much reduced in size, did not involve eosinophils, were generally monocytic, and did not appear necrotic in nature. It is possible that the specific pathogen-free housing of these animals contributed to their well-being. It might be fair to summarize that, although large granulomatous responses to schistosome eggs appear to be overzealous, largely unwarranted and pathogenic entities, some capability to respond to, and circumscribe, tissue-deposited eggs would seem beneficial. If this is true then a small tight granulomatous reaction, preferably only a few cells thick, might provide the "best of all possible worlds." We will later discuss the manner in which the host-parasite relationship has tried quite successfully to come up with this type of response (Section V.C).

e. Reactions to Egg Antigens

In vivo responses to soluble or particle-bound (but not egg-associated) egg antigens have been studied extensively in the form of skin tests and granuloma model systems. The clinical skin test studies have utilized both immediate and delayed testing [14,16,43] and in general indicate that hypersensitivity states do exist against egg antigens. They are not very useful diagnostically, and considerable differences exist in different studies as to their sensitivity and specificity [14,16,43]. Experimentally, delayed [307,386] and Arthus-type [381] reactions have been reported. The former responses were passively transferable with lymphoid cells but not with serum from infected mice, whereas the latter reaction was associated with serum transfer [386]. Experimental, passive, cutaneous anaphylaxis reactions evoked upon systemic challenge with SEA, 72 hr after intradermal serum injections, were also positive using sera from mice infected with *S. mansoni* for more than 7 weeks [387]. The delayed-type hypersensitivity reactions elicited by SEA in infected mice often contain over 50% eosinophils at 24 hr after challenge injection [388]. A unique model for studying granuloma formation against SEA, as well as other antigens, without the effect of the actual egg has been developed [389,390] and analyzed [391,392]. Particle bound antigens were seen to elicit the same sequence of histologic events in the pulmonary vasculature reported for egg-induced granuloma formation.

2. In Vitro

Several studies have reported on the ability of isolated, intact schistosome egg granulomas to elaborate lymphokine activities when cultured in vitro. These include migration inhibition factor [393], eosinophil stimulation promoter (ESP) [394], eosinophil chemotactic factor of lymphocytes (ECF-L) [395], and a fibroblast stimulating factor which induces replication and collagen synthesis [340]. Such studies provide something of a connecting link between in vitro observed phenomena and the occurrences in vivo within the actual lesion.

a. Antibody Responses

The in vitro detection of humoral responses against intact eggs primarily rests on the COPT [10,306], whereas numerous serologic assays have been used to determine the host's antibody responses to egg antigens [10,48,202,312,387, 396-398]. The methodologies used range from immunofluorescence to ELISA and radioimmunoassays, and it is clear that multiple antibodies are produced which react with the components of SEA.

b. Antibody-Dependent Cell-Mediated Reactions and Cell-Mediated Reactions against Eggs

Upon in vitro cocultivation of *S. mansoni* eggs and peritoneal exudate cells from *S. mansoni*-infected mice (a source rich in eosinophils), it was observed that approximately 20% of the eggs were destroyed and had eosinophils associated with them [399]. They were morphologically reminiscent of the in vivo observations described above [351,359] which showed eosinophil involvement in egg destruction within granulomas. It was shown that macrophages, lymphocytes, or neutrophils were ineffective in this process, as were eosinophils from normal (uninfected) mice [399]. Egg destruction was demonstrated both morphologically and functionally. When further examined, this eosinophil-mediated egg

damage was seen to be abrogated by trypsinization of the cells, whereas reincuba-
tion in sera from infected mice restored this ability [400]. Sera from *Trichinella
spiralis*-infected mice did not have this effect. If the *S. mansoni* serum was first
passed over an SEA-bound immunoaffinity column, the restorative capacity of
the serum was removed. It thus appears that either normal or trypsinized-"infected" eosinophils can destroy schistosome eggs in an ADCC-type reaction mediated by cytophilic anti-SEA antibodies [400]. However, this mechanism does
not seem to be the only interaction operative in this egg destruction-eosinophil
relationship [395]. When normal (non-egg destructive) eosinophils were exposed
to lymphokine-containing culture supernatant fluids, these cells were endowed
with significant destructive capabilities [395]. Therefore, two effector mechanisms involving eosinophils seem to be capable of inflicting damage on schistosome eggs in vitro. Recent studies demonstrating decreased egg destruction in
vivo with parallel increased mortality upon elimination of such eosinophil participation by the use of anti-eosinophil serum appear to substantiate the significance of this anti-egg capability in the overall relationship [360].

c. Cell-Mediated Responses

Experimental studies using artificial exposure to SEA [401], or following
active infection [49,261,387,398,402-404] of mice, guinea pigs, hamsters, or
rhesus monkeys, have demonstrated that cell-mediated responses against SEA
can be measured by either lymphocyte blastogenesis assays or by lymphokine
(MIF or ESP) production. There are some fairly repeatable patterns of responsiveness during the course of the infection, and these will be described in more
detail in Section V.C, which is concerned with regulation.

Through the recent development of an in vitro model of granuloma formation [405], it is becoming possible to further dissect the granulomatous process
and study the progression of cellular interactions which produce this lesion in
response to schistosome eggs. This system involves culturing adult worm pairs
in erythrocyte-containing cultures. The worm pairs produce eggs and, 5-7 days
after the addition of host spleen cells, granuloma formation is observed around
the eggs. The cells used could be from either previously sensitized mice or normal mice. If sensitized cells were used, granuloma formation was accelerated.
The reaction demonstrated specificity for schistosome eggs and did not occur
using spleen cells from nude mice [405].

Lymphocyte reactivity to SEA has also been examined in clinical schistosomiasis. One study has shown lymphokine production (ESP) upon challenge
[406], whereas several have now demonstrated varying degrees of responsiveness
of peripheral blood [17,51,53-57,262,264] and spleen [407] lymphocytes in
blastogenesis assays upon exposure of the cells to SEA. Except in early infections, most lymphoid responses to SEA have been of a rather low grade.

C. Regulation of Responsiveness

1. In Vivo

Andrade and Warren observed that, during chronic infections in mice, granuloma formation to newly deposited *S. mansoni* eggs decreased after having reached a maximum at 8 weeks of infection [408]. This phenomenon of diminished reactivity in the face of continued antigenic exposure (egg production being continuous) was termed "endogenous desensitization" and was characterized using the pulmonary egg embolism model [409]. The observation has been reconfirmed in both the active infection [387] and the lung model [398] and has been renamed spontaneous modulation [410,411]. There has been one report that the size of granulomas also decreases in humans infected with *S. mansoni* (Ref. 412 and the discussion in Ref. 411). This study examined granulomas obtained by rectal biopsy. Some tangential evidence exists that a similar decreased reactivity develops in hosts infected with *S. haematobium* or *S. japonicum* (reviewed in Ref. 411). The in vitro evidence that some SEA-specific immune responses similarly diminish will be discussed below.

The mechanism(s) of this experimental modulation or suppression of active granuloma formation has been studied in vivo by use of an adoptive transfer system [413-415]. It was initially shown that passive transfer of spleen or lymph node cells from chronically infected (20 week) mice to syngeneic recipients which were 6 weeks into their *S. mansoni* infection resulted in the recipients having smaller granulomas around hepatic eggs at 8 weeks of infection [413]. Sera from chronic mice did not give this suppressive effect, and earlier in infection the suppression was only transferable with spleen cells, not lymph node cells [413]. Subsequent analysis of the system led to the demonstration that Thy-1-bearing lymphocytes were essential for the expression of suppression, and administration of low doses of cyclophosphamide (CY) partially abrogated granuloma modulation in CY-treated chronic mice. Also, spleen cells from chronic mice treated with cyclophosphamide were incapable of transferring the normally observed suppression [414]. The regimen of cyclophosphamide used did not alter anti-SEA hemagglutinating antibody titers. Adult thymectomy at 6 weeks of infection did not change the level of peak granuloma formation at 8 weeks, but by 15 weeks after infection there developed significantly less modulation in hosts which had been thymectomized as adults than those which were sham thymectomized [415]. The ability to adoptively transfer this active suppression with Thy-1-bearing lymphoid cells from chronically infected mice has been confirmed and extended [416]. The suppressor cells or cells involved in the suppression are also Ia positive [416]. I-J region gene products are directly involved in this process [417]. They exert this suppression in an anti-gen specific manner. They can also suppress MIF production (see below) [416]. Furthermore, the representation of Ia-positive cells identified within modulated (late) granulomas is higher than observed in maximum-sized 8 week granulomas [416]. It seems clear that suppressor cells, probably of the T-cell lineage, play a prominent role in the regulation of in vivo granuloma formation in active schistosomiasis mansoni.

Other cell populations are also of interest in this regard. Although less direct evidence links them to modulation, it has been shown that the B lymphocyte population dynamics within hepatic granulomas are also intriguing [418]. Although B cells make up only 2% of the population of cells in 8 week granulomas, their representation rises to 10% in granulomas from chronically infected mice exhibiting modulation [418]. These data concomitantly parallel an increase in anti-SEA antibody titers [387,398], which has been hypothesized as perhaps indicative of an enhancement [290,291] form of suppression.

Another situation which concerns decreased responsiveness in the form of smaller granulomas was reported in the offspring of female mice which harbored mature heavy *S. mansoni* infections during their pregnancies [419]. At 8 weeks of age such offspring received *S. mansoni* eggs in the tail vein, and their pulmonary granulomas were measured 17 days later. When compared with lesions in comparable offspring of normal females, those from *S. mansoni*-infected mothers had significantly smaller granulomas [419]. This innovative study hints at the possibility of transplacental in utero tolerance induction. It has been followed by attempts to artificially induce such a state [420]. The original observation was confirmed, and the administration of extremely high doses of SEA to uninfected, pregnant mice was seen to lead to a transient state of relative unresponsiveness in the young [420]. Neonatal exposure was approximately comparable. The effects of artificial induction were not as dramatic or durable as those induced in utero and did not ameliorate granuloma formation if the mice were given active infections [410,420].

There is evidence of transplacental passage of schistosome-specific antibodies in maternal-child pairs in human schistosomiasis [421]. Also, active sensitization of uninfected children born to infected mothers is known to occur [422,423]. In the latter case it was seen 1-3 years after birth that 48% of the uninfected children born to infected mothers had a positive delayed skin test response to an adult worm antigen preparation. This value was 7% for children born to mothers not known to have had schistosomiasis [422]. Cord blood and skin test studies on maternal-child pairs using adult worm antigens again demonstrated a degree of sensitization in the children of infected mothers [423]. The known existence of circulating antigens, antibody, and immune complexes in this disease (see Section IV.A) provide many options for both sensitization and tolerization in utero, and this remains an area of considerable potential interest.

2. In Vitro

Regulation of anti-egg serum antibody production during schistosome infections, especially in regard to immunoglobulin class, has been observed by a variety of serologic analyses. For example, IgE antibody specific for SEA was easily detected in sera from acute cases of schistosomiasis but in only 10% of those from chronic patients [48]. A similar pattern was observed with longitudinal sera from mice when tested for anti-SEA, heat-labile, 72 hr skin-fixing reaginic antibody [387]. Similarly, IgA antibodies localized by focal staining on worm or granuloma sections were present early in infections and were lacking later [397].

There is a variety of in vitro evidence of regulatory changes in the SEA-induced responsiveness of lymphoid populations from experimentally infected animals [49,287,288,387,388]. Between 8 and 20 weeks after infection, during the establishment of granuloma modulation, there is a sustained elevation in the production of anti-SEA hemagglutinating antibody and the total waning of SEA-induced lymphokine (MIF and ESP) production [49,387,398]. The SEA elicited delayed skin test response also declined over this period, while PPD responsiveness in parallel-infected and tuberculin-sensitized mice remained positive [398]. SEA-induced lymphocyte blastogenesis remained positive in chronically infected guinea pigs [49] and mice but declined to low-positive levels in the mice [387].

As mentioned earlier, multiple alterations are seen to occur in the spleens of mice with chronic schistosomiasis [418]. Cells from such spleens, but not from normal mice, upon 48-hr exposure to SEA and treatment with mitomycin C, appeared to suppress either the PHA- or SEA-induced responsiveness of other lymphocyte cultures [287]. However, it is now apparent that the presumed suppression is in fact due to increased cell proliferation in control cultures [424]. It seems that this alteration in spleens of chronically infected mice involves both T lymphocytes and macrophates. The mitogenesis of control cultures can also be mediated by cell-free supernatant fluids obtained from stimulated spleen cells from chronically infected mice. Con A stimulation of such spleen cells led to less augmentation and is primarily sttributable to T lymphocyte involvement [424].

Through the development of an in vitro model of granuloma formation (see above), the actual modulatory process has been recently analyzed in vitro [405]. This system has confirmed a role in granuloma modulation for Thy-1-bearing lymphocytes and has demonstrated that the participation of Ly-2, 3$^+$ lymphocytes is essential for suppression [405].

Several nonspecific regulatory systems have been described in approximate kinetic relationship to the occurrence of modulation and decreased SEA responsiveness [425-428]. These studies include prolongation of allogeneic skin graft retention [428], depressed PHA- and ConA-induced lymphocyte responses [49,425,426], suppressed antibody responses to thymus dependent and independent antigens [427], and shifts in the splenic T-cell pool from Ly-1$^+$ to Ly-1$^+$, 2, 3$^+$ [427]. An apparent decrease in B lymphocytes may have been due to immune complex masking of complement-receptor lymphocytes [427]. The suppressed antibody responses were seen to be due to an active suppressor cell activity [427]. Also during this time frame it was observed that spleen cells from *S. mansoni*-infected mice were functionally impaired in their ability to generate alloantigen-specific cytotoxic T lymphocytes [426] via mixed lymphocyte simulation. In this system it was shown that an adherent/phagocytic suppressor cell was responsible for the decreased activity. Suppression could be removed by removal of these cells and inflicted on normal spleen cells by admixtures of these populations [426]. The cells were not depleted by anti-Thy-1 and complement treatment and were considered to be suppressor macrophages [426].

In vitro studies of regulatory mechanisms concerning SEA responsiveness in clinical schistosomiasis have focused primarily on SEA-induced lymphocyte blastogenesis [17,51,53-58,264]. It was observed that, during well-defined acute infections with *S. mansoni,* SEA responsiveness was quite strong, but this was lost upon the development of chronic disease [51]. In another series SEA responses were never very good, but earlier infections gave somewhat better responses [17]. The same pattern was reported with *S. japonicum* patients [264]. Detailed analysis of this apparent suppression has thus far revealed three modes of suppressor activity. The sera of chronically infected patients contain suppressor substances (as yet undefined) which, when included in cell cultures, decrease the already low responsiveness to SEA found in normal human serum-supplemented cultures [53,57]. The degree of suppressiveness observed in the sera has not correlated with anti-SEA antibody titers [57,429], and it was not observed to be effective if cells were only preincubated in its presence [53]. It also appears that for its expression it may need to work on a "susceptible" population of cells [58,59].

SEA-induced suppressor cell activity has been observed in approximately 35% of chronic patients tested (as compared with 88% when stimulated by ConA) [286]. In this series the suppressor effect was assayed on the PHA-responsiveness of autologous lymphocytes.

The effect of adherent suppressor cells has also been investigated in human schistosomiasis mansoni [54,56]. In one series of 24 chronic patients, removal of adherent/phagocytic cells elevated the SEA responses of only 25% of the patients [54]. In contrast, in another series of eight patients, removal of such cells resulted in substantial elevations in SEA-induced responsiveness in six patients, and the other two were elevated to a lesser degree [56]. Furthermore, "add-back" experiments could demonstrate the cellular requirement for this suppression. In an elegant follow-up study on one patient it was seen that adherent suppressor cells were not present at 4 months into his infection but had developed by 20 months [56]. In both studies it was clear that the adherent suppressor cell activity was schistosome antigen-specific and did not affect mitogen- or unrelated antigen-induced proliferation [54,56]. In another study of adehrent cell interactions in clinical, hepatosplenic schistosomiasis using peripheral blood and spleen cells [407], it has been observed that adherent splenic helper cells could be removed, resulting in lowered SEA responses.

Nonspecific suppression of the PHA responsiveness of patient's lymphocytes has been reported [264,407,430] but is by no means universally observed [14,51,55]. A totally nonspecific suppressive effect caused by the addition of SEA to PHA-responding cultures has been reported [55]. This suppression was expressed on lymphocytes from infected or normal individuals, was concentration dependent, operated regardless of adherent suppressor cells or serosuppression, and appeared to require an interaction with T lymphocytes. This effect was not due to toxicity [55].

D. Consequences and Conjecture

There is little doubt that extensive schistosome egg-induced granulomatous responses in a variety of tissues are pathogenic in humans and animals. The ability of the host to modulate this responsiveness while maintaining what appears to be a positive functional capability to contain the diffusion of egg contents in a smaller lesion makes incredibly good teleological sense. Whether this really is a primary mechanism which has evolved to tolerantly provide the parasite with a long-term home while minimizing the immunopathogenesis of the relationship remains to be tested.

Another egg-related phenomenon which was discussed previously (Section V.B) pertains to its possible role in the induction of protective responses during active infection [163,255-257,261]. It seems that the egg may yet play such a role, at least in mice, but it would currently appear that the role may be related to nonspecific aspects rather than egg antigen-induced specific responses. The focus of this effect may involve lung localization of eggs, and subsequent reactions to them may involve cells needed for protective reactions against migrating schistosomules. Granulomas have been shown to release chemotactic activities (active on eosinophils and monocytes) [395,431], which could be envisioned as participating in such a sequence.

1. Nonspecific Immunity

Others have studied the protective effects of nonspecific resistance and inflammatory processes on challenge infections with schistosome cercariae [364, 432-438]. The efficacy of BCG pretreatment was seen to depend upon whether viable organisms were presented intravenously [436] and was further dependent upon the strain of mouse studied. Responsiveness to BCG treatment as exhibited by protection to *S. mansoni* was not governed by MHC genes [437].

It will be of great interest to unravel these intertwining specific and nonspecific resistance patterns. If reactivity against the egg is indeed found to be essential for an optimal expression of resistance, then the currently considered "clean split" between immunopathology and acquired resistance in schistosomiasis may fade into the more complex situation typified by tuberculosis. On the other hand, if the egg-dependent resistance role is that of a well-timed nonspecific recruiter, then perhaps it could be successfully fulfilled by some other agent (BCG, cord factor, etc.). It would be fruitless to try to speculate as to the potential usefulness of such manipulations, but this kind of management would teach us much regarding the balancing of immune responses in chronic conditions.

2. Immunogenetics

Another aspect concerning the entire host-parasite interface is the genetic composition of the host. The immunogenetics of parasitic diseases is only now beginning to receive critical attention [58]. Though various differences have been observed regarding schistosomiasis in various strains of animals [72,73, 449], many such reports are as yet anecdotal. One such anecdotal racial predisposition has recently been quantitatively evaluated, and it appears that St. Lucia patients of East Indian heritage have a significantly increased predisposition toward the development of splenomegaly and hepatosplenic disease [439]. Experimentally it has been observed that different strains of hamsters develop widely different degrees of protective immunity to reinfection [440]. *Schistosoma mansoni* infections in Biozzi high- and low-responder mice revealed that, despite (due to ?) higher levels of humoral antibodies against schistosome antigens, the high responders tended to be more susceptible than low responders [441]. High responders also harbored more worms, larger worms, and more fecund worms than did low responders (enhancement?) [441]. A similar pattern has also been seen in the inverse correlation between antibody titer and acquired protection using the congenic inbred strains C3H/Sn (H-2^k) and C3H.B10 (H-2^b) [442]. A subsequent study demonstrated that, in this case, when the low responder C3H/Sn and the high responder C3H.B10 were compared, they did not show differences in worm burden or in in vitro lymphocyte responsiveness to adult worm antigens, SEA, or the purified egg antigen MSA_1. C3H.B10 mice did (under heavy infection) have higher mortality, greater antibody production, and stronger intradermal delayed-type hypersensitivity reactions to SEA. C3H/Sn developed higher peripheral blood eosinophilia and greater splenic involvement [443]. It may be remembered that H-2 differences did not account for the genetic differences involved in the degree of resistance induced in mice by BCG [437] or irradiated cercariae [73].

Several groups have suggested a relationship between the tendency to develop severe hepatosplenic schistosomiasis mansoni and blood group A [444-446]. Correlations between clinical classes of schistosomiasis and histocompatibility antigen patterns have been reported [447], and a relationship has been noted between HLA-A1 and HLA-B5 expression and hepatosplenism in Egypt [447]. However, this observation has not been universal. In St. Lucia, an HLA study of 200 hepatosplenic patients and 200 nonhepatosplenic patients, matched for age, sex and intensity of infection was negative in regard to any correlation between HLA type and clinical status (Goodgame and Bias, personal communication). Similarly, it has been reported that α_1-antitrypsin deficiency is not correlated with hepatosplenism [448]. Clearly, this area of investigation may yield substantial rewards which may be applicable in assisting our understanding of both resistance and pathogenesis in schistosomiasis.

VI. SUMMARY

It should be apparent that the study of the immunological aspects of mammalian schistosome infections is currently a thriving, active, and "occasionally" contradictory field of investigation. Clearly, this discipline is in a proliferative phase during which a wide variety of individual, and perhaps somewhat artificial, systems and phenomena are being described. One of the most exciting aspects of this often maddening trend is that the observations are no longer only being described, but many are now undergoing close in-depth scrutiny regarding the individual mechanisms at play. Some attempts are already being made to interrelate some of the various observations and their mechanisms being dissected. This will become an even greater challenge as we proceed. It is a task which requires the melding of expertise from the entire spectrum of biomedical knowledge. Already some bonuses have become apparent from this process. New information about unusual membrane biology, newly appreciated effector cell interactions, and the evaluation of the now oft described suppressor-regulatory systems at work in an actual chronic disease state are tantalizing examples of the richness available when scrutinizing the immunological aspects of the chronic, spectral disease schistosomiasis.

ACKNOWLEDGMENTS

The writing of this review and personal research cited were supported in part by the Research and Education Service of the Veterans Administration, The Edna McConnell Clark Foundation, and NIH Grant No. AI 11289. Special thanks goes to Judith O'Connell for her excellent secretarial assistance.

REFERENCES

1.   Warren K. S. (1971). In *Immunological Diseases*, 2nd ed. (M. Samter, Ed.). Little, Brown, Boston, Mass., p. 668.
2.   Warren, K. S. (1973). The pathology of Schistosome infections. *Helminth. Abs., Series A, Animal and Human Helminthol.* 42:591.

3. Lewert, R. M. (1970). Schistosomes. In *Immunity to Parasitic Animals.* Vol. 2 (G. J. Jackson, R. Herman, and I. Singer, Eds.). Appleton-Century-Crofts, New York, p. 981.

4. Smithers, S. R. (1972). Recent advances in the immunology of schistosomiasis. *Br. Med. Bull. 28:*49.

5. World Health Organization Memorandum. (1974). Immunology of schistosomiasis. *Bull. WHO 51:*553.

6. Smithers, S. R., and R. J. Terry. (1976). The immunology of schistosomiasis. *Adv. Parasitol. 14:*399.

7. Colley, D. G. (1977). The immunopathology of schistosomiasis. *Recent Adv. Clin. Immunol. 1:*101.

8. Phillips, S. M., and D. G. Colley (1978). Immunologic aspects of host responses to schistosomiasis: Resistance, immunopathology, and eosinophil involvement. *Progr. Allergy 24:*49.

9. Butterworth, A. E. (1977). The eosinophil and its role in immunity to helminth infection. *Cur. Top. Microbiol. Immunol. 77:*127.

10. Kagan, I. G., and J. Pellegrino (1961). A critical review of immunological methods for the diagnosis of bilharziasis. *Bull. WHO 25:*611.

11. Stirewalt, M. A. (1974). *Schistosoma mansoni:* Cercaria to schistosomule. *Adv. Parasitol. 12:*115.

12. Sadun, E. H., M. J. Schoenbechler, and M. Bentz (1965). Multiple antibody response in *Schistosoma mansoni* infections. Antigenic constituents in eggs, cercariae, and adults (excretions and secretions) determined by flocculation reactions, cross absorption and double diffusion studies. *Am. J. Trop. Med. Hyg. 14:*977.

13. Capron, A., J. Biguet, F. Rose, and A. Vernes (1965). Les antigénes de *Schistosoma mansoni.* II. Etude immunoélectrophorétique comparée de divers stades larvaires et des adultes des deux sexes. Aspets immunologiques des relations hôte-parasite de la cercaire et l'adulte de *S. mansoni. Annls. Inst. Pasteur (Paris) 109:*789.

14. Warren, K. S., R. W. Kellermeyer, P. Jordan, A. S. Littell, J. A. Cook, and I. G. Kagan (1973). Immunologic diagnosis of schistosomiasis. I. A controlled study of intradermal (immediate and delayed) and serologic tests in St. Lucians infected with *Schistosoma mansoni* and in uninfected St. Vincentians. *Am. J. Trop. Med. Hyg. 22:*189.

15. Katz, S. P., and D. G. Colley (1976). Induction of cellular humoral immunological responsiveness to a cercarial antigen preparation from *Schistosoma mansoni. Inf. Immunity 14:*502.

16. Moriearty, P., and R. M. Lewert (1974). Delayed hypersensitivity in Ugandan schistosomiasis. II. Epidemiologic patterns of intradermal responses. *Am. J. Trop. Med. Hyg. 23:*179.

17. Colley, D. G., J. A. Cook, G. L. Freeman, Jr., R. K. Bartholomew, and P. Jordan (1977). Immune responses during human schistosomiasis mansoni. I. In vitro lymphocyte blastogenic responses to heterogeneous antigenic preparations from schistosome eggs, worms, and cercariae. *Int. Arch. Allergy Appl. Immunol. 53:*420.

18. Stirewalt, M. A., and A. S. Evans (1955). Serologic reactions in *Schistosoma mansoni* infections. I. Cercaricidal, precipitation, agglutination and CHR phenomena. *Exp. Parasitol. 4:*123.

19. Sadun, E. H., R. I. Anderson, and J. S. Williams (1962). The nature of fluorescent antibody reactions and artificial immunizations with *Schistosoma mansoni. Bull. WHO 27:*151.

20. Kemp, W. M., R. T. Damian, and N. D. Greene (1973). *Schistosoma mansoni:* Immunohistochemical location of the CHR reaction in glycocalyx of cercariae. *Exp. Parasitol. 33:*27.

21. Kemp, W. M., N. D. Greene, and R. T. Damian (1974). Sharing of Cercarienhüllen Reaktion antigens between *Schistosoma mansoni* cercariae and adults and uninfected *Biomphalaria pfeifferi. Am. J. Trop. Med. Hyg. 23:* 197.

22. Kent. N. H. (1963). Comparative immunochemistry of larval and adult forms of *Schistosoma mansoni. Ann. N.Y. Acad. Sci. 113:*100.

23. Kronman, B. S. (1965). Immunochemistry of *Schistosoma mansoni* cercariae. *J. Immunol. 95:*13.

24. Sodeman, W. A., Jr. (1968). Studies on the protein composition of extracts of *Schistosoma mansoni* cercariae. *J. Parasitol. 54:*775.

25. Bogitsh, B. J., and S. P. Katz (1976). Immunocytochemical studies on *Schistosoma mansoni.* II. Soluble cercarial antigens in cercariae and schistosomules. *J. Parasitol. 62:*709.

26. Minard, P., K. D. Murrell, and M. A. Stirewalt (1977). Proteolytic, antigenic and immunogenic properties of *Schistosoma mansoni* cercarial secretion material. *Am. J. Trop. Med. Hyg. 26:*491.

27. Olivier, L. (1949). Schistosome dermatitis: A sensitization phenomenon. *Am. J. Hyg. 49:*290.

28. Macfarlane, W. V. (1949). Schistosome dermatitis in New Zealand. Part II. Pathology and immunology of cercarial lesions. *Am. J. Hyg. 50:*152.

29. Olivier, L., and P. P. Weinstein (1953). Experimental schistosome dermatitis in rabbits. *J. Parasitol. 38:*280.

30. Colley, D. G., A. Magalhães-Filho, R. Barros Coelho (1972). Immunopathology of dermal reactions induced by *Schistosoma mansoni* cercariae and cercarial extract. *Am. J. Trop. Med. Hyg. 21:*558.

31. Askenase, P. W., B. Hayden, and G. I. Higashi (1976). Cutaneous basophil hypersensitivity and inhibited macrophage migration in guinea pigs with schistomiasis. *Clin. Exp. Immunol. 23:*318.

32. Hsu, H. F., J. R. Davis, S. Y. L. Hsu, and J. W. Osborne (1963). Histopathology in albino mice and Rhesus monkeys infected with irradiated cercariae of *Schistosoma japonicum. Z. Tropenmed. Parasitol. 14:*240.

33. Sadun, E. H. (1963). Immunization in schistosomiasis by previous exposure to homologous and heterologous cercariae by inoculation of preparations from schistosomes and by exposure to irradiated cercariae. *Ann. N. Y. Acad. Sci. 113:*418.

34. Oda, T. (1973). Schistosome dermatitis in Japan. *Progr. Med. Parasitol. Japan V:*1.

35. Gazzinelli, G., F. J. Ramalho-Pinto, and W. Dias da Silva (1969). *Schisto-*

soma mansoni generation of anaphylatoxin by cercarial extracts. *Exp. Parasitol. 26:*86.

36. Machado, A. J., G. Gazzinelli, J. Pellegrino, and W. Dias da Silva (1975). *Schistosoma mansoni:* The role of the complement C_3-activating system in the cercaricidal action of normal serum. *Exp. Parasitol. 38:*20.

37. Colley, D. G., A. M. Savage, and F. A. Lewis (1977). Host responses induced and elicited by cercariae, schistosomula, and cercarial antigenic preparations. *Am. J. Trop. Med. Hyg. 26* (Suppl.):88.

38. Gazzinelli, G., F. J. Ramalho-Pinto, J. Pellegrino, and J. M. P. Memoria (1965). The intradermal test in the diagnosis of schistosomiasis mansoni. IV. Skin response to a purified fraction isolated from cercarial extracts. *J. Parasitol. 51:*753.

39. Sadun, E. H., and R. W. Gore (1970). *Schistosoma mansoni* and *S. haematobium:* Homocytotropic reagin-like antibodies in infections of man and experimental animals. *Exp. Parasitol. 28:*435.

40. Yuan, L., and K. W. Sell (1974). Immunochemical nature of schistosomal antigens in the induction of delayed hypersensitivity. *Immunochemistry 11:*235.

41. Hussain, R., W. E. Vannier, and K. D. Murrell (1975). Hypersensitivity to *Schistosoma mansoni* antigens. I. Immunochemical and biological characterization of an antigenic extract. *Immunochemistry 12:*561.

42. Pellegrino, J., and J. M. P. Memoria (1960). A reacao intradérmica na esquistossomose mansoni. I. Ensaios comparativos com antigenos de cerćaria, verme adulto, ôvo, e miracidio. *Rev. Inst. Med. Trop. São Paulo 2:*171.

43. Moriearty, P. L., and R. M. Lewert (1974). Delayed hypersensitivity in Ugandan schistosomiasis. I. Sensitivity, specificity, and immunological features of intradermal responses. *Am. J. Trop. Med. Hyg. 23:*169.

44. Katz, S. P., and D. G. Colley (1976). Analysis of the intradermal response against a soluble cercarial antigenic preparation from *Schistosoma mansoni. Inf. Immunity 14:*509.

45. Edwards, A. J., V. E. Jones, S. R. Smithers, and R. J. Terry (1966). The occurrence and properties of reagins in Rhesus monkeys infected with *Schistosoma mansoni. Ann. Trop. Med. Parasitol. 60:*280.

46. Kagan, I. G. (1968). Serologic diagnosis of schistosomiasis. *Bull. N.Y. Acad. Med. 44:*262.

47. Ruiz-Tiben, E., G. V. Hillyer, W. B. Knight, I. Gomez de Rios, and J. P. Woodall (1979). Intensity of infection with *Schistosoma mansoni:* Its relationship to the sensitivity and specificity of serologic tests. *Am. J. Trop. Med. Hyg. 28:*230.

48. Lunde, M. N., E. A. Ottesen, and A. W. Cheever (1979). Serological differences between acute and chronic schistosomiasis mansoni detected by enzyme-linked immunosorbent assay (ELISA). *Am. J. Trop. Med. Hyg. 28:*87.

49. Chen, P., and D. A. Dean (1977). Immune response of guinea pigs to *Schistosoma mansoni.* II. In vitro blastogenesis and macrophage migration inhibition factor production in response to cercarial, adult worm, and egg antigens. *Am. J. Trop. Med. Hyg. 26:*963.

50. Colley, D. G. (1974). Immunologic consequences of schistosome infection. *Progr. Immunol. II 4:*171.

51. Ottesen, E. A., R. A. Hiatt, A. W. Cheever, Z. R. Sotomayor, and F. A. Neva (1978). The acquisition and loss of antigen-specific cellular immune responsiveness in acute and chronic schistosomiasis in man. *Clin. Exp. Immunol. 33:*38.

52. Warren, K. S. (1978). Regulation of the prevalence and intensity of schistosomiasis in man. Immunology or ecology? *J. Infect. Dis. 127:*595.

53. Colley, D. G., S. E. Hieny, R. K. Bartholomew, and J. A. Cook (1977). Immune responses during human schistosomiasis mansoni, III. Regulatory effect of patient sera on human lymphocyte blastogenic responses to schistosomal antigen preparations. *Am. J. Trop. Med. Hyg. 26:*917.

54. Todd, C. W., R. W. Goodgame, and D. G. Colley (1979). Immune responses during human schistosomiasis mansoni, V. Suppression of schistosome antigen-specific lymphocyte blastogenesis by adherent/phygocytic cells. *J. Immunol. 122:*1440.

55. Colley, D. G., C. W. Todd, F. A. Lewis, and R. W. Goodgame (1979). Immune responses during human schistosomiasis mansoni. VI. In vitro non-specific suppression of phytohemagglutinin responsiveness induced by exposure to certain schistosomal preparations. *J. Immunol. 122:*1447.

56. Ottesen, E. A. (1979). Modulation of the host response in human schistosomiasis. I. Adherent suppresssor cells that inhibit lymphocyte proliferative responses to parasite antigens. *J. Immunol. 123:*1639.

57. Ottesen, E. A., and R. W. Poindexter (1980). Modulation of the host response in human schistosomiasis. II. Humoral factors which inhibit lymphocyte proliferative responses to parasite antigens. *Am. J. Trop. Med. Hyg. 29:*592.

58. Colley, D. G. (1980). The immunobiology of parasitism. In *Proceedings of the Conference on the Immunobiology of Parasitic Diseases.* University of South Florida, Tampa.

59. Todd, C. W., R. W. Goodgame, and D. G. Colley (1980). Immune responses during human schistosomiasis mansoni. VII. Further analysis of the interactions between patient sera and lymphocytes during in vitro blastogenesis to schistosome antigenic preparations. *Am. J. Trop. Med. Hyg. 29:*875.

60. Hsu, S. Y. L., H. F. Hsu, G. D. Penick, G. L. Lust, and L. K. Eveland (1977). *Schistosoma japonicum:* Highly irradiated cercariae as a test for specific immunity in Rhesus monkeys. *Exp. Parasitol. 43:*189.

61. Hsu, H. F., S. Y. L. Hsu, and J. W. Osborne (1962). Immunization against *Schistosoma japonicum* in Rhesus monkeys produced by irradiated cercariae. *Nature (Lond.) 194:*98.

62. Radke, M. G., and E. H. Sadun (1963). Resistance produced in mice by exposure to irradiated *Schistosoma mansoni* cercariae. *Exp. Parasitol. 13:*134.

63. Perlowagora-Szumlewicz, A. (1964). Studies on acquired resistance to

Schistosoma mansoni in mice exposed to X-irradiated cercariae. *Bull. WHO 30:*401.

64. Erickson, D. G., and W. L. Caldwell (1965). Acquired resistance in mice and rats after exposure to gamma-irradiated cercariae. *Am. J. Trop. Med. Hyg. 14:*566.

65. Hsu, S. Y. L., H. F. Hsu, and J. W. Osborne (1969). Immunization of rhesus monkeys against schistosome infection by cercariae exposed to high doses of X-radiation. *Proc. Soc. Exp. Biol. Med. 131:*1146.

66. Phillips, S. M., W. A. Reid, B. Doughty, and P. B. Khoury (1978). The cellular and humoral response to *Schistosoma mansoni* infections in inbred rats. III. Development of optimal protective immunity following natural infections and artificial immunizations. *Cell. Immunol. 38:*225.

67. Minard, P., D. A. Dean, R. H. Jacobsen, W. E. Vannier, and K. D. Murrell (1978). Immunization of mice with cobalt-60 irradiated *Schistosoma mansoni* cercariae. *Am. J. Trop. Med. Hyg. 27:*76.

68. Amin, M. A., and G. S. Nelson (1969). Studies on heterologous immunity in schistosomiasis. III. Further observations on heterologous immunity in mice. *Bull. WHO 41:*225.

69. Eveland, L. K., S. Y. L. Hsu, and H. F. Hsu (1969). Cross-immunity to *Schistosoma japonicum, S. mansoni* and *S. bovis* in rhesus monkeys. *J. Parasitol. 55:*279.

70. Taylor, M. G., G. S. Nelson, M. Smith, and B. J. Andrews (1973). Studies on heterologous immunity in schistosomiasis. 7. Observations on the development of acquired homologous and heterologous immunity to *Schistosoma mansoni* in baboons. *Bull. WHO 49:*57.

71. Smithers, S. R. (1962). Stimulation of acquired resistance to *Schistosoma mansoni* in monkeys: Role of eggs and worms. *Exp. Parasitol. 12:*263.

72. Dean, D. A., personal communication.

73. Murrell, K. D., S. Clark, D. A. Dean, and W. E. Vannier (1979). Influence of mouse strain on induction of resistance with irradiated *Schistosoma mansoni* cercariae. *J. Parasitol. 65:*829.

74. Miller, P., and R. A. Wilson (1978). Migration of the schistosomula of *Schistosoma mansoni* from skin to lungs. *Parasitology 77:*281.

75. Pellegrino, J., M. de Maria, and J. Faria (1965). Infection of the golden hamster with *Schistosoma mansoni* cercariae through the cheek pouch. *J. Parasitol. 51:*1015.

76. Wilson, R. A., T. Draskau, P. Miller, and J. R. Lawson (1978). *Schistosoma mansoni:* The activity and development of the schistosomulum during migration from the skin to the hepatic portal system. *Parasitology 77:*57.

77. Wilks, N. E. (1967). Lung to liver migration of schistosomes in the laboratory mouse. *Am. J. Trop. Med. Hyg. 16:*599.

78. Pereira, L. H., P. M. Z. Coelho, J. J. A. Fonseca, A. Bredt, and J. Pellegrino (1972). Migration of *Schistosoma mansoni* larvae in the albino mouse. *Rev. Inst. Med. Trop. São Paulo 14:*306.

79. Smithers, S. R., D. J. McLaren, and F. J. Ramalho-Pinto (1977). Im-

munity to schistosomes: The target. *Am. J. Trop. Med. Hyg. 26* (Suppl.):11.

80. James, E. R., and M. G. Taylor (1976). Transformation of cercariae to schistosomula: A quantitative comparison of transformation techniques and of infectivity by different injection routes of the organisms produced. *J. Helminthol. 50:*223.

81. Brink, L. H., D. J. McLaren, and S. R. Smithers (1977). *Schistosoma mansoni:* A comparative study of artificially transformed schistosomula and schistosomula recovered after cercarial penetration of isolated skin. *Parasitology 74:*73.

82. Sher, A., J. R. Kusel, H. Perez, and J. Clegg (1974). Partial isolation of a membrane antigen which induces the formation of antibodies lethal to schistosomules in vitro. *Clin. Exp. Immunol. 18:*357.

83. Hsu, S. Y. L., H. F. Hsu, P. Isacson, B. W. Kremenak, and H. F. Cheng (1976). In vitro effect of the lethal antibody on schistosomula in sera of rhesus monkeys immunized with highly irradiated cercariae. *J. Parasitol. 62:*914.

84. Murrell, K. D., W. E. Vannier, P. Minard, and V. D. Schinski (1977). *Schistosoma mansoni:* Extraction and partial characterization of membrane antigens using an assay based on competitive inhibition of human antibodies binding to schistosomules. *Exp. Parasitol. 41:*446.

85. Dean, D. A. (1977). Decreased binding of cytotoxic antibody on developing *Schistosoma mansoni:* Evidence for a surface change independent of host antigen adsorption and membrane turnover. *J. Parasitol. 63:*418.

86. Hsu, S. Y. L., H. F. Hsu, G. D. Penick, G. L. Lust, and J. W. Osborne (1974). Dermal hypersensitivity to schistosome cercariae in rhesus monkeys during immunization and challenge. I. Complex hypersensitivity reactions of a well-immunized monkey during the challenge. *J. Allergy Clin. Immunol. 54:*339.

87. von Lichtenberg, F., A. Sher, N. Gibbons, and B. L. Doughty (1976). Eosinophil-enriched inflammatory response to schistosomula in the skin of mice immune to *Schistosoma mansoni. Am. J. Pathol. 84:*479.

88. Sher, A. (1977). Immunity against *Schistosoma mansoni* in the mouse *Am. J. Trop. Med. Hyg. 26*(Suppl.):20.

89. Savage, A. M., and D. G. Colley (1980). The eosinophil in the inflammatory response to cercarial challenge of sensitized and chronically infected CBA/J mice. *Am. J. Trop. Med. Hyg. 29:*1268.

90. Hsu, S. Y. L., J. R. Davis, and H. F. Hsu (1965). Histopathology in rhesus monkeys infected four times with the Formosan strain of *Schistosoma japonicum. Z. Tropenmed. Parasitol. 16:*297.

91. Magalhães-Filho, A. (1959). Pulmonary lesions in mice experimentally infected with *Schistosoma mansoni. Am. J. Trop. Med. Hyg. 8:*527.

92. von Lichtenberg, F., A. Sher, and S. McIntyre (1977). A lung model of schistosome immunity in mice. *Am. J. Pathol. 87:*105.

93. Colley, D. G., and S. L. James (1979). Participation of eosinophils in

immunological systems. In *Cellular, Molecular and Clinical Aspects of Allergic Disorders: Comprehensive Immunology,* Vol. 6 (S. Gupta and R. A. Good, Eds.). Plenum, New York, p. 55.

94. Sher, A., S. R. Smithers, and P. Mackenzie (1975). Passive transfer of acquired resistance to *Schistosoma mansoni* in laboratory mice. *Parasitology 70:*347.

95. Sher, A., S. R. Smithers, P. Mackenzie, and K. Broomfield (1977). *Schistosoma mansoni.* Immunoglobulins involved in passive immunization of laboratory mice. *Exp. Parasitol. 41:*160.

96. Kassis, A. I., K. S. Warren, and A. A. F. Mahmoud (1979). Antibody-dependent complement-mediated killing of schistosomula in interperitoneal diffusion chambers in mice. *J. Immunol. 123:*1659.

97. Pellegrino, J., and N. Katz (1974). Failure to immunize mice by therapeutically killing developing schistosomula (*Schistosoma mansoni*). *J. Parasitol. 60:*727.

98. Perez, H., J. A. Clegg, and S. R. Smithers (1974). Acquired immunity to *Schistosoma mansoni* in the rat: Measurement of immunity by the lung recovery technique. *Parasitology 69:*349.

99. Knopf, P. M., T. B. Nutman, and J. A. Reasoner (1977). *Schistosoma mansoni:* Resistance to reinfection in the rat. *Exp. Parasitol. 41:*74.

100. Phillips, S. M., W. A. Reid, P. B. Khoury, and B. L. Doughty (1977). The cellular and humoral immune response to *Schistosoma mansoni* infections in inbred rats. IV. A posteriori interpretations. *Am. J. Trop. Med. Hyg. 26*(Suppl.):48.

101. Long, E., M. Doenhoff, and J. Bain (1978). Factors affecting the acquisition of resistance against *Schistosoma mansoni* in the mouse. 2. The time at which resistance to reinfection develops. *J. Helminthol. 52:*187.

102. James, E. R., and J. Farrant (1977). Recovery of infective *Schistosoma mansoni* schistosomula from liquid nitrogen: A step towards storage of a live schistosomiasis vaccine. *Trans. R. Soc. Trop. Med. Hyg. 71:*498.

103. Bickle, Q. D., and E. R. James (1978). Resistance against *Schistosoma mansoni* induced by immunization of mice with cryopreserved schistosomula. *Trans. R. Soc. Trop. Med. Hyg. 72:*677.

104. Stirewalt, M. A., F. A. Lewis, and K. D. Murrell (1979). *Schistosoma mansoni:* Cryopreservation of schistosomules. *Exp. Parasitol. 48*(2), 272.

105. Murrell, K. S., M. A. Stirewalt, and F. A. Lewis (1979). *Schistosoma mansoni:* Vaccination of mice with cryopreserved irradiated schistosomules. *Exp. Parasitol. 48*(2):265.

106. Colley, D. G., and S. K. Wikel (1974). *Schistosoma mansoni:* Simplified method for the production of schistosomules. *Exp. Parasitol. 35:*44.

107. Ramalho-Pinto, F. J., J. B. de Souza, and J. H. L. Playfair (1976). Stimulation and suppression of response of mouse T cells to the schistosomules of *Schistosoma mansoni* during infection. *Nature (Lond.) 259:*603.

108. Ramalho-Pinto, F. J., O. L. Goldring, S. R. Smithers, and J. H. L. Play-

fair (1976). T-cell helper response to antigens of *Schistosoma mansoni* in CBA mice. *Clin. Exp. Immunol. 26:*327.

109.   Ramalho-Pinto, F. J., S. R. Smithers, and J. H. L. Playfair (1979). Carrier effect during the course of experimental schistosomiasis: Suppression of the response to TNP-schistosomula in rats and inbred mice. *J. Immunol. 123:*507.

110.   James, S. L., and A. Sher (1980). Immune mechanisms which stimulate mouse leukocyte migration in response to schistosomula of *Schistosoma mansoni*. *J. Immunol. 124:*1837.

111.   Lewis, F. A., C. E. Carter, and D. G. Colley (1977). Eosinophils and immune mechanisms. V. Demonstration of mouse spleen cell-derived chemotactic activities for eosinophils and mononuclear cells and comparisons with eosinophil stimulation promoter. *Cell. Immunol. 32:*86.

112.   Tavares, C. A. P., G. Gazzinelli, T. A. Mota-Santos, W. Dias da Silva (1978). *Schistosoma mansoni:* Complement-mediated cytotoxic activity in vitro and effect of decomplementation on acquired immunity in mice. *Exp. Parasitol. 46:*145.

113.   Dean, D. A., R. Wistar, and K. D. Murrell (1974). Combined in vitro effects of rat antibody and neutrophilic leukocytes on schistosomula of *Schistosoma mansoni*. *Am. J. Trop. Med. Hyg. 23:*420.

114.   Sher, A., and S. L. McIntyre (1977). Receptors for C_3 on rat peritoneal mast cells. *J. Immunol. 119:*722.

115.   Ramalho-Pinto, F. J., D. J. McLaren, and S. R. Smithers (1978). Complement-mediated killing of schistosomula of *Schistosoma mansoni* by rat eosinophils in vitro. *J. Exp. Med. 147:*147.

116.   Santoro, F., P. J. Lachmann, A. Capron, and M. Capron (1979). Activation of complement by *Schistosoma mansoni* schistosomula: Killing of parasites by the alternative pathway and requirement of IgG for classical pathway activation. *J. Immunol. 123:*1551.

117.   Clegg, J. A., and S. R. Smithers (1972). The effects of immune rhesus monkey serum on schistosomula of *Schistosoma mansoni* during cultivation in vitro. *Int. J. Parasitol. 2:*79.

118.   Murrell, K. D., and B. Clay (1972). In vitro detection of cytotoxic antibodies to *Schistosoma mansoni* schistosomules. *Am. J. Trop. Med. Hyg. 21:*569.

119.   Capron, A., M. Capron, D. Camus, and A. Vernes (1973). Les phénomènes d'hypersensibilitè au cours des schistosomiasis humaines a *Schistosoma mansoni*. II. Etude in vitro de l'activité léthale des serums de malades pour les schistosomules de *Schistosoma mansoni*. Rapport avec les tests d'hypersensibilité. *Pathol. Biol. (Paris) 21:*1079.

120.   Smith, M. A., and G. Webbe (1974). Damage to schistosomula of *Schistosoma haematobium* in vitro by immune baboon and human sera and absence of cross reaction with *Schistosoma mansoni*. *Trans. R. Soc. Trop. Med. Hyg. 68:*70.

121.   Dean, D. A., R. Wistar, and P. Chen (1975). Immune response of guinea

pigs to *Schistosoma mansoni*. I. In vitro effects of antibody and neutrophils, eosinophils and macrophages on schistosomula. *Am. J. Trop. Med. Hyg. 24:*74.

122. Ramalho-Pinto, F. J., R. de Rossi, and S. R. Smithers (1979). Murine schistosomiasis mansoni: Anti-schistosomula antibodies and the IgG subclasses involved in the complement- and eosinophil-mediated killing of schistosomula in vitro. *Parasite Immunol. 1:*295.

123. Mahmoud, A. A. F., K. S. Warren, and P. A. Peters (1975). A role for the eosinophil in acquired resistance to *Schistosoma mansoni* infection as determined by antieosinophil serum. *J. Exp. Med. 142:*805.

124. Butterworth, A. E., R. F. Sturrock, V. Houba, and P. H. Rees (1974). Antibody-dependent cell-mediated damage to schistosomula in vitro. *Nature (Lond.) 252:*503.

125. Butterworth, A. E., R. F. Sturrock, V. Houba, A. A. F. Mahmoud, A. Sher, and P. H. Rees (1975). Eosinophils as mediators of antibody-dependent damage to schistosomula. *Nature (Lond.) 256:*727.

126. Butterworth, A. E., R. F. Sturrock, V. Houba, and R. Taylor (1976). *Schistosoma mansoni* in baboons. Antibody-dependent cell-mediated damage to [51]-Cr-labelled schistosomula. *Clin. Exp. Immunol. 25:*95.

127. Glauert, A., and A. E. Butterworth (1977). Morphological evidence for the ability of eosinophils to damage antibody-coated schistosomula. *Trans. R. Soc. Trop. Med. Hyg. 71:*392.

128. Butterworth, A. E., H. G. Remold, V. Houba, J. R. David, D. Franks, P. H. David, and R. F. Sturrock (1977). Antibody-dependent eosinophil-mediated damage to [51]CR-labeled schistosomula of *Schistosoma mansoni:* Mediation by IgG, and inhibition by antigen-antibody complexes. *J. Immunol. 118:*2230.

129. Butterworth, A. E., J. R. David, D. Franks, A. A. F. Mahmoud, P. H. David, R. F. Sturrock, and V. Houba (1977). Antibody-dependent eosinophil-mediated damage to ^{51}Cr-labeled schistosomula of *Schistosoma mansoni:* Damage by purified eosinophils. *J. Exp. Med. 145:*136.

130. Sturrock, R. F., A. E. Butterworth, V. Houba, S. D. Karamsadar, and R. Kimani (1978). *Schistosoma mansoni* in the Kenyan baboon (*Papio anubis*): The development and predictability of resistance to homologous challenge. *Trans. R. Soc. Trop. Med. Hyg. 72:*251.

131. Vadas, M. A., J. R. David, A. Butterworth, N. T. Pisani, and T. A. Siongok (1979). A new method for the purification of human eosinophils and neutrophils, and a comparison of the ability of these cells to damage schistosomula of *Schistosoma mansoni. J. Immunol. 122:*1228.

132. Butterworth, A. E., D. J. Wassom, G. J. Gleich, D. A. Loegering, and J. R. David (1979). Damage to schistosomula of *Schistosoma mansoni* induced directly by eosinophil major basic protein. *J. Immunol. 122:*221.

133. Butterworth, A. E., M. A. Vadas, and J. R. David (1980). Mechanisms of eosinophil-mediated helminthotoxicity. In *The Eosinophil in Health and Disease,* (A. A. F. Mahmoud and K. F. Austen, Eds.). Grune & Stratton, New York, pp. 253–273.

134. Mackenzie, C. E., F. J. Ramalho-Pinto, D. J. McLaren, and S. R. Smithers (1977). Antibody-mediated adherence of rat eosinophils to schistosomula of *Schistosoma mansoni* in vitro. *Clin. Exp. Immunol. 30:*97.

135. McLaren, D. J., F. J. Ramalho-Pinto, and S. R. Smithers (1978). Ultrastructural evidence for complement and antibody-dependent damage to schistosomula of *Schistosoma mansoni* by rat eosinophils in vitro. *Parasitology 77:*313.

136. Anwar, A. R. E., S. R. Smithers, and A. B. Kay (1979). Killing of schistosomula of *Schistosoma mansoni* coated with antibody and/or complement by human leukocytes in vitro: Requirement for complement in preferential killing by eosinophils. *J. Immunol. 122:*628.

137. Kassis, A. I., M. Aikawa and A. A. F. Mahmoud (1979). Mouse antibody-dependent eosinophil and macrophage adherence and damage to schistosomula of *Schistosoma mansoni. J. Immunol. 122:*398.

138. Capron, M., J. Rousseaux, C. Mazingue, H. Bazin, and A. Capron (1978). Rat mast cell-eosinophil interaction in antibody dependent eosinophil cytotoxicity to *Schistosoma mansoni* schistosomula. *J. Immunol. 121:* 2518.

139. Capron, M., A. Capron, G. Torpier, H. Bazin, D. Bout, and M. Joseph (1978). Eosinophil-dependent cytotoxicity in rat schistosomiasis. Involvement of IgG_{2a} antibody and role of mast cells. *Eur. J. Immunol. 8:*127.

140. McLaren, D. J., C. D. Mackenzie, and F. J. Ramalho-Pinto (1977). Ultrastructural observations on the in vitro interaction between rat eosinophils and some parasitic helminths (*Schistosoma mansoni, Trichinella spiralis,* and *Nippo strongylus brasiliensis*). *Clin. Exp. Immunol. 30:*105.

141. McLaren, D. J., and F. J. Ramalho-Pinto (1979). Eosinophil-mediated killing of schistosomula of *Schistosoma mansoni* in vitro: Synergistic effect of antibody and complement. *J. Immunol. 123:*1431.

142. Ellner, J. J., and A. A. F. Mahmoud (1979). Killing of schistosomula of *Schistosoma mansoni* by normal human monocytes. *J. Immunol. 123:* 949.

143. Ellner, J. J., G. R. Olds, and A. A. F. Mahmoud (1979). Schistosomula killing by human monocytes: Alterations in disease. Fourteenth Joint Conference on Parasitic Diseases of the United States-Japan Cooperative Medical Science Program, New Orleans, La., August, 1979.

144. Mahmoud, A. A. F., P. A. Peters, R. H. Civil, and J. S. Remington (1979). In vitro killing of schistosomula of *Schistosoma mansoni* by BCG and *C. parvum* activated macrophages. *J. Immunol. 122:*1655.

145. Perez, H. A., and S. R. Smithers (1977). *Schistosoma mansoni* in the rat: The adherence of macrophages to schistosomula in vitro after sensitization with immune serum. *Int. J. Parasitol. 7:*315.

146. Capron, A., J.-P. Dessaint, M. Capron, and H. Bazin (1975). Specific IgE antibodies in immune adherence of normal macrophages to *Schistosoma mansoni* schistosomules. *Nature (Lond.) 253:*474.

147. Capron, A., J.-P. Dessaint, M. Joseph, R. Rousseaux, M. Capron, and H. Bazin (1977). Interaction between IgE complexes and macrophages in the rat: A new mechanism of macrophage activation. *Eur. J. Immunol.* 7:315.

148. Joseph, M., A. Capron, A. E. Butterworth, R. F. Sturrock, and V. Houba (1978). Cytotoxicity of human and baboon mononuclear phagocytes against schistosomula in vitro: Induction by immune complexes containing IgE and *Schistosoma mansoni* antigens. *Clin. Exp. Immunol.* 33:48.

149. Smithers, S. R., and B. M. Ogilvie (1965). Reagin-like antibodies and the passive transfer of resistance in experimental schistosomiasis. *Parasitology 55:*2P.

150. Butterworth, A. E., M. A. Vadas, E. Martz, and A. Sher (1979). Cytolytic T lymphocytes recognize alloantigens on schistosomula of *Schistosoma mansoni,* but fail to induce damage. *J. Immunol.* 122:1314.

151. Sher, A., P. Mackenzie, and S. R. Smithers (1974). Decreased recovery of invading parasites from the lungs as a parameter of acquired immunity to schistosomiasis in the mouse. *J. Infect. Dis.* 130:626.

152. Phillips, S. M., W. A. Reid, J. I. Bruce, K. Hedlund, R. C. Colvin, R. Campbell, C. L. Diggs, and E. H. Sadun (1975). The cellular and humoral immune response to *Schistosoma mansoni* infections in inbred rats. I. Mechanisms during initial exposure. *Cell. Immunol.* 19:99.

153. Phillips, S. M., W. A. Reid, and E. H. Sadun (1977). The cellular and humoral response to *Schistosoma mansoni* infections in inbred rats. II. Mechanisms during reexposure. *Cell. Immunol.* 28:75.

154. Smithers, S. R., and R. J. Terry (1979). The immunology of schistosomiasis. *Adv. Parasitol.* 7:41.

155. Smithers, S. R., R. J. Terry, and D. J. Hockley (1969). Host antigens in schistosomiasis. *Proc. R. Soc. Lond. [Biol.]* 171:483.

156. Clegg, J. A. (1974). Host antigens and the immune response in schistosomiasis. In *Parasites in the Immunized Host: Mechanisms of Survival.* Ciba Foundation Symposium, No. 25. Elsevier North-Holland, Amsterdam, Holland, p. 161.

157. McLaren, D. J., J. A. Clegg, and S. R. Smithers (1975). Acquisition of host antigens by young *Schistosoma mansoni* in mice: Correlation with failure to bind antibody in vitro. *Parasitology 70:*67.

158. Goldring, O. L., J. A. Clegg, S. R. Smithers, and R. J. Terry (1976). Acquisition of human blood group antigens by *Schistosoma mansoni.* *Clin. Exp. Immunol.* 26:181.

159. Tavares, C. A. P., R. C. Soares, P. M. Z. Coelho, G. Gazzinelli (1978). *Schistosoma mansoni:* Evidence for a role of serum factors in protecting artificially transformed schistosomula against antibody-mediated killing in vitro. *Parasitology 77:*225.

160. Tavares, C. A. P., M. N. Cordeiro, T. A. Mota-Santos, and G. Gazzinelli (1980). Artificially transformed schistosomula of *Schistosoma mansoni:* Mechanism of acquisition of protection against antibody-mediated killing. *Parasitology 80*(1):95.

161. Imohiosen, E. A. E., A. Sher, and F. von Lichtenberg (1978). Early developmental changes of the schistosomula of *Schistosoma mansoni* in vitro and in mouse lung. *Parasitology 76:*317.

162. Goldring, O. L., A. Sher, S. R. Smithers, and D. J. McLaren (1977). Host antigens and parasite antigens of murine *Schistosoma mansoni. Trans. R. Soc. Trop. Med. Hyg. 71:*144.

163. Gazzinelli, G. (1979), personal communication.

164. Hockley, D. J., and D. J. McLaren (1973). *Schistosoma mansoni:* Changes in the outer membrane of the tegument during development from cercaria to adult worm. *Int. J. Parasitol. 3:*13.

165. Hockley, D. J., D. J. McLaren, B. J. Ward, and M. V. Nermut (1975). A freeze fracture study of the tegument of *Schistosoma mansoni* (Platyhelminthes: Trematoda). *Tissue Cell 7:*485.

166. Wilson, R. A., and P. E. Barnes (1974). The tegument of *Schistosoma mansoni:* Observations of the formation, structure, and composition of cytoplasmic inclusions in relation to tegument function. *Parasitology 68:*239.

167. Wilson, R. A., and P. E. Barnes (1977). The formation and turnover of the membranocalyx on the tegument of *Schistosoma mansoni. Parasitology 74:*61.

168. Minard, P., D. A. Dean, W. E. Vannier, and K. D. Murrell (1978). Effect of immunization on migration of *Schistosoma mansoni* through lungs. *Am. J. Trop. Med. Hyg. 27:*87.

169. Doenhoff, M., Q. Bickle, E. Long, J. Bain, and A. McGregor (1978). Factors affecting the acquisition of resistance against *Schistosoma mansoni* in the mouse. I. Demonstration of resistance to reinfection using a model system that involves perfusion of mice within three weeks of challenge. *J. Helminthol. 52:*173.

170. Warren, K. S., A. A. F. Mahmoud, P. Cummings, D. J. Murphy, and H. B. Houser (1974). Schistosomiasis mansoni in Yemeni in California: Duration of infection, presence of disease, therapeutic management. *Am. J. Trop. Med. Hyg. 23:*902.

171. Tsang, V. C. W., W. J. Hubbard, and R. T. Damian (1977). Coagulation factor XIIa (activated Hageman factor) inhibitor from adult *Schistosoma mansoni. Am. J. Trop. Med. Hyg. 26:*243.

172. Tsang, V. C. W., and R. T. Damian (1977). Demonstration and mode of action of an inhibitor for activated Hageman factor (factor XIIa) of the intrinsic blood coagulation pathways from *Schistosoma mansoni. Blood 49:*619.

173. Gershon, R. K., R. L. Carter, and K. Kondo (1967). On concomitant immunity in tumor bearing hamsters. *Nature (Lond.) 213:*674.

174. Kagan, I. G., and L. Norman (1963). Analysis of helminth antigens (*Echinococcus granulosus* and *Schistosoma mansoni*) by agar gel methods. *Ann. N.Y. Acad. Sci. 113:*130.

175. Damian, R. T. (1966). An immunodiffusion analysis of some antigens of *Schistosoma mansoni* adults. *Exp. Parasitol. 18:*255.

176. Biguet, J., A. Capron, and P. Tran Van Ky (1962). Les antigèns de *Schistosoma mansoni*. 1. Étude électrophorétique et immunoélectrophorétique charactérisation des antigèns spécifiques. *Ann. Inst. Pasteur (Paris) 103:*763.

177. Sawada, T., K. Sato, and S. Sato (1970). The further purification of antigen SST for schistosomiasis japonica skin tests by electrophoretic and gel-filtration techniques. In *Recent Advances in Researches on Filariasis and Schistosomiasis in Japan,* (M. Sasa, Ed.). University Park Press, Baltimore, Md., p. 365.

178. Bout, D., H. Dupas, M. Capron, A. el Gazawi, Y. Carlier, A. Delacourte, and A. Capron (1978). Purification, immunochemical and biological characterization of malate dehydrogenase of *Schistosoma mansoni*. *Immunochemistry 15:*633.

179. Rotmans, J. P. (1978). *Schistosoma mansoni*. Antigenic characterization of malate dehydrogenase isoenzymes and use in the defined antigen substrate spheres (DASS) system. *Exp. Parasitol. 46:*49.

180. Bout, D., H. Dupas, M. Capron, P. Tran Van Ky, and A. Capron (1977). Drugs as ligands of immunogenic molecules in parasites: An approach to the isolation of target antigens. *J. Immunol. Meth. 15:*1.

181. Hillyer, G. V., R. P. Pelley, and A. del Llano de Diaz (1979). Solubilization of antigens of *Fasciola hepatica* which react with antibodies to *Schistoma mansoni*. *J. Parasitol. 65:*55.

182. Hillyer, G. V. H., A. del Llano de Diaz, and C. N. Reyes (1977). *Schistosoma mansoni:* Acquired immunity in mice and hamsters using antigens of *Fasciola hepatica*. *Exp. Parasitol. 42:*348.

183. Christensen, N. Ø., P. Nansen, F. Frandsen, A. Bjørneboe, and J. Monrad (1978). *Schistosoma mansoni* and *Fasciola hepatica:* Cross-resistance in mice. *Exp. Parasitol. 46:*113.

184. Murrell, K. D., W. E. Vannier, and A. Ahmed (1974). *Schistosoma mansoni:* Antigenic heterogeneity of excretions and secretions. *Exp. Parasitol. 36:*316.

185. Kloetzel, K., and R. M. Lewert (1966). Pigment formation in *Schistosoma mansoni* infections in the white mouse. *Am. J. Trop. Med. Hyg. 15:*28.

186. Grimaud, J. A., R. Borojevic, and H. Araujo dos Santos (1976). Schistosomal pigment in human and murine infections with *Schistosoma mansoni*. *Trans. R. Soc. Trop. Med. Hyg. 70:*73.

187. Kusel, J. R., P. E. Mackenzie, and D. J. McLaren (1975). The release of membrane antigens into culture by adult *Schistosoma mansoni*. *Parasitology 71:*247.

188. Kusel, J. R., and P. E. Mackenzie (1975). The measurement of the relative turnover rates of proteins of the surface membranes and other fractions of *Schistosoma mansoni* in culture. *Parasitology 71:*261.

189. Wilson, R. A., and P. E. Barnes (1979). Synthesis of macromolecules by the epithelial surfaces of *Schistosoma mansoni:* An autoradiographic study. *Parasitology 78:*295.

190. Hayunga, E. G., K. D. Murrell, D. W. Taylor, and W. E. Vannier (1979). Isolation and characterization of surface antigens from *Schistosoma mansoni*. I. Evaluation of radioisotope labeling techniques for surface proteins from adult worms. *J. Parasitol. 65:*488.

191. Cordeiro, M. do N., and G. Gazzinelli (1979). *Schistosoma mansoni:* Resolution and molecular weight estimates of tegument glycoproteins by polyacrylamide gel electrophoresis. *Exp. Parasitol. 48:*337.

192. Berggren, W. L., and T. W. Weller (1967). Immunoelectrophoretic analysis of specific circulating antigen in animals infected with *Schistosoma mansoni. Am. J. Trop. Med. Hyg. 16:*606.

193. Gold, R., R. S. Rosen, T. H. Weller (1969). A specific circulating antigen in hamsters infected with *Schistosoma mansoni.* Detection of antigen in serum and urine, and correlation between antigenic concentration and worm burden. *Am. J. Trop. Med. Hyg. 18:*545.

194. Bawden, M. P., and T. H. Weller (1974). *Schistosoma mansoni* circulating antigen: Detection by complement fixation in sera from infected hamsters and mice. *Am. J. Trop. Med. Hyg. 23:*1077.

195. Madwar, M. A., and A. Voller (1975). Circulating soluble antigens and antibody in schistosomiasis. *Br. Med. J. 1:*435.

196. Bout, D., F. Santoro, and A. Capron (1975). Détection des immuncomplexes dans la bilharziose. *Méd. Mal. Infect. 5:*631

197. Bout, D., F. Santoro, Y. Carlier, J. C. Bina, and A. Capron (1977). Circulating immune complexes in schistosomiasis. *Immunology 33:*17.

198. Jones, C. E., F. W. Rachford, M. A. Ozcel, and R. M. Lewert (1977). *Schistosoma japonicum:* Semiquantitative assessment of circulating immune complexes, serum C1q and C_3, and the relationship of these parameters to renal pathology and hepatic fibrosis in rabbits. *Exp. Parasitol. 42:*221.

199. Smith, M. D., P. J. Verroust, L. Morel-Maroger, M. Geniteau, and J. P. Couland (1977). A study of the presence of circulating immune complexes in schistosomiasis. *Trans. R. Soc. Trop. Med. Hyg. 7:*343.

200. Deelder, A. M., D. P. Van Dalen, and J. G. Van Egmond (1978). *Schistosoma mansoni:* Microfluorometric determination of circulating anodic antigen and antigen-antibody complexes in infected hamster serum. *Exp. Parasitol. 44:*216.

201. Digeon, M., D. Droz, L. H. Noel, J. Riza, C. Rieumailhol, J. F. Bach, F. Santoro, and A. Capron (1979). The role of circulating immune complexes in the glomerular disease of experimental hepatosplenic schistosomiasis. *Clin. Exp. Immunol. 35:*329.

202. Lawley, T. J., E. A. Ottesen, R. A. Hiatt, and L. A. Gazze (1979). Circulating immune complexes in acute schistosomiasis. *Clin. Exp. Immunol. 37:*221.

203. Nash, T. E., B. Prescott, and F. A. Neva (1974). The characteristics of the circulating antigen in schistosomiasis. *J. Immunol. 112:*1500.

204. Nash, T. E., U. D. Nasir, and R. W. Jeanloz (1977). Further purification

and characterization of a circulating antigen in schistosomiasis. *J. Immunol. 119:*1627.

205. Nash, T. E. (1978). Antibody response to a polysaccharide antigen present in the schistosome gut. I. Sensitivity and specificity. *Am. J. Trop. Med. Hyg. 27:*939.

206. Nash, T. E. (1974). Localization of the circulating antigen within the gut of *Schistosoma mansoni. Am. J. Trop. Med. Hyg. 23:*1085.

207. von Lichtenberg, F., M. P. Bawden, and S. H. Shealey (1974). Origin of circulating antigen in the schistosome gut. An immunofluorescent study. *Am. J. Trop. Med. Hyg. 23:*1088.

208. Nash, T. E., E. A. Ottesen, and A. W. Cheever (1978). Antibody response to a polysaccharide antigen present in the schistosome gut. II. Modulation of antibody response. *Am. J. Trop. Med. Hyg. 27:*944.

209. Carlier, Y., D. Bout, J. C. Bina, D. Camus, J. F. M. Figueiredo, and A. Capron (1975). Immunological studies in human schistosomiasis. I. Parasitic antigen in urine. *Am. J. Trop. Med. Hyg. 24:*949.

210. Santoro, F., Y. Carlier, R. Borojevic, D. Bout, P. Tachon, and A. Capron (1977). Parasite "M" antigen in milk from mothers infected with *Schistosoma mansoni* (preliminary report). *Ann. Trop. Med. Parasitol. 71:*121.

211. Maddison, S. E., M. D. Hicklin, and I. G. Kagan (1973). Immediate, Arthus, and delayed-type skin reactions in Rhesus monkeys infected with *Schistosoma mansoni* or mycobacteria. *J. Allergy Clin. Immunol. 52:*131.

212. Camus, D., Y. Carlier, M. Capron, J. C. Bina, J. F. M. Figueiredo, A. Prata, and A. Capron (1977). Immunological studies in human schistosomiasis. III. Immunoglobulin levels, antibodies, and delayed hypersensitivity. *Am. J. Trop. Med. Hyg. 26:*482.

213. Billings, F. T., W. L. Winkenwerder, and A. V. Hunninen (1946). Studies on acute schistosomiasis japonica in the Phillipine Islands. I. A clinical study of 337 cases with a preliminary report on the results of treatment with Fuadin in 110 cases. *Bull. Johns Hopkins Hosp. 78:*21

214. Wei-Hsin, C. (1958). Acute schistosomiasis. Clinical manifestations of 96 cases. *Chin. Med. J. 76:*1.

215. Chin, D., T. Yen, C. Wei-Liang, S. Tsung-Jen, and T. Yi-Hsin (1958). Acute schistosomiasis. Clinicopathologic report of three cases. *Chin. Med. J. 76:*40.

216. Liu, J., C. Wei-Ju, H. Ming-Hsin, P. Ju-Sun, C. Shao-Chi, H. Chao-Yueh, H. Pao-Yuan, and T. Ching-Yi (1958). Acute schistosomiasis japonica. *Chin. Med. J. 76:*229.

217. Tsu-Fei, S., and C. Nai-Pin (1958). Schistosomiasis in children. *Chin. Med. J. 76:*361.

218. Diaz-Rivera, R. S., F. Ramos-Morales, E. Koppisch, M. R. Garcia-Palmieri, A. A. Cintron-Rivera, E. J. Marchand, O. Gonzalez, and M. V. Torregrosa (1956). Acute Manson's schistosomiasis. *Am. J. Med. 21:*918.

219. Oliveira, C. A., D. M. Bicalho, R. Pimenta-Filho, H. Katz, H. Ferreira, D. Bittencourt, R. P. Dias, R. J. Alvarenga, and C. B. Dias (1969). A fase

aguda da esquistossomose mansoni. Estude laparoscopico da disseminacao de granulomas esquistossomoticos. *GEN 23:*369.

220.   Bogliolo, L. (1967). The pathogenesis of schistosomiasis mansoni. In *Bilharziasis*. (F. K. Mostofi, Ed.). Springer-Verlag, New York, p. 184.

221.   Hillyer, G. V. (1969). Immunoprecipitins in *Schistosoma mansoni* infections. IV. Human infections. *Exp. Parasitol. 25:*376.

222.   Reis, A. P., N. Katz, and J. Pellegrino (1970). Immunodiffusion tests in patients with *Schistosoma mansoni* infection. *Rev. Inst. Med. Trop. São Paulo 12:*245.

223.   Hillyer, G. V., N. Hernandez-Almenas, W. B. Knight, and B. Cline (1976). Circulating antigens, antibodies, and immunoglobulins in the serum of humans with schistosomiasis mansoni. *Bol. Asoc. Med. P. R. 68:*128.

224.   von Lichtenberg, F. (1964). Studies on granuloma formation. III. Antigen sequestration and destruction in the schistosome pseudotubercle. *Am. J. Pathol. 45:*75.

225.   Gutekunst, R. R., H. G. Browne, and D. M. Meyers (1965). Influence of *Schistosoma mansoni* eggs on growth of monkey heart cells. *Exp. Parasitol. 17:*194.

226.   Cheever, A. W., W. B. DeWitt, and K. S. Warren (1965). Repeated infection and treatment of mice with *Schistosoma mansoni:* Functional, anatomic, and immunologic observations. *Am. J. Trop. Med. Hyg. 14:*239.

227.   von Lichtenberg, F., E. H. Sadun, A. W. Cheever, D. G. Erickson, A. J. Johnson, and H. W. Boyce (1971). Experimental infection with *Schistosoma japonicum* in chimpanzees. Parasitologic, clinical, serologic, and pathological observations. *Am. J. Trop. Med. Hyg. 20:*850.

228.   von Lichtenberg, F., E. H. Sadun, and J. I. Bruce (1972). Renal lesions in *Schistosoma japonicum* infected rabbits. *Trans. R. Soc. Trop. Med. Hyg. 66:*505.

229.   Andrade, Z. A., and M. Susin (1974). Renal changes in mice infected with *Schistosoma mansoni. Am. J. Trop. Med. Hyg. 23:*400.

230.   Hillyer, G. V., and R. M. Lewert (1974). Studies on renal pathology in hamsters infected with *Schistosoma mansoni* and *S. japonicum. Am. J. Trop. Med. Hyg. 23:*404.

231.   Sadun, E. H., W. A. Reid, A. W. Cheever, R. H. Duvall, K. G. Swan, K. M. Kent, J. I. Bruce, and F. von Lichtenberg (1975). Effects of portacaval shunting in chimpanzees: Dissociation of pipe-stem fibrosis and glomerulopathy. *Am. J. Trop. Med. Hyg. 24:*619.

232.   Tada, T., Y. Kondo, K. Okumura, M. Sano, and M. Yokogawa (1975). *Schistosoma japonicum:* Immunopathology of nephritis in *Macaca fascicularis. Exp. Parasitol. 38:*291.

233.   Natali, P. G., and D. Cioli (1976). Immune complex nephritis in *Schistosoma mansoni*-infected mice. *Eur. J. Immunol. 6:*359.

234.   Houba, F., R. F. Sturrock, and A. E. Butterworth (1977). Kidney lesions in baboons infected with *Schistosoma mansoni. Clin. Exp. Immunol. 30:*439.

235. Hillyer, G. V. (1973). Schistosome deoxyribonucleic acid (DNA), antibodies to DNA in schistosome infections, and their possible role in renal pathology. *Bol. Asoc. Med. P.R. 65*(Suppl.):1.

236. Andrade, Z. A., and A. C. Queiroz (1968). Lesões renais na esquistossomose hepatesplênica. *Rev. Inst. Med. Trop. São Paulo 10:*36.

237. Lima, R. R., E. Brito, and H. Rocha (1969). Glomerulonefrite crônica associada à hepatoesplenomegalia esquistossomótica. *Gaz. Med. Bah. 69:* 43.

238. Brito, T., J. Gunji, M. E. Camargo, D. O. Penna, and L. C. Silva (1970). Advanced kidney disease in patients with hepatosplenic Manson's schistosomiasis. *Rev. Inst. Med. Trop. São Paulo 12:*225.

239. Andrade, Z. A., S. G. Andrade, and M. Sadigursky (1971). Renal changes in patients with hepatosplenic schistosomiasis. *Am. J. Trop. Med. Hyg. 20:*77.

240. Queiroz, F. P., E. Brito, R. Martinelli, and H. Rocha (1973). Nephrotic syndrome in patients with *Schistosoma mansoni* infection. *Am. J. Trop. Med. Hyg. 22:*622.

241. Falcao, A., and B. Gould (1975). Immune complex nephropathy in schistosomiasis. *Ann. Intern. Med. 83:*148.

242. Hillyer, G. V., J. A. Campos, R. Lluberer, and J. L. Cangiano (1975). Schistosomal nephropathy? I. Preliminary studies of a patient with schistosomiasis mansoni and glomerulonephritis in Puerto Rico. *Bol. Asoc. Med. P.R. 67:*339.

243. Rocha, H., T. Cruz, E. Brito, and M. Susin (1976). Renal involvement in patients with hepatosplenic schistosomiasis mansoni. *Am. J. Trop. Med. Hyg. 25:*108.

244. Hoshino-Shimizu, S., T. Brito, H. Y. Kanamura, A. L. Canto, A. O. Silva, A. R. Campos, D. O. Penna, and L. C. Silva (1976). Human schistosomiasis: *Schistosoma mansoni* antigen detection in renal glomeruli. *Trans. R. Soc. Trop. Med. Hyg. 70:*492.

245. Barsoum, R. S., S. Bassily, O. K. Baligh, M. Eissa, N. el-Sheemy, N. Affify, and A-M. Hassaballa (1977). Renal disease in hepatosplenic schistosomiasis, a clinicopathological study. *Trans. R. Soc. Trop. Med. Hyg. 71:* 387.

246. Moriearty, P. L., and E. Brito (1977). Elution of renal antischistosome antibodies in human schistosomiasis mansoni. *Am. J. Trop. Med. Hyg. 26:*717.

247. Sadigursky, M., Z. A. Andrade, R. Danner, A. W. Cheever, I. A. Kamel, and A. M. Elwi (1976). Absence of schistosomal glomerulopathy in *Schistosoma haematobium* infection in man. *Trans. R. Soc. Trop. Med. Hyg. 70:*322.

248. Smithers, S. R., and R. J. Terry (1967). Resistance to experimental infection with *Schistosoma mansoni* in rhesus monkeys induced by the transfer of adult worms. *Trans. R. Soc. Trop. Med. Hyg. 61:*517.

249. Hsu, S. Y. L., and H. F. Hsu (1969). Immunization against schistosome

infection in rhesus monkeys with living worms by intraperitoneal injection. *Parasitology 59:*601.

250. Maddison, S. E., I. G. Kagan, F. W. Chandler, D. Gold, G. V. Hillyer, S. B. Slemanda, and V. Tsang (1979). Immunization against *Schistosoma mansoni* in rhesus monkeys and the requirement of activation of both cell-mediated and humoral mechanisms. *Inf. Immunity. 25:*237.

251. Webbe, G., and C. James (1973). Acquired resistance to *Schistosoma haematobium* in the baboon (*Papio anubis*). *Trans. R. Soc. Trop. Med. Hyg. 67:*151.

252. Damian, R. T., N. D. Greene, K. F. Meyer, A. W. Cheever, W. J. Hubbard, M. E. Hawes, and J. D. Clark (1976). *Schistosoma mansoni* in baboons. III. The course and characteristics of infection, with additional observations on immunity. *Am. J. Trop. Med. Hyg. 25:*299.

253. Sadun, E. H., and J. I. Bruce (1964). Resistance induced in rats by previous exposure to and by vaccination with fresh homogenates of *Schistosoma mansoni. Exp. Parasitol. 15:*32.

254. Hillyer, G. V., J. Chiriboga, R. Menendez-Corrada, J. Pellegrino, and F. Liard (1970). An attempt to induce resistance in mice to *Schistosoma mansoni* infection using millipore diffusion chambers. *Rev. Inst. Med. Trop. São Paulo 12:*149.

255. Bickle, Q., J. Bain, A. McGregor, and M. Doenhoff (1979). Factors affecting the acquisition of resistance against *Schistosome mansoni* in the mouse. III. The failure of primary infections with cercariae of one sex to induce resistance to reinfection. *Trans. R. Soc. Trop. Med. Hyg. 73:* 37.

256. Dean, D. A., P. Minard, M. A. Stirewalt, W. E. Vannier, and K. D. Murrell (1978). Resistance of mice to secondary infection with *Schistosoma mansoni.* I. Comparison of bisexual and unisexual initial infections. *Am. J. Trop. Med. Hyg. 27:*951.

257. Dean, D. A., P. Minard, K. D. Murrell, and W. E. Vannier (1978). Resistance of mice to secondary infection with *Schistosoma mansoni.* II. Evidence for a correlation between egg deposition and worm elimination. *Am. J. Trop. Med. Hyg. 27:*957.

258. Smith, M. A., and J. A. Clegg (1979). Different levels of immunity to *Schistosoma mansoni* in the mouse: The role of variant cercariae. *Parasitology 78:*311.

259. Doenhoff, M., and E. Long (1979). Factors affecting the acquisition of resistance against *Schistosoma mansoni* in the mouse. IV. The inability of T cell-deprived mice to resist reinfection, and other in vivo studies on the mechanisms of resistance. *Parasitology 78:*171.

260. von Lichtenberg, F., E. H. Sadun, and J. I. Bruce (1963). Host response to eggs of *Schistosoma mansoni.* III. The role of eggs in resistance. *J. Infect. Dis. 113:*113.

261. Maddison, S. E., S. B. Slemenda, G. V. Hillyer, F. W. Chandler, and I. G. Kagan (1979). Immune responses to *Schistosoma mansoni* in rhesus

monkeys with multiple chronic and early primary infections. *Inf. Immunity. 25:*249.

262. Weiss, N., U. P. Oberlin, and A. Degrémont (1976). Stimulation of hamster and human lymphocyte cultures by soluble egg antigens (SEA) of *Schistosoma haematobium* and *S. mansoni. Trans. R. Soc. Trop. Med. Hyg. 70:*317.

263. Vernes, A., D. Camus, A. Capron, M. Capron, M. Gentilini, and E. Crouzet (1973). Les phenomenes d'hypersensibilite au cours des schistosomiases humaines a *Schistosoma mansoni* et *Schistosoma haematobium.* I. Étude de l'hypersensibilite retardée in vivo par intradermo-réaction et in vitro par le test de migration leucocytaire et un test mixte derivé du test d'inhibition de l'étalement des macrophages. *Pathol. Biol. (Paris) 21:* 1073.

264. Lewert, R. M., M. G. Yogore, and B. L. Blas (1979). Lymphocyte responsiveness to phytohemagglutinin and to worm and egg antigens in human schistosomiasis japonicum. *Am. J. Trop. Med. Hyg. 28:*92.

265. Ky, N. T., B. Halpern, and L. Roche (1977). Lymphocyte culture in the immunological diagnosis of human Bilharziasis. *Ann. Allergy 38:*353.

266. Clegg, J. A., S. R. Smithers, and R. J. Terry (1970). "Host" antigens associated with schistosomes: Observations on their attachment and their nature. *Parasitology 61:*87.

267. Cioli, D. (1976). *Schistosoma mansoni:* A comparison of mouse and rat worms with respect to host antigens detected by the technique of transfer into hamsters. *Int. J. Parasitol. 6:*355.

268. Lewert, R. M., M. G. Yogore, J. M. Para, and M. A. Ozcel (1977). Rejection of mouse-derived *Schistosoma japonicum* and serum lethality of hosts immunized with mouse globulin or mouse erythrocytes. *J. Parasitol. 63:*825.

269. Boyer, M. H., L. J. Kalfayan, and D. G. Ketchum (1977). The host antigen phenomenon in experimental murine schistosomiasis. III. Destruction of parasites transferred from mice to hamsters. *Am. J. Trop. Med. Hyg. 26:*254.

270. Coelho, P. M. Z., J. R. Melo, L. H. Pereira, and E. Nascimento (1979). Transplantation of adult *Schistosoma mansoni* from mice to the portal system of *Cebus* monkeys immunized against the donor host. *Trans. R. Soc. Trop. Med. Hyg. 73:*113.

271. Coelho, P. M. Z., D. G. Colley, J. Pellegrino, and L. H. Pereira (1976). Survival of schistosomula (*Schistosoma mansoni*) transferred from hamsters to mice immunized against the donor host. *J. Parasitol. 62:*159.

272. Boyer, M. H., and D. G. Ketchum (1976). The host antigen phenomenon in experimental murine schistosomiasis. II. Failure to demonstrate destruction of parasites transferred from hamsters to mice. *J. Immunol. 116:*1093.

273. Kemp, W. M., S. C. Merritt, M. S. Bogucki, J. G. Rosier, and J. R. Seed (1977). Evidence for adsorption of heterospecific host immunoglobulin on the tegument of *Schistosoma mansoni. J. Immunol. 119:*1849.

274. Kemp, W. M., S. C. Merritt, and J. G. Rosier (1978). *Schistosoma mansoni:* Identification of immunoglobulins associated with the tegument of adult parasites from mice. *Exp. Parasitol. 45:*81.

275. Sher, A., B. J. Hall, and M. A. Vadas (1978). Acquisition of murine major histocompatibility complex gene products by schistosomula of *Schistosoma mansoni. J. Exp. Med. 148:*46.

276. Dean, D. A., and K. W. Sell (1972). Surface antigens on *Schistosoma mansoni.* II. Adsorption of a Forssman-like host antigen by schistosomula. *Clin. Exp. Immunol. 12:*525.

277. Torpier, G., A. Capron, and M. A. Quaissi (1979). Receptor for IgG (F_c) and human β_2-microglobulin on *S. mansoni* schistosomula. *Nature (Lond.) 278:*447.

278. Smith, H. V., and J. R. Kusel (1979). The acquisition of antigens in the intercellular substance of mouse skin by schistosomula of *Schistosoma mansoni. Clin. Exp. Immunol. 36:*430.

279. Damian, R. T. (1964). Molecular mimicry: Antigen sharing by parasite and host and its consequences. *Am. Natural. 98:*129.

280. Damian, R. T., N. D. Greene, and W. J. Hubbard (1973). Occurrence of mouse α_2-macroglobulin antigenic determinants on *Schistosoma mansoni* adults, with evidence on their nature. *J. Parasitol. 59:*64.

281. Kemp, W. M., R. T. Damian, N. D. Greene, and W. B. Lushbaugh (1976). Immunocytochemical localization of mouse alpha 2-macroglobulin-like antigenic determinants on *Schistosoma mansoni* adults. *J. Parasitol. 62:*413.

282. Hockley, D. G., and S. R. Smithers (1970). Damage to adult *Schistosoma mansoni* after transfer to a hyperimmune host. *Parasitology 61:*95.

283. Mota-Santos, R. B., G. Gazzinelli, F. J. Ramalho-Pinto, J. Pellegrino, and W. Dias da Silva (1976). Immunodepression in mice following *Schistosoma mansoni* infection. *Rev. Inst. Med. Trop. São Paulo 18:*246.

284. Mota-Santos, T. A., C. A. P. Tavares, G. Gazzinelli, and J. Pellegrino (1977). Immunosuppression mediated by adult worms in chronic schistosomiasis mansoni. *Am. J. Trop. Med. Hyg. 26:*727.

285. Dessaint, J. P., D. Camus, E. Fischer, and A. Capron (1977). Inhibition of lymphocyte proliferation by factor(s) produced by *Schistosoma mansoni. Eur. J. Immunol. 7:*624.

286. Colley, D. G., F. A. Lewis, and R. W. Goodgame (1978). Immune responses during human schistosomiasis mansoni. IV. Induction of suppressor cell activity by schistosome antigen preparations and concanavalin A. *J. Immunol. 120:*1225.

287. Kayes, S. G., and D. G. Colley (1979). Immunoregulation in experimental schistosomiasis: In vitro induction and assay of spleen cell suppressor activity. *J. Immunol. 122:*2340.

288. Goodwin, J. S., R. P. Messner, A. D. Bankhurst, G. T. Peake, J. H. Saiki, and R. C. Willians (1977). Prostaglandin producing suppressor cells in Hodgkin's disease. *N. Engl. J. Med. 297:*963.

289. Goodwin, J. S., R. DeHoratius, H. Isreal, G. T. Peake, and R. P. Messner (1979). Suppressor cell function in sarcoidosis. *Ann. Intern. Med. 90:* 169.

290. Baldwin, R. W., and R. A. Robins (1976). Factors interfering with immunological rejection of tumours. *Br. Med. Bull. 32:*118.

291. Gorczynski, R. M., D. G. Kilburn, R. A. Knight, C. Norbury, D. C. Parker, and J. B. Smith (1975). Nonspecific and specific immunosuppression in tumour-bearing mice by soluble immune complexes. *Nature (Lond.) 254:* 141.

292. Gershon, R. L., S. Orbach-Arbouys, and C. Calkins (1974). B cell signals which activate suppressor T cells. *Progr. Immunol. II 2:*123.

293. Moretta, L., M. Ferrarini, M. C. Mingari, A. Moretta, and S. R. Webb (1976). Subpopulations of human T cells identified by receptors for immunoglobulins and mitogen responsiveness. *J. Immunol. 117:*2171.

294. Moretta, L., S. R. Webb, C. E. Grossi, P. M. Lydyard, and M. D. Cooper (1977). Functional analysis of two human T-cell subpopulations: Help and suppression of B-cell responses by T cells bearing receptors for IgM or IgG. *J. Exp. Med. 146:*184.

295. Binz, H., and H. Wigzell (1977). Idiotypic, alloantigen-reactive T lymphocyte receptors and their use to induce specific transplantation tolerance. *Progr. Allergy 23:*154.

296. Hubbard, W. J. (1978). Hypothesis. Alpha-2 macroglobulin-enzyme complexes as suppressors of cellular activity. *Cell. Immunol. 39:*388.

297. Smyth, J. D., and J. A. Clegg (1959). Egg-shell formation in trematodes and cestodes. *Exp. Parasitol. 8:*286.

298. Stenger, R. J., K. S. Warren, and E. A. Johnson (1967). An ultrastructural study of hepatic granulomas and schistosome egg shells in murine hepatosplenic schistosomiasis mansoni. *Exp. Mol. Pathol. 8:*116.

299. Race, G. J., J. H. Martin, D. V. Moore, and J. E. Larsh, Jr. (1971). Scanning and transmission electronmicroscopy of *Schistosoma mansoni* eggs, cercariae and adults. *Am. J. Trop. Med. Hyg. 20:*914.

300. Ford, J. W., and H. D. Blankenspoor (1979). Scanning electron microscopy of the eggs of three human schistosomes. *Int. J. Parasitol. 9:*141.

301. Cheever, A. W. (1969). Quantitative comparison of the intensity of *Schistosoma mansoni* infections in man and experimental animals. *Trans. R. Soc. Trop. Med. Hyg. 63:*781.

302. Smith, T. M., H. L. Lucia, B. L. Doughty, and F. C. von Lichtenberg (1971). The role of phospholipids in schistosome granulomas. *J. Infect. Dis. 123:*629.

303. Smith, M. A. (1974). Radioassays for the proteolytic enzyme secreted by living eggs of *Schistosoma mansoni. Int. J. Parasitol. 4:*681.

304. Dresden, M. (1979). The proteinases of *Schistosoma mansoni* cercariae, adults, and eggs. Fourteenth Joint Conference on Parasitic Diseases of the United States-Japan Cooperative Medical Science Program, New Orleans, La., August, 1979.

305.   Stjernholm, R. L., and K. S. Warren (1974). *Schistosoma mansoni:* Utilization of exogenous metabolites by eggs in vitro. *Exp. Parasitol. 36:*222.

306.   Oliver-Gonzales, J. (1954). Anti-egg precipitins in the serum of human infected with *Schistosoma mansoni. J. Infect. Dis. 95:*86.

307.   Boros, D. L., and K. S. Warren (1970). Delayed hypersensitivity-type granuloma formation and dermal reaction induced and elicited by a soluble factor isolated from *Schistosoma mansoni* eggs. *J. Exp. Med. 132:* 488.

308.   Carter, C. E., and D. G. Colley (1978). An electrophoretic analysis of *Schistosoma mansoni* soluble egg antigen preparation. *J. Parasitol. 64:* 385.

309.   Pelley, R. P., R. J. Pelley, J. Hamburger, P. A. Peters, and K. S. Warren (1976). *Schistosoma mansoni* soluble egg antigens. I. Identification and purification of three major antigens, and the employment of radioimmunoassay for their further characterization. *J. Immunol. 117:*563.

310.   Hamburger, J., R. P. Pelley, and K. S. Warren (1976). *Schistosoma mansoni* soluble egg antigens. II. Determination of the stage and species specificity of their serologic reactivity by radioimmunoassay. *J. Immunol. 117:*1561.

311.   Pelley, R. P., and R. J. Pelley (1976). *S. mansoni* soluble egg antigens. IV. Biochemistry and immunochemistry of major serological antigens with particular emphasis on MSA$_1$. In *Biochemistry of Parasites and Host-Parasite Relationships* (H. Van den Bossche, Ed.). Elsevier North-Holland Biomedical Press, Amsterdam, Holland, p. 283.

312.   Pelley, R. P. (1977). Purification of *Schistosoma mansoni* egg antigens: Theory and practice. *Am. J. Trop. Med. Hyg. 26*(Suppl.):104.

313.   Boros, D. L., R. Tomford, and K. S. Warren (1977). Induction of granulomatous and elicitation of cutaneous sensitivity by partially purified SEA of *Schistosoma mansoni. J. Immunol. 118:*373.

314.   Brown, A. P., H. G. Remold, K. S. Warren, and J. R. David (1977). Partial purification of antigens from eggs of *Schistosoma mansoni* that elicit delayed hypersensitivity. *J. Immunol. 119:*1275.

315.   Carter, C. E., and D. G. Colley (1979). Partial purification and characterization of *Schistosoma mansoni* soluble egg antigen using Con A-Sepharose chromatography. *J. Immunol. 122:*2204.

316.   Harrison, D. J., C. E. Carter, and D. G. Colley (1979). Immunoaffinity purification of *Schistosoma mansoni* soluble egg antigens. *J. Immunol. 122:*2210.

317.   Carter, C. E., and D. G. Colley (1980). Immunoaffinity purification of a *Schistosoma japonicum* soluble egg antigen. *Mol. Immunol.* (in press).

318.   Boctor, F. N., T. E. Nash, and A. W. Cheever (1979). Isolation of a polysaccharide antigen from *Schistosoma mansoni* eggs. *J. Immunol. 122:* 39.

319.   Warren, K. S., E. O. Domingo, and R. B. T. Cowan (1967). Granuloma

formation around schistosome eggs as a manifestation of delayed hypersensitivity. *Am. J. Pathol. 51:*735.

320. Warren, K. S., D. L. Boros, L. M. Hang, and A. A. F. Mahmoud (1975). The *Schistosoma japonicum* egg granuloma. *Am. J. Pathol. 80:*279.

321. Warren, K. S. (1972). The immunopathogenesis of schistosomiasis: A multidisciplinary approach. *Trans. R. Soc. Trop. Med. Hyg. 66:*417.

322. von Lichtenberg, F., D. G. Erickson, E. H. Sadun (1973). Comparative histopathology of schistosome granulomas in the hamster. *Am. J. Pathol. 72:*149.

323. Warren, K. S. (1963). The contribution of worm burden and host response to the development of hepatosplenic schistosomiasis mansoni in mice. *Am. J. Trop. Med. Hyg. 12:*34.

324. Cheever, A. W. (1965). A comparative study of *Schistosoma mansoni* infections in mice, gerbils, multimammate rats and hamsters. I. The relation of portal hypertension to size of hepatic granulomas. *Am. J. Trop. Med. Hyg. 14:*211.

325. Cheever, A. W. (1965). A comparative study of *Schistosoma mansoni* in mice, gerbils, multimammate rats, and hamsters. II. Qualitative pathological differences. *Am. J. Trop. Med. Hyg. 14:*227.

326. von Lichtenberg, F., J. H. Smith, and A. W. Cheever (1966). The Hoeppli phenomenon in schistosomiasis. Comparative pathology and immunopathology. *Am. J. Trop. Med. Hyg. 15:*886.

327. Warren, K. S. (1966). The pathogenesis of "clay-pipe stem cirrhosis" in mice with chronic schistosomiasis mansoni, with a note on the longevity of the schistosomes. *Am. J. Pathol. 49:*477.

328. Domingo, E. O., and K. S. Warren (1969). Pathology and pathophysiology of the small intestine in murine schistosomiasis mansoni, including a review of the literature. *Gastroenterology 56:*231.

329. Warren, K. S., and E. G. Berry (1972). Induction of hepatosplenic disease by single pairs of the Phillipine, Formosan, Japanese, and Chinese strains of *Schistosoma japonicum*. *J. Infect. Dis. 126:*482.

330. Erickson, D. G., E. H. Sadun, H. L. Lucia, F. von Lichtenberg, and A. W. Cheever (1971). *Schistosoma haematobium:* Infections in five species of primates. *Exp. Parasitol. 29:*126.

331. Kuntz, R. E., B. J. Myers, J. A. Moore, and T. C. Huang (1971). *Schistosoma haematobium:* Experimental infection in Capuchin monkey, *Cebus apella*. *Exp. Parasitol. 29:*33.

332. Webbe, G., C. James, and G. S. Nelson (1974). *Schistosoma haematobium* in the baboon (*Papio anubis*). *Am. Trop. Med. Parasitol. 68:*187.

333. Cheever, A. W. (1968). A quantitative post-mortem study of schistosomiasis mansoni in man. *Am. J. Trop. Med. Hyg. 17:*38.

334. Kamel, I. A., A. M. Elwi, A. W. Cheever, J. E. Mosimann, and R. Danner (1978). *Schistosoma mansoni* and *S. haematobium* infections in Egypt. IV. Hepatic lesions. *Am. J. Trop. Med. Hyg. 27:*939.

335. Sadun, E. H., F. von Lichtenberg, A. W. Cheever, and D. G. Erickson

(1970). Schistosomiasis mansoni in the chimpanzee. The natural history of chronic infections after single and multiple exposures. *Am. J. Trop. Med. Hyg. 19:*258.

336. Cheever, A. W. (1972). Pipe-stem fibrosis of the liver. *Trans. R. Soc. Trop. Med. Hyg. 66:*946.

337. Warren, K. S. (1972). Pipe-stem fibrosis of the liver. *Trans. R. Soc. Trop. Med. Hyg. 66:*948.

338. Dunn. M. A., M. Rojkind, K. S. Warren, P. K. Hait, L. Rifas, and S. Seifter (1977). Liver collagen synthesis in murine schistosomiasis. *J. Clin. Invest. 59:*666.

339. Johnson, R. L., and M. Ziff (1976). Lymphokine stimulation of collagen accumulation. *J. Clin. Invest. 58:*240.

340. Wyler, D. J., S. M. Wahl, and L. M. Wahl (1978). Hepatic fibrosis in schistosomiasis: Egg granulomas secrete fibroblast stimulating factor in vitro. *Science 202:*438.

341. Canto, A. L., A. Sesso, and T. de Brito (1977). Human chronic mansonian schistosomiasis—Cell proliferation and fibre formation in the hepatic sinusoidal wall: A morphometric, light and electron-microscopy study. *J. Pathol. 123:*35.

342. Grimaud, J. A., and R. Borojevic (1977). Myofibroblasts in hepatic schistosomal fibrosis. *Experimentia 33:*890.

343. von Lichtenberg, F. (1962). Host response to eggs of *S. mansoni*. I. Granuloma formation in the unsensitized laboratory mouse. *Am. J. Pathol. 41:*711.

344. Akpom, C. A., M. F. Abdel-Wahab, and K. S. Warren (1970). Comparison of formation of granulomata around eggs of *Schistosoma mansoni* in the mouse, guinea pig, rat and hamster. *Am. J. Trop. Med. Hyg. 19:*996.

345. Kassis, A. I., K. S. Warren, and A. A. F. Mahmoud (1978). The *Schistosoma haematobium* egg granuloma. *Cell. Immunol. 38:*310.

346. Erickson, D. G., C. E. Jones, and D. B. Tang (1974). Schistosomiasis mansoni, haematobia and japonica in hamsters: Liver granuloma measurements. *Exp. Parasitol. 35:*425.

347. Hsu, S. Y. L., H. F. Hsu, G. L. Lust, J. R. Davis, and L. K. Eveland (1973). Comparative studies on the lesions caused by eggs of *Schistosoma japonicum* and *Schistosoma mansoni* in the liver of hamsters, guinea pigs, and albino rats. *Ann. Trop. Med. Parasitol. 67:*349.

348. Warren, K. S., D. I. Grove, and R. P. Pelley (1978). The *Schistosoma japonicum* egg granuloma. II. Cellular composition, granuloma size, and immunologic concomitants. *Am. J. Trop. Med. Hyg. 27:*271.

349. von Lichtenberg, F., and P. Raslavicius (1967). Host response to eggs of *Schistosoma mansoni*. V. Reactions to purified miracidia and egg shells and to viable and heat-killed whole eggs. *Lab. Invest. 16:*892.

350. Hang, L. M., K. S. Warren, and D. L. Boros (1974). *Schistosoma mansoni:* Antigenic secretions and the etiology of egg granulomas in mice. *Exp. Parasitol. 35:*288,

351. Bogitsh, B. J. (1971). *Schistosoma mansoni:* Cytochemistry of eosinophils in egg-caused early hepatic granulomas in mice. *Exp. Parasitol. 29:* 493.

352. Smith, M. D. (1977). The ultrastructural development of the schistosome egg granuloma in mice. *Parasitology 75:*119.

353. Bogitsh, B. J., and S. K. Wikel (1974). *Schistosoma mansoni:* Ultrastructural observations on the small intestine of the murine host. *Exp. Parasitol. 35:*68.

354. Moore, D. L., D. I. Grove, and K. S. Warren (1976). The *Schistosoma mansoni* egg granuloma: Quantitation of cell populations. *J. Pathol. 121:*41.

355. Mahmoud, A. A. F., K. S. Warren, and R. C. Graham, Jr. (1975). Anti-eosinophil serum and the kinetics of eosinophilia in schistosomiasis mansoni. *J. Exp. Med. 142:*560.

356. Warren, K. S., and E. O. Domingo (1970). Granuloma formation around *Schistosoma mansoni, S. haematobium* and *S. japonicum* eggs in unsensitized mice: Size and rate of development, cellular composition, cross-reactivity, and rate of egg destruction. *Am. J. Trop. Med. Hyg. 19:*292.

357. Cheever, A. W., and L. A. Anderson (1971). Rate of destruction of *Schistosoma mansoni* eggs in the tissues of mice. *Am. J. Trop. Med. Hyg. 20:*62.

358. Cheever, A. W., and K. G. Powers (1971). Rate of destruction of *Schistosoma mansoni* eggs and adult worms in the tissues of rhesus monkeys. *Am. J. Trop. Med. Hyg. 20:*69:

359. Edungbola, L. D., and E. L. Schiller (1979). Histopathology of hepatic and pulmonary granulomata experimentally induced with eggs of *Schistosoma mansoni. J. Parasitol. 65:*253.

360. Olds, G. R., and A. A. F. Mahmoud (1980). Role of host granulomatous response in murine schistosomiasis mansoni. Eosinophil-mediated destruction of eggs. *J. Clin. Invest. 66:*1191.

361. Magalhães-Filho, A., I. M. Krupp, and E. A. Malek (1965). Localization of antigen and presence of antibody in tissues of mice infected with *Schistosoma mansoni,* as indicated by fluorescent antibody techniques. *Am. J. Trop. Med. Hyg. 14:*84.

362. Sogandares-Bernal, F., and S. Brandt (1976). Antibodies sequestered in the liver granulomata of 8-week infections of CF_1 mice by *Schistosoma mansoni* Sambon, 1907. *Z. Parasitenkd. 50:*331.

363. Davis, B. H., A. A. F. Mahmoud, and K. S. Warren (1974). Granulomatous hypersensitivity to *Schistosoma mansoni* eggs in thymectomized and bursectomized chickens. *J. Immunol. 113:*1064.

364. Maddison, S. E., F. W. Chandler, J. S. McDougal, S. B. Slemenda, and I. G. Kagan (1978). *Schistosoma mansoni* infection in intact and B cell deficient mice: The effect of pretreatment with BCG in these experimental models. *Am. J. Trop. Med. Hyg. 27:*966.

365. Warren, K. S., and E. O. Domingo (1970). *Schistosoma mansoni:* Stage

specificity of granuloma formation around eggs after exposure to irradiated cercariae, unisexual infections, or dead worms. *Exp. Parasitol. 27:*
60.

366.   Domingo, E. O., R. B. T. Cowan, and K. S. Warren (1967). The inhibition of granuloma formation around *Schistosoma mansoni* eggs. I. Immunosuppressive Drugs. *Am. J. Trop. Med. Hyg. 16:*284.

367.   Domingo, E. O., and K. S. Warren (1967). The inhibition of granuloma
formation around *Schistosoma mansoni* eggs. II. Thymectomy. *Am. J.
Pathol. 51:*757.

368.   Domingo, E. O., and K. S. Warren (1968). The inhibition of granuloma
formation around *Schistosoma mansoni* eggs. III. Heterologous and
antilymphocyte serum. *Am. J. Pathol. 52:*613.

369.   Perrotto, J. L., and K. S. Warren (1969). Inhibition of granuloma formation around *Schistosoma mansoni* eggs. IV. X-irradiation. *Am. J. Pathol.
56:*279.

370.   Warren, K. S. (1969). Inhibition of granuloma formation around *Schistosoma mansoni* eggs. V. "Hodgkin's-like Lesion" in SJL/J mice. *Am.
J. Pathol. 56:*293.

371.   Warren, K. S., A. A. F. Mahmoud, D. L. Boros, T. W. Rall, M. A. Mandel,
and C. C. J. Carpenter, Jr. (1974). In vivo suppression by cholera toxin
of cell-mediated and foreign body inflammatory responses. *J. Immunol.
112:*996.

372.   Boros, D. L., and K. S. Warren (1971). Effect of antimacrophage serum
on hypersensitivity (*Schistosoma mansoni* egg) and foreign body (divinyl-
benzene copolymer bead) granulomas. *J. Immunol. 107:*534.

373.   Mahmoud, A. A. F., and K. S. Warren (1974). Anti-inflammatory effects of tartar emetic and niridazole: Suppression of schistosome egg
granuloma. *J. Immunol. 112:*222.

374.   Knauft, R. F., and K. S. Warren (1969). The effect of calorie and protein malnutrition on both the parasite and the host in acute murine
schistosomiasis mansoni. *J. Infect. Dis. 120:*560.

375.   Mahmoud, A. A. F. (1979). Host-parasite relationship in schistosomiasis
mansoni in the mutation diabetic mouse (db/db). *Am. J. Trop. Med.
Hyg. 28:*286.

376.   Byram, J. E., A. Sher, J. DiPietro, and F. von Lichtenberg (1979). Potentiation of schistosome granuloma formation by lentinan-A T-cell adjuvant.
*Am. J. Pathol. 94:*201.

377.   Fine, D. P., R. D. Buchanan, and D. G. Colley (1973). *Schistosoma mansoni* infection in mice depleted of thymus-dependent lymphocytes. *Am.
J. Pathol. 71:*193.

378.   Buchanan, R. D., D. P. Fine, and D. G. Colley (1973). *Schistosoma mansoni* infection in mice depleted of thymus-dependent lymphocytes. II.
Pathology and altered pathogenesis. *Am. J. Pathol. 71:*207.

379.   Hsu, C. K., S. H. Hsu, R. A. Whitney, Jr., and C. T. Hansen (1976). Immunology of schistosomiasis in athymic mice. *Nature (Lond.) 262:*397.

380. Phillips, S. M., J. J. DiConza, J. A. Gold, and W. A. Reid (1977). Schistosomiasis in the congenitally athymic (nude) mouse. I. Thymic dependence of eosinophilia, granuloma formation, and host morbidity. *J. Immunol. 118:*594.

381. Byram, J. E., and F. von Lichtenberg (1977). Altered schistosome granuloma formation in nude mice. *Am. J. Trop. Med. Hyg. 26:*944.

382. Doenhoff, M., R. Musallam, J. Bain, and A. McGregor (1979). *Schistosoma mansoni* infections in T-cell deprived mice, and the ameliorating effect of administering homologous chronic infection serum. I. Pathogenesis. *Am. J. Trop. Med. Hyg. 28:*260.

383. Byram, J. E., M. J. Doenhoff, R. Musallam, L. H. Brink, and F. von Lichtenberg (1979). *Schistosoma mansoni* infections in T-cell deprived mice, and the ameliorating effect of administering homologous chronic infection serum. II. Pathology. *Am. J. Trop. Med. Hyg. 28:*274.

384. Doenhoff, M., R. Musallam, J. Bain, and A. McGregor (1978). Studies on the host-parasite relationship in *Schistosoma mansoni*-infected mice: The immunological dependence of parasite egg excretion. *Immunology 35:* 771.

385. Epstein, W. L., K. Fukuyama, K. Danno, and E. Kwan-Wong (1979). Granulomatous inflammation in normal and athymic mice infected with *Schistosoma mansoni:* An ultrastructural study. *J. Pathol. 127:*207.

386. Colley, D. G. (1972). Intradermal immune responses to a schistosomal egg antigen during experimental murine *Schistosoma mansoni* infection. *Proc. Soc. Exp. Biol. Med. 140:*772.

387. Colley, D. G. (1975). Immune responses to a soluble schistosomal egg antigen preparation during chronic primary infection with *Schistosoma mansoni. J. Immunol. 115:*150.

388. Colley, D. G. (1980). Lymphokine-related eosinophil responses. In *Lymphokine Reports,* Vol. 1. Academic Press, New York, p. 133.

389. von Lichtenberg, F., T. M. Smith, H. L. Lucia, and B. L. Doughty (1971). New model for schistosome granuloma formation using soluble egg antigen and bentonite particles. *Nature (Lond.) 299:*199.

390. Boros, D. L., and K. S. Warren (1971). Specific granulomatous hypersensitivity elicited by bentonite particles coated with soluble antigens from schistosome eggs and tubercle bacilli. *Nature (Lond.) 299:*200.

391. Boros, D. L., and K. S. Warren (1973). The bentonite granuloma: Characterization of a model system for infectious and foreign body granulomatous inflammation using soluble mycobacterial, histoplasma and schistosoma antigens. *Immunology 24:*511.

392. Dunsford, H. A., H. L. Lucia, B. L. Doughty, and F. von Lichtenberg (1974). Artificial granulomas from bentonite and latex carrier particles. *Am. J. Trop. Med. Hyg. 23:*203.

393. Boros, D. L., K. S. Warren, and R. P. Pelley (1973). The secretion of migration inhibitory factor by intact schistosome egg granulomas maintained in vitro. *Nature (Lond.) 246:*224.

394. James, S. L., and D. G. Colley (1975). Eosinophils and immune mechanisms: Production of the lymphokine eosinophil stimulation promoter (ESP) in vitro by isolated intact granulomas. *J. Reticuloendothel. Soc. 18:*283.

395. James, S. L., and D. G. Colley (1978). Eosinophil-mediated destruction of *Schistosoma mansoni* eggs in vitro. III. Lymphokine involvement in the induction of eosinophil functional abilities. *Cell. Immunol. 38:*48.

396. Hillyer, G. V., and L. P. Frick (1967). Immunoprecipitins in *Schistosoma mansoni* infections. I. Mouse infection. *Exp. Parasitol. 20:*321.

397. Kanamura, H. Y., S. Hoshino-Schimizu, M. E. Camargo, and L. C. da Silva (1979). Class specific antibodies and fluorescent staining patterns in acute and chronic forms of schistosomiasis mansoni. *Am. J. Trop. Med. Hyg. 28:*242.

398. Boros, D. L., R. P. Pelley, and K. S. Warren (1975). Spontaneous modulation of granulomatous hypersensitivity in schistosomiasis mansoni. *J. Immunol. 114:*1437.

399. James, S. L., and D. G. Colley (1976). Eosinophil-mediated destruction of *Schistosoma mansoni* eggs. *J. Reticuloendothel. Soc. 20:*359.

400. James, S. L., and D. G. Colley (1978). Eosinophil mediated destruction of *Schistosoma mansoni* eggs in vitro. II. The role of cytophilic antibody. *Cell. Immunol. 38:*35.

401. Boros, D. L., H. J. Schwartz, A. E. Powell, and K. S. Warren (1973). Delayed hypersensitivity, as manifested by granuloma formation, dermal reactivity, macrophage migration inhibition, and lymphocyte transformation, induced and elicited in guinea pigs with soluble antigens of *Schistosoma mansoni* eggs. *J. Immunol. 110:*1118.

402. Colley, D. G. (1971). Schistosomal egg antigen-induced lymphocyte blastogenesis in experimental murine *Schistosoma mansoni* infection. *J. Immunol. 107:*1477.

403. Colley, D. G. (1973). Eosinophil and immune mechanisms. I. Eosinophil stimulation promoter (ESP): A lymphokine induced by specific antigen or phytohemagglutinin. *J. Immunol. 110:*1419.

404. Pelley, R. P., R. Karb, A. A. F. Mahmoud, and K. S. Warren (1976). Antigen dose response and specificity of production of the lymphokine eosinophil stimulation promoter. *J. Infect. Dis. 134:*230.

405. Doughty, B. L., A. G. Bentley, and S. M. Phillips (1979). In vitro modulation of granulomatous hypersensitivity in schistosomiasis mansoni. *Fed. Proc. 38:*1275 (Abstract).

406. Kazura, J. W., A. A. F. Mahmoud, K. S. Karb, and K. S. Warren (1975). The lymphokine eosinophil stimulation promoter and human schistosomiasis mansoni. *J. Infect. Dis. 132:*702.

407. Reiner, N. E., R. Kamel, G. I. Higashi, A. el Naggar, M. Aguib, J. J. Ellner, and A. A. F. Mahmoud (1979). Concurrent responses of peripheral blood and splenic mononuclear cells to antigenic and mitogenic stimulation in human hepatosplenic schistosomiasis. *J. Infect. Dis. 140*(2):162.

408. Andrade, Z. A., and K. S. Warren (1964). Mild prolonged schistosomiasis in mice: Alterations in host response with time and the development of portal fibrosis. *Trans. R. Soc. Trop. Med. Hyg. 58:*53.

409. Domingo, E. O., and K. S. Warren (1968). Endogenous desensitization: Changing host granulomatous response to schistosome eggs at different stages of infection with *Schistosoma mansoni. Am. J. Pathol. 52:*369.

410. Warren, K. S. (1974). Modulation of immunopathology in schistosomiasis. In *Parasites in the Immunized Host: Mechanisms of Survival.* Ciba Foundation Symposium, No. 25 Elsevier North-Holland, Amsterdam, Holland, p. 243.

411. Warren, K. S. (1977). Modulation of immunopathology and disease in schistosomiasis. *Am. J. Trop. Med. Hyg. 26*(Suppl.):113.

412. Rocklin, R. E., A. Brown, K. S. Warren, R. P. Pelley, V. Houba, and A. E. Butterworth (1977). Immunologic modulation in children with schistosomiasis. *Clin. Res. 25:*486A.

413. Colley, D. G. (1976). Adoptive suppression of granuloma formation. *J. Exp. Med. 143:*696.

414. Colley, D. G., F. A. Lewis, and C. W. Todd (1979). Adoptive suppression of granuloma formation by T lymphocytes and by lymphoid cells sensitive to cyclophosphamide. *Cell. Immunol. 45:*192.

415. Colley, D. G. (1981). T lymphocytes that contribute to the immunoregulation of granuloma formation in chronic murine schistosomiasis. *J. Immunol. 126* (in press).

416. Chensue, S. W., and D. L. Boros (1979). Modulation of granulomatous hypersensitivity. I. Characterization of T lymphocytes involved in the adoptive suppression of granuloma formation in *Schistosoma mansoni* infected mice. *J. Immunol. 123:*1409.

417. Green, W. F., and D. G. Colley (1981). Modulation of *Schistosoma mansoni* egg-induced granuloma formation: I-J restriction of T cell-mediated suppression in a chronic parasitic infection. *Proc. Natl. Acad. Sci. USA. 78* (in press).

418. Chensue, S. W., and D. L. Boros (1979). Population dynamics of T and B lymphocytes in the lymphoid organs, circulation, and granulomas of mice infected with *Schistosoma mansoni. Am. J. Trop. Med. Hyg. 28:*291.

419. Lewert, R. M., and S. Mandlowitz (1969). Schistosomiasis: Prenatal induction of tolerance to antigens. *Nature (Lond.) 224:*1029.

420. Hang, L. M., D. L. Boros, and K. S. Warren (1974). Induction if immunological hyporesponsiveness to granulomatous hypersensitivity in *Schistosoma mansoni* infection. *J. Infect. Dis. 130:*515.

421. Hillyer, G. V., R. Menendez-Corrada, R. Lluberes, and F. Hernandez-Morales (1970). Evidence of transplacental passage of specific antibody in schistosomiasis mansoni in man. *Am. J. Trop. Med. Hyg. 19:*289.

422. Camus, D., Y. Carlier, J. C. Bina, R. Borojevic, A. Prata, and A. Capron (1976). Sensitization to *Schistosoma mansoni* antigen in uninfected children born to infected mothers. *J. Infect. Dis. 134:*405.

423. Tachon, P., and R. Borojevic (1978). Mother-child relationship in human schistosomiasis mansoni: Skin test and cord blood reactivity to schistosomal antigens. *Trans. R. Soc. Trop. Med. Hyg. 72:*605.

424. Kayes, S. G., and D. G. Colley. Immunoregulation in experimental schistosomiasis. Comparisons between concanavalin A- and soluble egg antigen-induced changes in spleen cells from chronically infected mice. (In preparation.)

425. Pelley, R. P., J. J. Ruffier, and K. S. Warren (1976). The suppressive effect of a chronic helminth infection, schistosomiasis mansoni, on the in vitro responses of spleen and lymph node cells to the T cell mitogens PHA and Con A. *Inf. Immunity. 13:*1176.

426. Coulis, P. A., R. M. Lewert, and F. W. Fitch (1978). Splenic suppressor cells and cell-mediated cytotoxicity in murine schistosomiasis. *J. Immunol. 120:*1074.

427. Attallah, A. M., A. H. Smith, K. D. Murrell, T. Fleischer, J. Woody, W. E. Vannier, I. Scher, A. Ahmed, and K. W. Sell (1979). Characterization of the immunosuppressive state during *Schistosoma mansoni* infection. *J. Immunol. 122:*1413.

428. Araujo, F. G., P. M. Z. Coelho, L. H. Pereira, and J. Pellegrino (1977). *Schistosoma mansoni:* Impairment of the cell-mediated immune response in mice. *Clin. Exp. Immunol. 28:*289.

429. Goodgame, R. W., D. G. Colley, C. C. Draper, F. A. Lewis, M. L. McLaren, and R. P. Pelley (1978). Humoral immune responses in human hepatosplenic schistosomiasis mansoni. *Am. J. Trop. Med. Hyg. 27:*1174.

430. Wilkins, H. A., and J. Brown (1977). *Schistosoma haematobium* in a Gambian community. II. Impaired cell-mediated immunity and other immunological abnormalities. *Ann. Trop. Med. Parasitol. 71:*59.

431. Tsuda, S., K. Fukuyama, and W. L. Epstein (1979). Low molecular weight eosinophil chemotactic factor in granulomatous liver of murine schistosomiasis. *J. Immunol. 122:*2554.

432. Capron, A., and M. A. Lesoin (1969). Rôle protecteur du BCG dans la schistosomiase expérimentale. *C.R. Acad. Sci. [D] (Paris) 269:*2110.

433. Smith, M. A., J. A. Clegg, J. R. Kusel, and G. Webbe (1975). Lung inflammation in immunity to *Schistosoma mansoni. Experientia 31:*595.

434. Mahmoud, A. A. F., K. S. Warren, and G. T. Strickland (1976). Acquired resistance to infection with *Schistosoma mansoni* induced by *Toxoplasma gondii. Nature (Lond.) 263:*56.

435. Bout, D., H. Dupas, Y. Carlier, D. Afchain, and A. Capron (1977). High resistance induced by young live Bacillus Calmette-Guerin (BCG) to *Schistosoma mansoni* infection in mice. *Ann. Immunol. (Paris) 128*(C): 811.

436. Civil, R. H., K. S. Warren, and A. A. F. Mahmoud (1978). Conditions for Bacille Calmette-Guerin-induced resistance to infection with *Schistosoma mansoni* in mice. *J. Infect. Dis. 137:*550.

437. Civil, R. H., and A. A. F. Mahmoud (1978). Genetic differences in BCG-

induced resistance to *Schistosoma mansoni* are not controlled by genes within the major histocompatibility complex of the mouse. *J. Ummunol. 120:*1070.

438. Olds, G. R., L. Chedid, E. Lederer, and A. A. F. Mahmoud (1980). Induction of resistance to *Schistosoma mansoni* by natural and synthetic cord factor and its lower homologues. *J. Infect. Dis. 141:*473.

439. Goodgame, R. W., J. A. Cook, and P. Jordan (1980). Racial predisposition in hepatosplenic schistosomiasis mansoni. (Submitted for publication.)

440. Smith, M. A., and J. A. Clegg (1976). Different levels of acquired immunity to *Schistosoma mansoni* in two strains of hamster. *Parasitology 73:* 47.

441. Blum, K., and D. Cioli (1978). Behavior of Biozzi high and low responder mice upon infection with *Schistosoma mansoni*. *Eur. J. Immunol. 8:*52.

442. Deelder, A. M., F. H. J. Claas, and R. R. P. DeVries (1978). Influence of the mouse H-2 gene complex on experimental infections with *Schistosoma mansoni*. *Trans. R. Soc. Trop. Med. Hyg. 72:*321.

443. Claas, F. H. J., and A. M. Deelder (1979). H-2 linked immune response to murine experimental *Schistosoma mansoni* infections. *J. Immunogen. 6:*167.

444. Khattab, M., M. T. El-Gengehy, and M. Sharaf (1968). ABO blood group in bilharzial hepatic fibrosis. *J. Egypt. Med. Assoc. 51:*245.

445. Camus, D., J. C. Bina, Y. Carlier, F. Santoro (1977). A, B, O blood groups in clinical forms of schistosomiasis mansoni. *Trans. R. Soc. Trop. Med. Hyg. 71:*182.

446. Lima-Perreira, F. E., E. R. Bortolini, J. L. A. Carneiro, C. R. Mello da Silva, and R. C. Neves (1979). A, B, O blood groups and hepatosplenic form of schistosomiasis mansoni (Symmer's fibrosis). *Trans. R. Soc. Trop. Med. Hyg. 73:*238.

447. Abdel-Salam, E., S. Ishaac, and A. A. F. Mahmoud (1979). Histocompatability-linked susceptibility for hepatosplenomegaly in human schistomiasis mansoni. *J. Immunol. 123:*1829.

448. Goodgame, R. W., and R. K. Bartholomew (1978). Lack of association of hepatosplenic schistosomiasis and alpha-1-antitrypsin deficiency. *Am. J. Trop. Med. Hyg. 27:*779.

449. Colley, D. G., and G. L. Freeman, Jr. (1980). Differences in adult *Schistosoma mansoni* worm burden requirements for the establishment of resistance to reinfection in inbred mice. I. CBA/J and C57BL/6 mice. *Am. J. Trop. Med. Hyg. 29:*1279.

2

Immune Responses in Malaria

ANIL N. JAYAWARDENA   Yale University School of Medicine, New Haven, Connecticut

I.	Introduction	86
II.	The Host-Parasite Relationship	86
	A. The Parasite	86
	B. The Immune System: Its Response	87
III.	Protective Responses to Erythrocytic Infections	88
	A. General Considerations	88
	B. Role of T Cells	89
	C. Role of Antibody	97
	D. The Cellular Component in Resistance to Malaria	103
IV.	Active Immunization against Erythrocytic Infections	108
V.	Immune Responses to Pre-erythrocytic Infections	110
VI.	Regulatory Responses	112
	A. Immunosuppression	112
	B. Hypergammaglobulinemia	117
	C. Autoimmunity	118
	D. Bidirectional Effects of the Immune Response	120
VII.	Concluding Remarks	121
	References	122

I. INTRODUCTION

There is currently a resurgence of interest in the immunology of malaria. This "reawakening" is perhaps long overdue since malaria has remained the most serious of the major parasitic diseases—its incidence in the tropics is estimated at 150 million cases per annum [1].

Several reasons underlie the current interest in the immunology of malaria: (1) The development of a vaccine against malaria appears to be a viable proposition [2,3]. (2) New chemotherapeutic approaches may depend on an increased understanding of the host response since antimalarial drugs act synergistically with the immune system [4]. (3) Fundamental insights into the role of the immune response in the establishment and evolution of host-parasite and even host-tumor relationships [5] may be gained by studying the immune responses activated in a disease such as malaria.

The possibility of carrying out detailed studies of the immune response, in terms of our current understanding of its cellular, molecular, and genetic bases, is greatly facilitated by the existence of a series of well-defined murine models of the disease [6]. This review will focus primarily on the host response in these model systems. It will attempt to examine, in particular, the manner in which the immune system contributes to both positive and negative attributes of the host response and thus regulates the host-parasite relationship.

II. THE HOST-PARASITE RELATIONSHIP

A. The Parasite

Malaria is caused by protozoan parasites of the genus *Plasmodium,* first described 100 years ago [7]. The disease in humans is caused by four species of *Plasmodium* (*P. falciparum, P. vivax, P. malariae,* and *P. ovale*). Malaria also occurs in other mammals (apes and rodents) and in birds and reptiles.

The complexity of the host response is not surprising when one examines the life cycles of these organisms. They consist of a series of distinct developmental stages—both extracellular and intracellular—which provide the host with a constantly changing antigenic stimulus. The life cycle involves a phase of development in an invertebrate host (mosquito), followed by a phase of development in a vertebrate host. In mammalian malaria, the infective forms (sporozoites) are injected by a female anopheline mosquito into the host. The sporozoites circulate in the blood stream for a few hours and then enter parenchymal cells of the liver where they undergo a cycle of growth and asexual reproduction (exoerythrocytic or pre-erythrocytic development). Merozoites produced through exoerythrocytic development either reinfect liver cells or enter red blood cells (RBC) where they either initiate a cyclic phase of asexual multiplication result-

ing in the release of merozoites which reinvade RBC or differentiate into gameto-
cytes which are infective for mosquitoes. For a detailed description of life cycles
and the biology of the malaria parasites, see Garnham, 1966 [8].

B. The Immune System: Its Response

It is increasingly clear that the mammalian immune system can best be viewed as
a complex network of cells continuously responding to signals from both within
and without to maintain a "steady state." When confronted with an exogenous
stimulus such as a rapidly multiplying malaria parasite, the steady state appears to
be disrupted. The series of events which ensue and which constitute the host response can be viewed as an attempt on the part of the host to reach a new state of
equilibrium. In the case of a host infected with malaria, the events involved are
necessarily complex and include (1) responses which are primarily "protective"
and are aimed at limiting the spread of the organism (e.g., the production of specific antibody against the parasite), (2) responses which appear to be "regulatory"
or "suppressive" and which inhibit the development of a protective response
(e.g., the activation of suppressor cells), and (3) responses which are neither
directly protective nor inhibitory but rather appear to be symptomatic of a
breakdown of normal regulatory mechanisms (e.g., the development of certain
forms of autoimmunity). The extent to which any particular response is triggered would depend on the antigenic makeup of the parasite and the ability of
the host to recognize and respond to these antigens. The outcome of a specific
host-parasite relationship would in turn depend not on any single response but
on the net balance between these diverse and often opposing manifestations of
the host response. In successful host-parasite relationships a new level of equilibrium, "immunity"—is achieved; in others immunity is not achieved, resulting
in the elimination of both host and parasite.

Malarial infections in rodent and simian hosts provide a spectrum of such
relationships in which varying levels of equilibrium are reached. In certain host-
parasite combinations—*Plasmodium vinckei* or *Plasmodium berghei* in mice and
Plasmodium knowlesi in rhesus monkeys (*Macaca mulatta*)—effective immunity
is not induced, and the infections prove rapidly fatal. The failure to induce immunity can be attributed to a lack of adaptation since these parasites are not in
their natural hosts. If the same parasites are in their natural hosts—African
thicket rats (*Thamnomys* sp.) [9] and the Kra monkey (*Macaca irus*), respectively [8] —they activate an effective immune response and coexist harmoniously
with the host for several years. Other models which *simulate* natural host-
parasite associations are *Plasmodium yoelii* (17X) in mice and *P. berghei* in
adult rats.

In most "natural" host-parasite associations after the primary infection is controlled, the host becomes resistant to reinfection with the homologous parasite (immune). In certain model systems it has been claimed that the development of this resistance is associated with the complete elimination of the parasite, i.e., the immunity developed is "sterile" [10,11]. However, in systems which have been carefully examined, small numbers of parasites appear to persist in the immune host [12]. This phenomenon has been termed premunition [13], or concomitant immunity [14]. Most instances in which immunity to malaria develops under natural conditions, including the immunity to *P. falciparum* shown by adults living in hyperendemic areas, can be attributed to a form of premunition, or concomitant immunity. The dynamic and often tenuous nature of the balance between host and parasite in these situations is emphasized by the fact that either complete eradication of the parasite (via chemotherapy) or a reduction in host immunocompetence as a result of aging, malnutrition, pregnancy, or some other factor can once more disrupt the equilibrium between host and parasite and result in a loss of immunity.

III. PROTECTIVE RESPONSES TO ERYTHROCYTIC INFECTIONS

A. General Considerations

Resistance to blood-induced malarial infections operates at two levels: (1) innate or natural resistance mechanisms which in large measure determine whether an animal is susceptible to infection or not and (2) protective immunological mechanisms which control the spread of the parasite and maintain a state of immunity in a susceptible host. The innate factors which operate at the level of the RBC include the presence or absence of appropriate receptors for the parasite [15], the age of the RBC [16], enzyme activity [17], and hemoglobin type [18]. In the rodent malarias the age of the red cell is a particularly critical factor [19]; although certain parasites invade both mature and immature red cells (e.g., certain strains of *P. berghei*), others invade reticulocytes preferentially (e.g., *P. yoelii* 17X). In the latter case, maneuvers which increase or decrease reticulocyte production cause radical changes in the intensity of the infection. For a detailed description of innate resistance mechanisms, see Miller and Carter [20] and Luzzato [21]. Protective immunological mechanisms elicited in an infected host include the production of host protective antibody and the activation of cellular resistance mechanisms; these mechanisms will form the main focus of this section of the review. Although systems such as the natural killer (NK) cell system will also be discussed, it should be pointed out that this system shows no immunological specificity and can more accurately be regarded as a form of innate resistance.

Both innate and immunological resistance mechanisms are under genetic control and probably underlie the marked variation in the susceptibility of different strains of mice to erythrocytic infections of malaria [22]. Using duration and severity as parameters of resistance, strains such as the A/J, BALB/cJ, and C57BL/6J appear to be highly susceptible to nonfatal *P. yoelii* (17X) infections, whereas strains such as the CBA/CaJ are relatively resistant (Jayawardena, unpublished results). An essentially similar pattern of strain variation also occurs in *P. chabaudi* infections [23,24]. Interestingly, the A/J, AKR, A/HeJ, and C56BL/6J strains of mice have also been found to be highly susceptible to sporozoite-induced *P. berghei* infections [25]. Examination of *P. yoelii* (17X) infections in B-10 mice congenic at the H-2 locus representing $H-2^a$, $H-2^b$, $H-2^d$ and $H-2^k$ haplotypes has not revealed an obvious association between H-2 and the intensity of these infections (Jayawardena and Murphy, unpublished results). However, since a multiplicity of immunological and nonimmunological mechanisms are probably involved in resistance to malaria, these observations do not rule out the possibility that some form of H-2-linked control may be involved in the very complex responses to *Plasmodium* spp. One factor contributing to the pattern of strain variation observed appears to be the NK potential of these mice (see Section III.D).

B. Role of T Cells

1. T-Cell Dependence of Protective Immunity

The development of protective immunity to malaria is clearly thymus dependent. This is implied by three main lines of evidence: (1) T-cell-deficient animals are unable to respond effectively to malaria, (2) the development of protective immunity is associated with T-cell activation, and (3) T cells from animals immune to malaria transfer such immunity to nonimmune recipients.

a. Effect of T-Cell Deprivation

The first direct evidence that the thymus played a role in controlling malarial infections came from the demonstration that *P. berghei* infections were more severe in neonatally thymectomized rats than in intact controls [26,27]. The absolute T-cell dependency of the immune response was demonstrated more convincingly in subsequent studies on *P. yoelii* (17X) infections in mice. Normal mice respond effectively to this parasite and control infections in 2-3 weeks, after which they are resistant to reinfection (immune). In contrast, congenitally athymic or T-cell-deprived mice are unable to mount an effective response, and infections prove uniformly fatal in 30-35 days [12,28] (Figure 1). Even if infections in T-cell-deficient mice are controlled temporarily by chemotherapy, resistance fails to develop [29], implying an absolute requirement for T cells in the induction of immunity to this parasite. Interestingly, parasitemias in T-cell-deficient mice tend to be significantly lower than in normal mice around day 10 or 11 of infection [12]. Although this could be due to increase of a non-T-cell-dependent form of immunity—such as the NK system, or decrease in a T-cell-

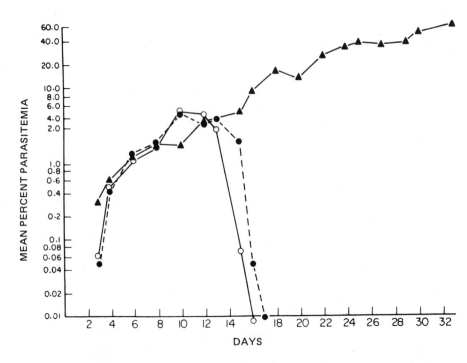

Figure 1 Mean parasitemias in normal (○), sham-deprived (●), and T-cell-deprived (▲) CBA mice infected with 10^4 *P. yoelii* (17X) parasitized RBC. (From Jayawardena et al. [12].)

dependent suppressor mechanism of some kind—it should be noted that, as T cells regulate hematopoiesis [30], the lower parasitemia may reflect a decrease in the rate of production of immature RBC which are preferentially parasitized by *P. yoelii* (17X). Furthermore, although T-cell deprivation always results in a worsening of the disease in host-parasite systems in which effective immunity is induced (e.g., *P. yoelii* (17X) in mice; *P. berghei* in adult rats), the same manipulation usually has a beneficial rather than deleterious effect on systems where the parasite appears not to activate an effective immune response and kills its host, e.g., *P. berghei* in mice (see Section VI.D).

b. T-Cell Activation

Malaria parasites have been shown to activate T cells both in vivo and in vitro. *Plasmodium yoelii* (17X) infected mouse radiation chimeras, in which T cells were identified by virtue of the T_6 chromosome marker, showed massive

T-cell proliferation which lasted until the infection was controlled [31]. When these mice were rechallenged with the homologous parasite, a second brief burst of T-cell mitosis occurred (Jayawardena, unpublished results). In contrast, *P. berghei* (ANKA) infections, which kill CBA mice in 20 to 25 days, elicited considerably less T-cell activity, and this activity waned despite a progressive infection [31]. Essentially similar results have been reported in studies in which the T-cell responses to *P. yoelii* (17X) and *P. berghei* (K 173) were monitored using a surface antigenic marker (Thy-1) for T cells [32], Hence, there appears to be a clear positive correlation between T-cell activation and the induction of protective immunity.

The ability of malarial antigens to activate T cells has also been demonstrated in vitro [33]. Splenic T cells from normal mice and mice immune to *P. yoelii* (17X) transformed when exposed to either *P. yoelii* (17XL)* parasitized red blood cells (PRBC) or a lysate of the parasitized cells. The degree and kinetics of proliferation of the unprimed cells differed from that of the primed cells and was thought to reflect either primary in vitro antigenic stimulation or polyclonal activation in response to a parasite-derived mitogen. Specifically sensitized T cells can also be detected in infected animals because they produce lymphotoxin when exposed to malarial antigens. Using this assay, sensitized T cells have been demonstrated in *P. yoelii* (17X) infected mice from within 5 days of infection to 150 days after recovery (Jayawardena and Ruddle, in preparation).

c.   Transfer of Resistance with T Cells

Animals that recover from the acute phase of malaria are usually resistant to reinfection with the homologous parasite. Spleen cells from such animals transfer resistance to nonimmune recipients [34,35]. Fractionation of the spleen cells in rats immune to *P. berghei* and mice immune to *P. yoelii* has shown that both immune T and B cells have the capacity to transfer resistance [35-37].

2.   T-Cell-Dependent Manifestations of Immunity

While there is little doubt that T cells are essential for the generation of an effective immune response, the precise manner in which they contribute to the development of a protective response remains to be identified. Several manifestations of the host response are thymus dependent (see Table 1); those responses that appear to be relevant to the development of protective immunity will be discussed.

---

*A lethal strain of *P. yoelii* (17X) which kills mice in 7-10 days.

Table 1 T-Cell-Dependent Manifestations of Immunity in Murine Malaria

Response	Reference
Splenomegaly	Jayawardena et al. [12]
	Roberts and Weidanz [38]
Germinal center response	Jayawardena et al. [12]
DTH responses to parasitized RBC	Whitelaw et al. [39]
Lymphotoxin production	Jayawardena and Ruddle, in preparation
Blood monocyte production and activation	Jayawardena et al. [12]
Macrophage activation	Roberts and Weidanz [38]
Production of monocyte chemotactic factor	Wyler and Gallin [40]
Specific IgM, IgG1, and IgG2 antibody production	Jayawardena et al. [12]
Nonspecific immunoglobulin production	Rosenberg [41]
Anti-erythrocyte autoantibody production	Rosenberg [41]
Anemia	Roberts and Weidanz [38]
Suppressor cell activation	Jayawardena [42]

a. The Response of the Spleen

CBA mice infected with *P. yoelii* (17X) show about a 10-fold increase in spleen size during the acute phase of the infection. In contrast, T-cell-deprived mice show only a modest increase in spleen size [12]. Furthermore, fatal *P. berghei* (ANKA) infections induce substantially less splenomegaly than *P. yoelii* [43].

The splenomegaly in *P. yoelii*-infected mice is associated mainly with reactive changes in the malpighian follicles. These changes are of two main types: infiltration of the periarteriolar regions by pyroninophilic lymphoid cells, and a vigorous germinal center response [12]. Pyroninophilic lymphoid cells accumulate in the thymus-dependent periarteriolar zones in the first week of infection (Figure 2). At the peak of infection, the response is maximal—the periarteriolar regions are packed with pyroninophilic cells; with regression of the infection, the response recedes. This response is T-cell dependent in that only small numbers of pyroninophilic cells are found cuffing the central arterioles in T-cell-deprived mice [12]. *Plasmodium yoelii*-infected mice also show a prominent germinal center response. In weeks 2 and 3 of infection, the germinal centers are large and active and are the dominant feature of the white pulp (Figure 3). In infected, T-cell-deprived mice the white pulp remains inconspicuous throughout the infec-

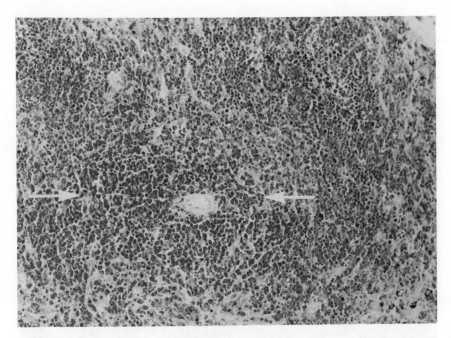

Figure 2 Spleen of CBA mouse: day 7 *P. yoelii* (17X) infection. Central arteriole surrounded by darkly staining pyroninophilic cells (arrows) (magnification X98). (From Jayawardena [43].)

tion, and only small, poorly delineated germinal centers are seen. The response is restored in T-cell-deprived mice reconstituted with thymus grafts [12]. Comparative studies of the responses of CBA mice to *P. yoelii* and *P. berghei* have shown that, although fatal *P. berghei* infections induce a significant degree of germinal center activity, the response is clearly less marked than in *P. yoelii* infections (Figure 4) [43,44].

b. Delayed-Type Hypersensitivity Responses

Mice sensitized to the erythrocytic stages of malaria show delayed-type hypersensitivity (DTH) responses when PRBC are injected into the ear or footpad. Using the ear assay, positive DTH responses to a strain of *P. berghei* were elicited in sensitized BALB/c nu/+ mice, but hypothymic BABL/c nu/nu mice failed to mount DTH responses to *P. berghei*-infected RBC, indicating that this response was T-cell dependent [39]. DTH responses were also elicited in sensitized CBA/H and SJL mice. No genetic restriction could be demonstrated in

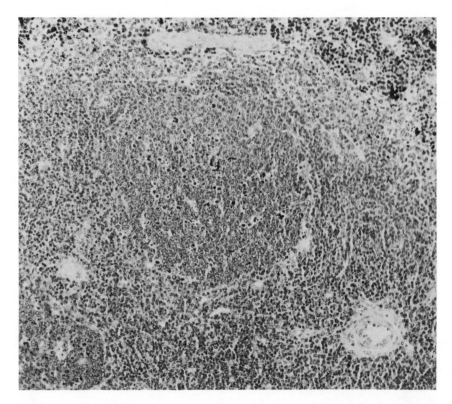

Figure 3 Spleen of CBA mouse: day 21 *P. yoelii* (17X) infection; large well-defined germinal center (gc) (magnification ✕117). (From Jayawardena [43].)

this system since responses were not affected by the genotype of the PRBC used to sensitize or elicit the reactions. Similarly, the ability of sensitized T cells to transform and produce lymphotoxin when exposed to *P. yoelii* PRBC in vitro is not affected by the genotype of the PRBC (Jayawardena and Ruddle, unpublished results). Hence, the antigens which elicit these responses appear to be parasitic rather than modified—host cell antigens.

c. Blood Monocyte and Macrophage Responses

Plasmodium yoelii (17X) infections induce a massive blood monocyte response in normal CBA mice [12] . Monocyte levels increase from 380 ± 71 mm^3 in uninfected mice to a peak of $29,206 \pm 4635$ mm^3 13 days after infection. This response is impaired in T-cell-deprived mice—monocyte counts are lower

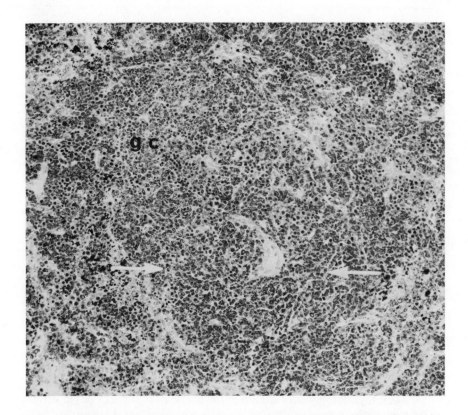

Figure 4 Spleen of CBA mouse: day 23 *P. berghei* (ANKA) infection; shows poorly demarcated white pulp segments surrounded by hyperplastic red pulp. Germinal centers (gc) are present, but are not very active. Pyroninophilic cell response in the periarteriolar region is maximal (arrows). (From Jayawardean [43].)

throughout most of the infection [12,43]. Furthermore, monocytes show marked signs of "activation" in normal mice, but not in T-cell-deprived mice (Jayawardena, unpublished observations). As with other responses, the monocyte response is reduced in *P. berghei* infections [43]. Both the accumulation and functional activity of splenic macrophages are also influenced by T cells. Fewer macrophages accumulate in the spleens of nude mice infected with *P. yoelii* or *P. berghei* than in normal mice. Furthermore, although *P. yoelii*-infected thymus-bearing mice show enhanced phagocytosis as judged by accelerated carbon clearance, this is not observed in athymic mice at a similar stage of infection [38].

d. Antibody Responses

Malarial infections usually induce a vigorous and sustained antibody response which is largely thymus dependent. CBA mice infected with *P. yoelii* (17X) show a rapid increase in IgM, IgG1, and IgG2 fluorescent antibodies to PRBC. In T-cell-deprived mice the IgG1 response is virtually absent; IgG2 and IgM antibody responses also show a high degree of thymus dependency [12].

3. Characterization of T-Cell Subsets

It is now clear that T cells are not a homogeneous population but rather consist of distinct subclasses or sets which mediate different functions [45]. Various approaches have been used to separate these cells and analyze their function. Raff and Cantor [46] suggested a classification of T cells based on their sensitivity to adult thymectomy (T_1) and anti-lymphocyte serum (T_2). More recently, alloantisera that define cell surface antigens (Ly, Qa-1, etc.) on T cells have been used to identify several T-cell subsets with distinct immunological functions [47-50]. Since several manifestations of the host response to parasites such as *P. yoelii* (17X) are T-cell dependent, it is not unlikely that different aspects of host immunity will be mediated by distinct T-cell subsets. At present, information is available only regarding the subsets involved in the control of acute blood stage infections.

a. Adult Thymectomy and Anti-Lymphocyte Serum

Adult thymectomy does not affect the course of *P. yoelii* (17X) infections in CBA mice even 6 months after thymectomy (Jayawardena, unpublished results). Hence T_1 cells, which decline after thymectomy [45], do not play an important role in controlling the acute phase of these infections. However, treatment of CBA mice with anti-lymphocyte serum (ALS) does result in a substantial increase in the severity of *P. yoelii* infections [43]. Similarly, if adult rats are treated with ALS before infection, their ability to control *P. berghei* infections is reduced [51]; if treated after the acute phase has been controlled, the infections recrudesce [52]. Hence, based on the classification of Raff and Cantor [46], the control of acute primary malarial infections appears to depend mainly on a T_2-type cell.

b. Ly Characterization

Based on the expression of the Ly antigens, the peripheral T-cell pool can be subdivided into at least three functionally distinct T-cell subsets:

$Ly-1^+, 23^-$: inducer cells (includes helpers in antibody production and delayed-type hypersensitivity responses)

Ly-1$^-$, 23$^+$: cytotoxic and suppressor cells
Ly-1$^+$, 23$^+$: regulatory cells (includes feedback suppressor cells)

To identify the Ly phenotypes of the T cells mediating resistance to *P. yoelii* (17X), a cell transfer system was developed (Jayawardena et al., in preparation). The system involves the transfer of highly purified immune T cells into T-cell-deprived CBA/CaJ recipients; *P. yoelii* (17X) infections prove fatal in these recipients in 30-40 days [12]. If the recipients are injected with immune T cells, the infections are controlled. Treatment of the T cells with anti-Ly-1.1 serum abrogates the immunity transferred. Treatment with anti-Ly-2.1 serum reduces the immunity transferred very slightly. Mixtures of anti-Ly-1.1 and anti-Ly-2.1-treated T cells, i.e., populations specifically devoid of Ly-1$^+$, 23$^+$ cells, transfer immunity as effectively as unselected T cells. Hence, the T cells which transfer immunity to *P. yoelii* are primarily of the Ly-1$^+$, 23$^-$ phenotype [53]. Several important conclusions can be drawn from this experiment. (1) There has always been speculation that cytotoxic T cells may be involved in resistance to malaria [54], although there has been no convincing demonstration of cytotoxicity against PRBC using chromium release assays. The Ly-phenotyping data suggest that Ly-23$^+$ cells which include cytotoxic T cells are not the major component of the resistance mechanism. (2) Since resistance maps mainly to the Ly-1 population, and since these cells reconstitute the ability of T-cell-deprived mice to make specific antibody and elicit DTH responses to malarial antigens (Jayawardena et al., in preparation), these Ly-1 T cells could be helpers in antibody secretion and/or in DTH responses. Since these experiments have also demonstrated synergy between Ly-1 cells and purified B cells, both in terms of increased resistance and increased secretion of specific antiplasmodial antibody, one of the functions mediated by these Ly-1 T cells is clearly that of a helper in antibody synthesis. How these cells may also contribute to cell-mediated mechanisms, and the relative importance of such mechanisms, awaits further investigation.

C. Role of Antibody

1. Nature of the Antibody Response

The erythrocytic phase of a malarial infection is a potent stimulator of immunoglobulin (Ig) synthesis. Part of the Ig produced represents specific antibody against the parasite [55], which can be detected by a variety of techniques including indirect immunofluorescence [56], direct and indirect agglutination [57-59], and the enzyme-linked immunoabsorbent assay [60].

The nature and kinetics of the antibody response to blood stage infections are essentially similar in most human and experimental malarias. In *P. vivax* or *P. falciparum* malaria an early increase in IgM is soon followed by a rise in IgG fluorescent antibody levels. Some elevation of IgA generally occurs, but

IgD and IgE levels remain unchanged [61-64]. Essentially similar changes in indirect fluorescent antibody (IFA) levels occur in *P. yoelii* [65], *P. berghei* [31], *P. vinckei* [66], *P. chabaudi* [66], and *Babesia microti* [67] infections in mice. In the rodent systems, high levels of IgM and IgG antibody persist after natural (*P. yoelii* and *P. chabaudi*) or drug-induced (*P. vinckei*) recovery from the acute phase of the infection, and there is no evidence that the IgM response is suppressed after the appearance of IgG [65,66]. In contrast, preferential suppression of the IgM response, but persistence of the IgG response to *P. vivax*, has been reported in individuals treated with chloroquine [68,69].

Although increased levels of IgM and IgG antibodies are a constant feature of blood stage infections, they do not necessarily correlate with the level of host immunity. During the acute phase of the disease in rodents, there is generally a good positive correlation between antibody levels and the development of an effective immune response; nonfatal *P. yoelii* (17X) infections induce higher antibody levels in mice than do fatal *P. berghei* or *P. yoelii* (17XL) infections [31, 182]. Similarly, if mice are infected with nonfatal *P. chabaudi*, they develop higher antibody levels than when infected with *P. vinckei* (a fatal infection), even if the *P. vinckei* infections are controlled by chemotherapy [66]. However, in certain other situations a clear correlation does not obtain. Animals resistant to reinfection after immunization [70] or recovery from a blood stage infection [71] may have little or no detectable antibody. Conversely, an actively immunized animal with high fluorescent antibody levels may be susceptible to challenge [70]. The most direct evidence indicating that antibody is involved in protection is (1) the increased severity of infections in animals with B-cell deficiencies and (2) the ability to transfer immunity with B cells and hyperimmune sera.

2. The Effects of B-Cell Depletion

Mice depleted of B cells by treatment with anti-μ serum from birth are unable to resist normally nonfatal *P. yoelii* infections [72], implying a role for B cells and antibody in the development of protective immunity. (It should, however, be noted that these mice also lack a subset of Ig-dependent T cells [73] whose possible role in malarial infections has yet to be critically examined.) The findings with *P. yoelii* infections in μ-suppressed mice are consistent with earlier observations on *Plasmodium gallinaceum* and *Plasmodium lophurae* infections which were found to be more severe in chickens made B cell deficient by bursectomy [74,75].

Although μ-suppressed mice and agammaglobulinemic chickens are unable to control a primary infection effectively, control of the acute infections by chemotherapy has been reported to result in the development of "resistance to reinfection" in these B-cell-deficient animals [71,75]. If *P. yoelii* infections in congenitally athymic nude mice are controlled in a similar manner, resistance does not develop. Hence, although antibody appears to contribute to the control of acute malarial infections, once control is achieved, T-cell-dependent mech-

anisms in which antibody plays little or no role may be sufficient for maintaining a state of immunity.

3. Effects of the X-Linked B-Cell Defect

The importance of B cells in general, and of certain subsets in particular, has been further emphasized by recent experiments involving the CBA/N mouse. These mice have an X-linked recessive gene which results in a defect in certain B-cell subsets, particularly those involved in the response to a certain class of thymus-independent antigens [76-78]. Both *P. yoelii* and *B. microti* infections are more severe in mice carrying the X-linked gene [79,80] (Figure 5). The reduced resistance to these parasites is associated with a striking deficiency in a thymus-dependent IgM antibody response and with a delay in the kinetics of the IgG1 and IgG2 antibody responses to parasitized RBC. However, once these defective mice recover from a primary *P. yoelii* infection, they are highly resistant to reinfection despite the fact that B cells from these mice are clearly deficient in transferring immunity to nonimmune recipients [79]. These results and the observations made on μ-suppressed mice suggest a shift of emphasis to antibody-independent mechanisms once the acute phase of a *P. yoelii* infection is brought under control. In contrast to the situation with *P. yoelii*, primary *P. chabaudi* infections are controlled relatively effectively by CBA/N mice (Jayawardena unpublished results). Hence, the antibody responses which CBA/N mice are deficient in appear to be more important in the control of certain *Plasmodium* spp. than others.

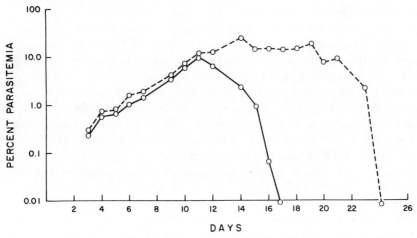

Figure 5 Mean parasitemias in normal (BALB $\times$ CBA/N) F_1 male mice (o——o) and defective (CBA/N $\times$ BALB) F_1 male mice (o – – –o) infected with 10^4 *P. yoelii* (17X) PRBC i.p. (From Jayawardena and Kemp [80].)

4. Transfer of Immunity with B Cells

B cells from mice immune to *P. yoelii* and from rats immune to *P. berghei* transfer resistance to nonimmune recipients [35,36]. In the *P. yoelii* system, adoptively transferred immune B cells have a more immediate effect on infections in naive recipients than do a similar number of immune T cells [79]. The transferred cells induce the production of high levels of antiplasmodial antibody (Jayawardena, unpublished results) and, as in the *P. berghei*-rat model, appear to exert a protective effect mainly by providing a source of protective antibody [81].

In general, even small numbers of immune B cells transfer better immunity than do large quantities of serum from the same donors. Although there are many possible explanations for the greater efficacy of cells, it should be noted that the B-cell preparations (prepared by treatment of whole spleen with anti-Thy-1.2 serum and complement) could either be contaminated with small numbers of T cells or contain some other cell type which also contributes to development of resistance.

5. Transfer of Immunity with Serum

The ability of passively transferred immune sera to decrease or delay parasitemia in nonimmune recipients has been demonstrated in a number of host-parasite systems [35,81,82]. However, there are many instances in which "protective activity" has not been detected in the sera of immune hosts [35]. Examination of the various attempts to transfer immunity with serum reveals certain trends regarding the nature of passively transferred antimalarial immunity. (1) In general, although hyperimmune sera (raised by multiple immunizations) are effective, immune sera from animals recovered from a single infection (e.g., *P. yoelii*) are without effect [35]. (2) Even with the most effective sera, the protective effects are not absolute except against low-challenge inocula [35]. Protection is generally short-lived [81] and is seen as a delay in the onset of a new infection or as temporary inhibition of an already existing infection. (3) Sera with protective activity are less effective when transferred into T-cell-deprived [35] or splenectomized recipients [84]. Hence, the protective effects seen in normal animals may depend in part on synergistic or simultaneous mobilization of other T-cell-dependent responses such as monocyte or macrophage activation. (4) Protective activity is associated with both IgM and IgG antibodies [83,85]. In the *P. berghei* rat system a combination of IgM and IgG is more protective than antibody of either isotype alone [85]. Furthermore, purified IgG appears to be less effective than whole serum in the *P. knowlesi*-rhesus monkey system [86]. Although, in studies of the passive transfer of immunity to *P. falciparum*, Cohen and MacGregor transferred a substantial though temporary immunity with repeated injections of purified IgG [87], the recipients of the serum had ongoing malarial infections and may, therefore, have had high levels of antibody of other isotypes (e.g., IgM) and also a suitably "activated" mononuclear phagocytic system. (5) Certain sera from immune mice tend to enhance rather than suppress infections in nonimmune recipients [35]. Hence, the limited effects of some sera may well imply the presence of inhibitory agents such as "blocking" antibodies, suppressor factors, and antigen-antibody complexes which might mask the protective components of these sera.

In summary, although these experiments indicate that serum antibody does have a protective role, the limited effects of passively transferred immune sera tend to suggest that immunity to malaria is unlikely to depend exclusively on humoral mechanisms.

6. Site of Action of Protective Antibody

The blood stages of *Plasmodium* spp. consist of a series of distinct developmental forms—both intracellular and extracellular (merozoite). The serum of immune animals has been shown to contain antibodies which react specifically with (1) free merozoites (of *P. knowlesi* and *P. falciparum*) and (2) cell surface antigens of PRBC.

a. Antimerozoite Antibodies

The possibility that protective antibodies acted on extracellular merozoites was first indicated by the serum transfer experiments of Cohen and MacGregor [87]. They found that inhibitory sera did not damage intracellular parasites but acted upon the mature schizont or free merozoite. In subsequent experiments using *P. knowlesi* parasites in vitro, they found that immune sera inhibited parasite growth only at schizogony. On the basis of these observations they suggested that the antibody blocked the attachment of merozoites to red blood cells and thus prevented invasion [88]. The merozoite inhibitory antibody was shown to be species specific, non-complement dependent, and mediated by IgG and its $(Fab^1)_2$ fragments, or IgM [89]. Merozoite inhibitory antibodies have been demonstrated in *P. knowlesi* and *P. falciparum* infections. The levels of such merozoite inhibitory antibody have been found to correlate with the immune status of repeatedly infected or immunized rhesus monkeys [90]. However, instances in which there was no correlation between these antibodies and the level of protective immunity of either chronically infected monkeys [91] or vaccinated monkeys [92] have also been reported. More recently, monoclonal IgG antibodies which bind to *P. yoelii* (17XL) merozoite antigens have been reported to protect against lethal *P. yoelii* (17XL) infections [93].

b. Antibodies to Cell Surface Antigens

Plasmodium spp., like many other intracellular parasites, induce new antigens in the plasma membranes of the cells they parasitize. Antibodies directed at these antigens are produced by the infected host: variant-specific schizont-infected cell agglutinins and opsonins are produced in *P. knowlesi* infections [94, 95] ; antibodies specific for "knoblike" alterations on mature *P. falciparum* PRBC are found in the sera of immune hosts [96] ; antibodies which react with cell surface antigens also occur in *P. yoelii* and *P. berghei* infections. These antibodies may be directed at parasitic antigens which are inserted into the red cell membrane, at altered red cell antigens, or at red cell antigens which are normally cryptic but are expressed as a consequence of parasitization.

The red cell agglutinins induced in *P. knowlesi* infections have been used to characterize antigenically distinct variants of the parasite and are thought to be directed against parasitic antigens inserted into the red cell membrane [95]. Similarly, the antibodies which react with the knoblike protrusions on *P. falciparum* PRBC cannot be absorbed out with normal erythrocytes and the knobs are therefore thought to consist primarily of parasitic antigens [96]. The role of these antigens in protection has not been established.

Antibodies to red cell antigens are also induced in malarial infections, and there is increasing evidence that these antibodies contribute to the development of protective immunity. In mice infected with *P. berghei,* erythrocyte-associated immunoglobulins (Ig) have been demonstrated by agglutination and radioimmunoassay [97]. Both IgG and IgM are present, and the amounts of these Igs increase as the infection progresses. Both parasitized and nonparasitized reticulocytes have larger amounts of membrane bound immunoglobulin than do mature nonparasitized RBC. These observations are consistent with several earlier reports. *P. berghei*-infected rats were found to have cold-reactive agglutinins to trypsinized erythrocytes [98]. *Plasmodium vivax* infections have been reported to induce Coomb's positive anemia [99], and IgM antibodies to RBC have been found in patients with *P. falciparum* infections [100]. Recent experiments using CBA/N mice suggest that the anti-red blood cell antibodies generated in malaria may have a protective role. These mice are unable to control *P. yoelii* and *B. microti* infections effectively [79,80]. The reduced resistance is associated with a reduction in erythrocyte-associated Igs on RBC from infected mice, a marked deficiency in the specific IgM antibody response to red cells from infected animals, and an inability to produce anti-erythrocyte autoantibodies to bromelain-treated mouse RBC. These observations are consistent with the possibility that a "protective autoantibody" directed at modified red cell determinants may contribute to the control of malarial infections. Such an antibody could exert its primary effect on the membrane of the RBC, rendering the cell unsuitable for parasite growth. Alternatively, an anti-erythrocyte antibody may act by blocking merozoite penetration; since the membranes of "normal" uninfected RBC are altered during infection (Howard et al., cited in Mitchell, 1980 [101]), this is clearly a possibility.

D. The Cellular Component in Resistance to Malaria

Protective antibodies form one component of the response to blood stage infection. However, several observations discussed in Section III.C imply that immunity is not mediated exclusively by humoral mechanisms. Furthermore, there is clearly an activation of the "cellular" components of the immune system as evidenced by the activation of natural killer cells, monocytes, and macrophages in malarial infections. These and other lines of evidence (see Section III.B) indicate that, in common with other intracellular pathogens, cell-mediated resistance mechanisms form an important component of the repertoire of host-protective immune mechanisms against *Plasmodium* spp. Such cellular resistance mechanisms can be induced either by specific immune responses involving sensitized T cells or by nonspecific mechanisms; the expression of such immunity is generally nonspecific. Both T-cell dependent and independent forms of nonspecific immunity appear to be activated in malarial infections.

1. Activation of Nonspecific Immunity

One of the most compelling reasons for invoking cellular resistance mechanisms as a factor in the host response are the effects of various immunostimulants on erythrocytic infections. A wide range of agents known to have nonspecific immunostimulatory activity have been shown to augment resistance to certain *Plasmodium* and *Babesia* spp.; they include Bacillus Calmette-Guerin (BCG), *Corynebacterium parvum, Brucella abortus, Escherichia coli* lipopolysaccharide (LPS), Freund's complete adjuvant (FCA), and poly 1-C (see Table 2).

Of all these immunostimulatory agents, the effects of BCG and *C. parvum* have been studied most extensively, and it is worth considering the nature of the resistance induced by these agents in some detail.

Live BCG (Glaxo) or killed *C. parvum* administered intravenously (IV) or intraperitoneally (IP), but not subcutaneously (SC), has been shown to protect CBA mice completely against the piroplasms *B. microti* and *Babesia rhodhani* and to increase resistance to otherwise fatal *P. vinckei* infections [102,103]; the protection induced by BCG increases over the first 3 weeks of infection and lasts up to 6 months [113]. These agents do not protect CBA mice against blood-induced infections of *P. berghei* (K 173) [103] and have either a very modest effect or no effect on *P. yoelii* (17X) infections (Refs. 102 and Jayawardena, unpublished results). *Corynebacterium parvum* has also been found to induce a significant level of protection against sporosoite-induced *P. berghei* infections [104].

Once treated with BCG, protection to subsequent challenge with *B. microti* is unaffected by x-irradiation, cyclophosphamide (300 mg/kg body weight), or

Table 2 Induction of Non-Specific Immunity to *Plasmodia* spp. and *Babesia* spp.

Agent	Host-Parasite System	Protection	Reference
1. BCG (Glaxo) 2×10^7 live organisms IV	*B. microti, B. rhodhani,* and *P. vinckei* (Antwerp strain) in CBA mice	Complete	Clarke et al. [102]
	P. yoelii in CBA mice	Partial	Clarke et al. [102]; Jayawardena, unpublished
2. *Corynebacterium parvum,* live	*B. microti, B. rhodhani, P. vinckei,* and *P. chabaudi* in CBA mice	Complete	Clarke et al. [103]
Corynebacterium parvum (heat inactivated)	*P. berghei* (K173)	No protection	Clarke et al. [103]
	P. berghei sporozoite challenge	Complete protection or increase in prepatent period	Nussenzweig [104]
3. *Brucella abortus* (strain 19) IV or IP	*B. microti* in CBA mice	Complete	Herod et al. [105]
4. *Coxiella burnetti*	*B. microti, B. rhodhani,* and *P. vinckei petteri*	Complete	Clark [106]
5. Interferon inducers: Newcastle disease virus	*P. berghei* in mice	Increase in mean survival time	Schultz et al. [107]
Statolon, Newcastle disease virus, poly 1-C	*P. berghei* sporozoite challenge	Complete or partial	Jahiel et al. [108,109]
6. *Escherichia coli* (endotoxin)	*P. berghei* in mice and rats	Moderate suppression of infection	Martin et al. [110]; MacGregor et al. [111]
7. Freund's complete adjuvant (FCA) IP	*P. berghei* in mice	Reduced parasitemia in first week after challenge	Jerusalem [112]

splenectomy. BCG also augments the resistance of nude mice to *B. microti*, but the level of resistance induced is clearly less than in similarly treated thymus-bearing littermates. If BCG-treated mice are splenectomized or treated with cortisone acetate after infection, the disease relapses. Furthermore, BCG-treated, infected mice make only low levels of parasite-specific antibody, and the parasites appear to degenerate within RBC at the time the infection is controlled [113,114].

This group of observations indicates that agents such as BCG have powerful protective effects against certain intraerythrocytic protozoa but not against others. The resistance does not appear to involve production of specific antibodies to surface antigens of PRBC. Furthermore, since the resistance of nude mice can be potentiated with BCG, a significant component of the BCG-induced protection appears not to involve mature T cells. The most likely explanation for the effects of BCG is that it activates a powerful form of nonspecific immunity [114] mediated by multiple effector mechanisms. The most likely effectors of this form of immunity are NK cells, monocytes, and macrophages.

2. Mediators of Nonspecific Immunity

a. Natural Killer Cells

NK cells—a recently described system of cells distinct from T cells, B cells, and macrophages [115]—are thought to play a significant role in resistance to tumors [116]. There is increasing evidence that they may also form an important defense mechanism to many other infectious agents, including parasites.

The first suggestion that they may be involved in resistance to malaria was made as a result of the correlation observed between the degree of resistance and the levels of NK cell activity in different strains of mice. Using *P. chabaudi*, both Wigzell [24] and Allison [23] found that strains of mice known to have low levels of NK activity, such as the A/J [117], were very susceptible to infection, whereas strains known to have high NK activity, such as the CBA, were the most resistant. A similar correlation between the severity of *P. yoelii* (17X) infections in different strains of mice and their levels of NK activity has also been observed (Jayawardena, unpublished results).

NK cells also appear to be activated during malarial infections. Using the lysis of ^{51}Cr-labeled YAC cells as an index of NK cell activity, the kinetics of NK cell activation have been examined in the spleens of mice infected with *P. yoelii* (17X). A substantial increase in NK activity is seen during the early phase of the infection (day 6; see Table 3), but by day 12 (the time at which infections are being controlled), NK levels in infected mice are similar to those in uninfected controls. *Plasmodium yoelii*-infected T-cell-deprived mice also show an increase in NK cell activity—an observation consistent with the notion that mature T cells are not involved in the induction of this activity.

Table 3 NK Cell Activity in the Spleens of CBA Mice Infected with
P. yoelii (17X): Day 6 of Infection

	Lysis (%)[a]				
Effector Cells	12:1	25:1	50:1	100:1	200:1
Normal spleen	6.0	9.8	17.1	26.1	25.1
Infected spleen	19.7	32.9	46.8	48.9	34.6
Normal spleen (nylon purified)	6.4	15.2	22.6	24.8	21.5
Infected spleen (nylon purified)	28.5	41.7	53.8	37.7	34.5

[a]Effector cells were incubated with ^{51}Cr-labeled target YAC cells for 4 h at
the effector tp target cell ratios indicated. Assays were performed according
to the method of Kiessling et al. [117].

More recent evidence that NK cells may be involved in resistance to
Plasmodium spp. has come from experiments in which the ability of mice carrying the beige (bj) mutation to resist malaria has been tested. Mice with the beige
mutation appear to have normal T- and B-cell function but have been found to
lack NK cells [118]; they are also known to have defective polymorph [119,
120] and monocyte function [121]. *Plasmodium yoelii* (17X) infections are
far more severe in mice with the beige mutation than in nonmutant controls
(Jayawardena, in preparation). Although the data available at present do not
completely eliminate the possibility that the increased susceptibility maps to a
cell other than the NK cell, such as the blood monocyte, this result is consistent
with a role for the NK system in resistance to malaria.

Furthermore, many of the agents (BCG and *C. parvum*) shown to increase
nonspecific immunity to malaria do increase NK cell activity [122,123]. Also,
the characteristics of this form of immunity—its insensitivity to x-irradiation
and the existence of a thymus-independent component—are consistent with the
possible involvement of the NK system. The recent finding that interferon and
interferon inducers increase NK cell activity both in vivo [124] and in vitro [125]
is particularly interesting. Interferon inducers have been shown to exert significant protective effects on malarial infections [107-109,126], and the presence
of interferon has been demonstrated in the serum of mice infected with *P. berghei*
[127]. Furthermore, agents such as BCG and *C. parvum* are known to induce the
production of interferon [128]. Hence, parasite derived or induced interferon
may lead to NK cell activation as an "early" response to infection—before conventional immune mechanisms are brought into play. Intensification of this re-

sponse by interferon inducers or exogenous interferon may be sufficient to suppress an infection completely.

b. Monocytes and Macrophages

The involvement of the mononuclear phagocytic system (MPS) in the response to malaria has been apparent since the classic histologic studies of Taliaferro and Cannon [129,130]. These workers observed parasites in various stages of phagocytosis within free and fixed macrophages in infected and superinfected animals and reasoned that the MPS was an important element in the host response to *Plasmodium* spp. Many recent observations support the idea that the blood monocyte and tissue macrophage are involved in the control of primary infections and in resisting reinfection.

Mice infected with malaria show a massive increase in the numbers and functional state of both the blood monocyte and the splenic macrophage (see Section III.B). Mobilization of these cells is T-cell dependent. Both responses correlate closely with the development of immunity. In mice infected with *P. yoelii* (17X), maximum blood monocyte counts occur at the time the infection is controlled; *P. berghei* (ANKA) infections induce a weaker monocyte response, which fails in the later stages of infection [43]. Similarly, Shear et al. [131] found that macrophage activation in the spleens of *P. berghei*-infected mice was maximal in the second week of infection but was suppressed at later stages of infection.

There is only limited information regarding the nature and mechanism of monocyte or macrophage activation in malaria. It appears to involve sensitized Ly-1$^+$ T cells (Jayawardena et al., in preparation), and by analogy with other systems [132], these cells probably produce soluble factors which then activate monocytes and macrophages in a nonspecific manner. A recent study [131] examined some of the characteristics of macrophage activation in *P. berghei* infections. Splenic macrophages were "activated" as judged by increased size, spreading, and ability to phagocytize parasitized RBC and opsonized or nonopsonized sheep erythrocytes. Peritoneal macrophages showed no evidence of activation. The ingestion of parasitized RBC appeared to be mediated by cold agglutinin-type immunoglobulins. Ingestion of PRBC was inhibited late in the infection, and this inhibition was thought to be mediated by immune complexes. In an earlier study, Brown [52] showed that activated peritoneal macrophages from BCG-treated mice phagocytized *P. knowlesi* PRBC more readily than did normal macrophages in the presence of specific antibody.

Although monocytes and macrophages are activated as a consequence of infection, and together with the NK system are probably the main mediators of nonspecific immunity, the precise mechanisms by which these cells affect their targets remain to be established. Although opsonization of PRBC has been demonstrated in vitro, and parasites within macrophages have been observed in the blood and tissues of infected animals, convincing evidence that opsonization constitutes a *primary* mechanism of control in vivo has yet to be obtained. Attempts at in vivo depletion of macrophages using macrophage poisons have had no significant effects on the course of infection. Furthermore, the evidence suggesting that certain *Plasmodium* and *Babesia* spp. die *within* RBC [133] argues against a primary role for a phagocytic mechanism. Alternative possibilities are the production of soluble mediators capable of affecting the parasite via an effect on the RBC membrane, or contact lysis by antibody-independent or antibody-dependent cell mediated cytotoxic (ADCC) mechanisms.

IV. ACTIVE IMMUNIZATION AGAINST ERYTHROCYTIC INFECTIONS

Significant levels of protective immunity to blood stage infections can be induced in rodent, simian, and avian hosts by vaccination with the erythrocytic stages of *Plasmodium* spp. (reviewed in Refs. 2 and 134). Immunity has been induced (1) with unselected PRBC (rendered noninfectious by x-irradiation [135-138], formalin fixation [139,140], and exposure to heat [141]); (2) with selected developmental stages (schizonts [142,143], merozoites [144], and gametes [145]); and (3) with a purified histidine-rich protein [146]. The immunity induced by these blood stage vaccines is stage specific, i.e., it will not prevent pre-erythrocytic development. The immunity is also generally specific for the species, strain, and variant of the parasite used to immunize the host. However, recent studies suggest that merozoite vaccines may induce broader strain- and variant-specific immunity [2,3].

The level of resistance induced by a particular vaccine appears to depend on a number of factors. They include its intrinsic immunogenicity, the form, route, and quantity of antigen administered, and the use of appropriate adjuvants.

The blood stages of certain parasites appear to be more immunogenic than others. For instance, a single IV injection of formalin-fixed *P. yoelii* (17X) induces significantly stronger immunity in mice than a similar vaccine made from the lethal variant *P. yoelii* (17XL) (Jayawardena, in preparation). The antigens involved in the induction of immunity to these parasites have not been characterized, but it is worth noting that *P. yoelii* (17X) invades reticulocytes preferentially, whereas lethal *P. yoelii* (17 XL) is found predominantly in mature RBC. Hence, host antigens on the reticulocyte, such as H-2, may have an inductive role in the development of resistance. Recognition of PRBC may involve both host and parasite antigens expressed on the red cell membrane as in the case of virus-infected cells [147,148]. However, efforts to demonstrate a role for host antigens in T cell responses to PRBC have not been successful (see Section III.B).

The protection induced by a weakly immunogenic parasite such as *P. berghei* can be improved by increasing the amount of antigen administered and/ or by the use of suitable adjuvants. A single injection of formalin-fixed PRBC induces a limited degree of immunity in mice, but repeated injections protect mice effectively against otherwise lethal challenge [140]. Various adjuvants including *Bordetella pertussis*, BCG, and *C. parvum* have also been shown to potentiate the resistance induced by *P. berghei* vaccines [149,150]. The form in which the antigen is administered and the route of administration also appear to be critical; soluble malarial antigens do not induce effective immunity; intravenous injection is the most effective route.

The mechanisms by which many of the blood stage vaccines work have not been examined in detail. In general, vaccinated challenged animals show increased levels of specific antibody and heightened CMI responses. Mice vaccinated with *P. yoelii* (17X) produce specific IgM and IgG antibody responses [151,152], elicit DTH responses to malarial antigens [153,154], and their spleen cells produce lymphotoxin and proliferate when exposed to specific antigen (Jayawardena and Ruddle, in preparation). The relative importance of antibody versus cell-mediated mechanisms have not been critically evaluated. Furthermore, although spleen cells from immunized rodents transfer immunity adoptively [155], the contributions of T and B cells to this resistance is unclear.

Targett [70] vaccinated rhesus monkeys with formalin-fixed *P. knowlesi* schizonts in FCA and found that indirect fluorescent antibody titers (IFAT) to PRBC did not correlate with the degree of protection achieved. Similarly, the levels of anti-merozoite antibodies do not always correlate with protection in monkeys vaccinated with merozoites in FCA [2]. Hence, unlike naive, unprimed animals in which there appears to be an absolute requirement for antibody to control the acute phase of the disease, animals primed by vaccination have a need for antibody that may be minimal, and protection may be mediated mainly by cell-mediated mechanisms. This is reminiscent of the situation in mice recovered from *P. yoelii* where once immunity develops it can be maintained even in animals with severe B cell deficiencies.

Although considerable progress has been made towards the development of a vaccine against erythrocytic malarial infections, there are still many features of the antigens involved and the immune responses to them which need further study. A finer characterization of the protective antigens of *Plasmodium* spp. is required. The possible existence of "common" antigens which transcend strain and variant barriers needs to be examined. The role of host antigens, such as modified red cell antigens, in inducing immunity needs to be investigated. There is also clearly a need for a finer analysis of the immune responses in vaccinated animals. It is necessary to identify the critical form(s) of immunity induced by effective vaccines and to optimize their development by more effective presentation and/or modification of the relevant antigens. The regulatory circuits activated by immunization should also be explored; the limited and sometimes harmful effects of certain vaccines may be due to preferential activation of suppressor mechanisms or disruption of normal homeostasis.

V. IMMUNE RESPONSES TO PRE-ERYTHROCYTIC INFECTIONS

When sporozoites are injected into the bloodstream, they circulate for 1-2 hr [156] and then enter parenchymal cells of the liver where they initiate a phase of pre-erythrocytic or exoerythrocytic (EE) development. The existence of immunity to this phase of the infection has been questioned [157], and initial attempts to demonstrate immunity using live sporozoites were unsuccessful; Bray and Garnham [157] reported that the pre-erythrocytic development of *Plasmodium cynomolgi bastianelli* in monkeys was unaffected by previous sporozoite-induced infections. However, in subsequent studies, both Verhave [158] and Beaudoin et al. [159] found that, compared with untreated controls, rats maintained on chloroquine to suppress blood stage infections developed fewer EE forms when repeatedly injected with live sporozoites.

Mature sporozoites are clearly immunogenic: sporozoites attenuated by a variety of methods, including ultraviolet (UV) light, heat, and x-irradiation, induce significant levels of protection against live sporozoite challenge [160-164]. Since attenuated sporozoites induce better protection than killed sporozoites [161], it has been suggested that limited exoerythrocytic development of the sporozoite may be necessary for the induction of this immunity [164]. X-irradiated sporozoites induce the most effective immunity; mice injected IV with multiple doses of x-irradiated *P. berghei* sporozoites are completely resistant to a live sporozoite challenge [165]. The immunity is relatively short-lived, lasting for about 40 days [163]. Immunized animals produce anti-sporozoite antibodies which can be detected by the circumsporozoite (CSP) reaction [166] or by immunofluorescence [167]. The immunity developed is stage specific in that mice immunized with sporozoites are completely susceptible to blood-induced infections [168]. Possibly the most important aspect of the immunity induced with x-irradiated sporozoites is that in the rodent [163], but not in the simian [169], systems investigated, sporozoite vaccination induces extensive cross protection between different species of *Plasmodium*. Mice immunized with *P. berghei* (NK 65) sporozoites are also protected against *P. chabaudi* and *P. vinckei* sporozites [163]; the cross protection is paralleled by demonstrable serologic cross reactivity [113]. This contrasts with the situation in blood stage infections where erythrocytic infections of *P. berghei* confer no cross protection to either *P. chabaudi* or *P. vinckei* [170,171]. These observations raise the interesting possibility that, during the sporogonic phase of development in the mosquito, there may be reversion to a "common" or "basic" antigenic type. Although the bloodstream forms of African trypanosomes show considerable antigenic lability (reviewed in Ref. 172), there is some evidence that after development in the tsetse fly they revert to a basic antigenic type expressed on the metacyclic forms [173,174]. It is therefore possible that analogous changes in antigen expression may operate in other hemoprotozoan infections such as malaria.

The nature of the antigens on the sporozoites of different species of *Plasmodium* have yet to be characterized in detail. However, Nussenzweig and her colleagues recently produced hybridomas by fusing spleen cells from *P. berghei*-sporozoite-immunized mice with a plasmacytoma (P3U1) and found that the monoclonal antibodies produced by these hybrid cells bound to a protein (mol. wt. 44,000) enveloping the surface membrane of the sporozoite [175]. This protein appears to be the major surface antigen expressed by the sporozoite.

The precise effector mechanisms involved in immunity to the pre-erythrocytic phase (of development) have yet to be identified, but the basic cellular requirements necessary for inducing protection with x-irradiated sporozoites have been investigated. The induction of immunity is clearly T-cell dependent since neither athymic nude mice nor T-cell-deprived mice develop any resistance when treated with x-irradiated sporozoites [176,177]. Resistance can, however, be induced in μ-suppressed mice [176], suggesting that an absolute requirement for antibody does not exist. The resistance of vaccinated mice can be transferred with spleen cells, and their protective effect can be abrogated by treatment with anti-Thy-1.2 serum and complement (Verhave, cited by Spitalny et al., 1977 [177]). The cell-mediated nature of the response is also indicated by the fact that granuloma formation and mononuclear cell infiltration have been observed in the livers of immunized mice [178]. Furthermore, immunostimulatory agents such as *C. parvum* [104], BCG [179], and interferon inducers [108, 109] increase the resistance of mice to sporozoite challenge.

Sporozoite vaccination also induces a substantial CSP antibody response, but there is little correlation between CSP antibody levels and the degree of protection [164]. Serum from vaccinated mice has been found to accelerate the clearance of sporozoites [156], and the passive transfer of immune serum delays, but does not prevent, sporozoite-induced infections [163]. In a more recent series of experiments, monoclonal antibodies against the sporozoite (prepared as described earlier) have been found to abolish the infectivity of sporozoites in vitro and also to protect completely in passive transfer experiments [180], these sera had anti-sporozoite antibody titers from 10^2 to 10^3 times higher than those obtained directly from vaccinated mice [175]. All these observations taken together suggest that the pre-erythrocytic phase of infection is susceptible to attack by multiple immune mechanisms.

Antibodies against the sporozoite, if present in sufficiently high titers, can presumably inactivate the extracellular sporozoite and delay or prevent exo-erythrocytic development. However, a second form of T-cell-dependent immu-nity, not involving antibody, appears to be sufficient to induce protection against sporozoite challenge [176]. Since the induction and expression of this immunity is not affected by splenectomy [178], it probably represents a "local" CMI response in the liver involving macrophage activation or direct T-cell-medi-ated cytotoxicity of infected hepatocytes. A role for NK cells cannot be dis-counted particularly since some of the strains most susceptible to sporozoite challenge [25] have low levels of NK cell activity [117].

VI. REGULATORY RESPONSES

A. Immunosuppression

1. General Characteristics

Animals infected with *Plasmodium* spp. display a marked state of immuno-logical hyporesponsivensss. T- and B-cell function and the ability to produce antibody and/or cell-mediated immune responses to unrelated antigens are re-duced during infection. The degree to which these responses are affected varies considerably in different host-parasite systems. However, in many instances, there does appear to be a positive correlation between the severity of the sup-pression and the severity of the disease.

2. Responses to Mitogens

Spleen cells from mice infected with *P. yoelii* (17X) or *P. berghei* (ANKA) show a rapid loss in responsiveness to both T (phytohemagglutinin [PHA]) and B (LPS) cell mitogens [31,181,182]. In *P. yoelii* suppression is maximal at peak parasitemia, but with regression of the infection responsiveness returns. How-ever, the response to LPS remains significantly reduced for several weeks after recovery [181,182]. Comparative kinetic analysis of PHA and LPS responses in *P. yoelii* (17X) and *P. berghei* (ANKA) infections indicate that fatal *P. berghei* infections induce greater reduction of these responses than do *P. yoelii* (Figure 6) infections. Similarly, virulent *P. yoelii* (17XL) causes a more rapid shutdown of the LPS response than the nonvirulent strain [182]. Furthermore, the DNA synthetic response of spleen cells to LPS is suppressed significantly less in (*P. yoelii* [17X] and *P. berghei* [ANKA]) infected nude mice than in thymus-bear-ing controls (Figure 6), indicating that T-cell-dependent mechanisms are in-volved in the suppression observed [42].

3. Antibody Responses

Infected animals also show suppressed antibody responses to unrelated thymus dependent and independent antigens. *Plasmodium yoelii* (17X) infected

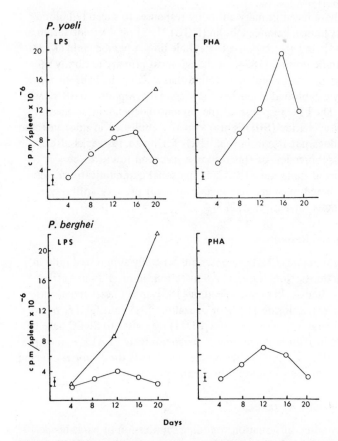

Figure 6 DNA synthetic responses of spleen cells from *P. yoelii* (17X) and *P. berghei* (ANKA) infected normal (○) and nude (△) mice to PHA and LPS. Because of the splenomegaly occurring during the disease, responses are expressed as the increment in counts per minute (cpm) per spleen, calculated thus:

$$\text{Increment cpm per spleen} = \frac{\text{increment cpm per culture}}{\text{number of cells per culture}} \times \text{number of cells per spleen}$$

where increment = cpm stimulated culture – cpm unstimulated culture. Each time point represents the mean responses of three mice whose spleens were cultured individually; all cultures were set up in triplicate. Standard errors did not differ by more than 10% of the mean for infected mice. Normal, uninfected controls were included in each experiment; mean responses ±SE of these controls are shown (●). For culture conditions see Table 4. (Data from A. N. Jayawardena and G. A. W. Rook, unpublished observations.)

mice have drastically reduced primary antibody responses to sheep red blood cells (SRBC) [183], human gammaglobulin (HGG) [183], and bovine serum albumin (BSA) [184], but the response to keyhole limpet hemocyanin (KLH) has been reported to be normal [183]. Although most primary antibody responses are suppressed, Greenwood et al. found that *P. yoelii* had absolutely no effect on an already established response—the secondary response to SRBC was unaffected [183]. The PFC response to the thymus-independent antigen-pneumococcal polysaccharide (SIII) is also virtually abolished in mice infected with *P. yoelii* and does not regain normal levels for up to 12 weeks after recovery [185,186]; suppression of this response has been found to be less pronounced in infected nude mice (Weidanz, personal communication). *Plasmodium berghei*-infected mice are also unable to elicit primary antibody responses to a wide range of antigens [187].

4. Cell-Mediated Responses

Cell-mediated immune (CMI) responses are generally suppressed only in severe malarial infections. Nonfatal *P. yoelii* infections in mice do not affect most CMI responses such as skin graft rejection [183] and contact hypersensitivity responses to picryl chloride [183] or oxazalone [31], but fatal *P. berghei* infections suppress these responses [31,188]. DTH responses to SRBC have been found to be reduced in both *P. yoelii*- and *P. berghei*-infected BALB/c mice [189]. However, since BALB/c mice are low responders to malaria the *P. yoelii*-infected mice had relatively high parasitemias in these experiments.

5. Parasite-Specific Responses

There is very limited information regarding suppression of parasite-specific immune responses. Weinbaum et al. [181] compared the in vitro proliferative responses of spleen cells from mice infected with nonfatal *P. yoelii* (17X) and fatal *P. yoelii* (17XL) to PRBC. They observed an early increase, followed by suppression and then recovery of responsiveness in the nonfatal infection; in fatal infections, the early increase was less marked and the onset of suppression was more rapid. There have been no studies carried out on immunosuppression using purified parasitic antigens. It is clearly important to monitor responses to such antigens and to determine whether the immunosuppression observed extends to parasite-specific antigens.

6. Mechanism of Suppression

There have been several suggestions put forward to explain the immunosuppression observed in malaria. These include the depletion of T and B cells, defective macrophage function, parasite-derived B-cell mitogens (Section VI.B), and the activation of suppressor cells.

The results of enumeration studies of T- and B-cells by immunofluorescence are not compatible with the idea that suppression of immune responsiveness is due to an actual depletion of immunocompentent cells. In fact there is an increase rather than a decrease in splenic T- and B-cell numbers in *P. yoelii* and *P. berghei* infections [32] at stages when significant immunosuppression is observed. Lymphocyte depletion and thymic involution occur only in the terminal stages of infections (*P. berghei*) [43,190] and are more likely to be a *consequence* of a suppression of immunity rather than the primary reason for it. The idea that suppression in the early phase of these infections is not due to a permanent depletion of responsive cells is also suggested by the fact that suppressed responses can be improved by removal of certain cell types on glass wool and Sephadex G10 columns (Table 4 and Ref. 42).

A second explanation has been that suppression is due to a defect in macrophage function. Loose et al. injected SRBC into the peritoneal cavity of normal and *P. berghei*-infected mice and then transferred the peritoneal exudate cells (macrophages) into normal recipients; macrophages from infected animals induced lower PFC responses than those from normal animals [191]. Warren and Weidanz [192] found that adherent cells from the spleens of mice infected with *P. yoelii* (17X) were defective in reconstituting the in vitro antibody response of nonadherent spleen cells to horse red blood cells (HRBC). These observations have led to the suggestion that macrophages from malarious mice are defective—possibly in processing antigen. Attempts to demonstrate "blocking" of the reticuloendothelial system in infected animals have not been successful. The clearance of ^{51}Cr-labeled SRBC and colloidal carbon appear to be increased rather than decreased in infected animals [193,194]; the increase appears to be due mainly to greater uptake by the liver; splenic uptake was similar to that observed in normal mice [193].

"Active" suppressor mechanisms have also been implicated in the suppression observed. Spleen cells from *P. yoelii* (17X) and *P. berghei* (ANKA) infected CBA mice show a rapid loss in their ability to elicit primary in vitro PFC responses to SRBC as the infections progress [42]. If spleen cells from *P. yoelii* (17X) or *P. berghei* infected mice are added to cultures of normal cells, they suppress the anti-SRBC PFC response of the normal cells if taken at day 7 or 8 of infection; *P. yoelii* (17X) spleen cells enhance the response if taken soon after infection (day 2-3) (Jayawardena, unpublished results). Suppression can be mediated by nylon-purified T cells and by plastic adherent cells (macrophages) from infected animals. Spleen cells from T-cell-deficient mice are less suppressive than spleen cells from normal mice at the same stage of infection [42]. The involvement of T cells in the suppression observed is also implied by the fact that the DNA synthetic responses to LPS are suppressed less in T-cell-deficient mice.

The general features of the suppression observed in murine malaria are similar to those reported in mice infected with *Trypanosoma brucei* (S42) [195,196], although comparative studies suggest the suppression is more severe

Table 4   The Effect of Adherent Cell Depletion on the DNA Synthetic Responses of Spleen Cells from Normal and *P. berghei* (ANKA) Infected Mice to Mitogens

Spleen cells[a]	Column Treatment	Mean cpm Culture ± SE[b]		
		Unstimulated	ConA	PHA
Normal Uninfected	None	1,145 ± 72	14,743 ± 111	9,587 ± 628
	Glass wool	848 ± 2	16,986 ± 1,201	14,864 ± 402
	Sephadex G10	447 ± 48	18,784 ± 1,496	15,678 ± 113
P. berghei Infected (day 8)	None	1,034 ± 62	5,690 ± 34	3,072 ± 20
	Glass wool	686 ± 159	12,469 ± 2,077	10,644 ± 1,691
	Sephadex G10	949 ± 64	12,336 ± 934	14,020 ± 1,874

[a](C57 X BALB/c)F$_1$ mice were used.
[b]Cultures consisted of 5×10^5 cells in 0.2 ml RPMI 1640 containing 5% fetal calf serum and optimal concentrations of mitogens. Cultures were incubated for 72 hr in a humidified atmosphere of 5% CO_2 in air at 37°C and were pulsed with 1 μCi [^{3}H] thymidine 16 hr before collection.

Source: A. N. Jayawardena and G. A. W. Rook, unpublished observations.

in the latter system. In the case of *T. brucei,* the T cells which suppressed the anti-SRBC PFC response were insensitive to ALS, sensitive to the long-term effects of adult thymectomy, and of the Ly-1$^+$, 23$^+$ phenotype, while the early helper cell was sensitive to ALS, not affected by adult thymectomy, and of the Ly-1$^+$, 23$^-$ phenotype [196]. It was suggested that in African trypanosomiasis, malaria, and related diseases, the parasite or a parasite-derived product such as a mitogen induced Ly-1 cells to exert nonspecific helper activity; as a consequence, Ly-1$^+$, 23$^+$ cells were stimulated to suppressor activity. Although phenotyping studies on the malarial systems are incomplete, the results to date are compatible with this model. Furthermore, the recent demonstration that an extract of *P. falciparum* has T-cell mitogenic activity [197] provides further support for the idea that activation of Ly-1$^+$ cells by a T-cell mitogen in a manner analogous to the ConA system [198,199] is a critical factor in the induction of suppression in malaria.

While suppressor cells appear to be *one* of the factors contributing to the immunological hyporesponsiveness observed, it is clearly not the only reason for the reduced responsiveness to a wide range of immunological stimuli. Other factors are also involved, particularly in the later stages of chronic or fatal infections. Although the early suppression can be alleviated by depletion of certain lymphocyte subpopulations and/or macrophages, it is generally more difficult in both malaria and trypanosomiasis to reverse the suppression in the later stages of infection. While this could be due to surface changes on the relevant cells resulting in increased resistance to anti-sera and/or loss of adherence characteristics, it is more likely to reflect intrinsic defects in T- and B-cell function independent of active suppressor mechanisms. Malarial infections induce massive T- and B-cell activation. B-cell activation could lead to defects in B-cell function as a result of the polyclonal stimulation and consequent terminal differentiation of B-cell clones. Similar lesions could occur at the level of the T cell and macrophage in situations where the "early" suppression is not counterbalanced by an adequate helper response.

B. Hypergammaglobulinemia

It has long been recognized that malarial infections cause huge increases in immunoglobulin levels. Much of the Ig produced appears not to be specific for the parasite. Based on absorption studies it has been estimated that less than 5% of the total Ig is directed at the parasite [200]. Similar increases in nonspecific Igs also occur in other parasitic infections—most notably in African trypanosomiasis [201]. There has been considerable speculation regarding the mechanism underlying the hypergammaglobulinemia. Polyclonal B-cell activation induced by a parasite-derived B-cell mitogen was suggested as a possible mechanism [202-204].

The occurrence of polyclonal B-cell activation in malaria is no longer in doubt. Rosenberg [41], using the reverse plaque assay (a technique which detects PFC of all specificities and is therefore a measure of polyclonal B-cell activation), demonstrated an approximate 100-fold increase of Ig-secreting cells in the spleens of mice infected with *P. yoelii* (17XL). More recently she confirmed that this increase in Ig-secreting cells is not class restricted and truly polyclonal (Rosenberg, personal communication). The massive increase in Ig-secreting cells could not be simulated by the injection of parasites rendered noninfective by x-irradiation, suggesting that a live replicating parasite was necessary to induce B-cell activation. *Plasmodium berghei* (K 173) and *P. yoelii* (17X) infections have also been reported to cause 30- to 50-fold increases in "background" PFC responses to SRBC and HRBC [206], which is suggestive of polyclonal B-cell activation. This increase in "background" PFC could also be induced by the injection of supernatants derived from parasitized RBC.

The ability of *Plasmodium* spp. to induce polyclonal B-cell activation has been demonstrated convincingly, but there is little or no evidence to support the original contention that it is due to direct triggering of B cells by a LPS-like substance. The increase of Ig-secreting cells as monitored by the reverse plaque assay is not found in nude mice [41]. Also, the increase of serum Ig levels in *P. yoelii* (17X) infections is drastically reduced in T-cell-deficient mice [43]. Hence, the hypergammaglobulinemia in malaria is clearly T-cell dependent. This is consistent with other situations such as the hypergammaglobulinemia induced by the repeated injection of protein antigens which has also been found to be T-cell dependent [206,207].

Based on the observations already discussed, and on the finding that soon after *P. yoelii* (17X) infection there appears to be an increase in nonspecific helper T-cell activity (Jayawardena et al., unpublished results), it is likely that the increased Ig levels are due to the production of soluble factors by activated Ly-1 helper cells, which then trigger B cells into nonspecific Ig production. The inductive influence for this form of T-cell activation may derive in part from a T-cell mitogen produced by the malaria parasite.

Polyclonal B cell activation can lead to intrinsic defects in B-cell function. In addition, there is increasing evidence that activated B cells are potent inducers of "feedback" suppressor T-cell activity [208]. Hence, the polyclonal B-cell activation in malaria may contribute to the immunosuppression by more than one mechanism.

C. Autoimmunity

The huge increase in Ig found in malaria includes autoantibodies of various specificities [209]. The antibodies produced by hosts infected with malaria include (1) anti-red cell antibodies [210]. (2) antinuclear antibodies [211], and (3) rheumatoid-factor-like antibodies [212]. Furthermore, individuals living in endemic areas and having high titers of antimalarial antibody (mainly IgM) were found to have a high incidence of antibodies to heart, thyroid, and parietal cells [213]. It has also been suggested that autoantibodies may contribute to the kidney disease (glomerulonephritis) characteristic of certain forms of malaria. Hence, various manifestations of autoimmunity are triggered as a consequence of infection and may contribute to much of the immunopathology associated with this disease.

In addition to *inducing* various forms of autoimmunity, malarial infections also appear to be capable of *suppressing* autoimmunity in certain situations. Female (NZB X NZW) F_1 mice showed high mortality due to the spontaneous developing of severe renal disease at 12 months of age, but those mice given *P. yoelii* (17X) at 1 month showed no clinical features of the disease or mortality (at a comparable time) [214]. Similar, though less striking, trends, including a delay in the onset of Coombs' positivity, were observed in *P. yoelii*-infected NZB mice [215].

The reasons underlying the induction and expression of autoimmunity in malarial infections are unclear. However, a consideration of other situations in which similar autoimmune phenomena are observed is perhaps relevant to the malaria situation. (1) Many of the autoimmune reactions seen in malaria are also triggered by other parasitic infections [209]. (2) Autoimmunity also develops spontaneously in certain strains of mice (such as the NZB and MRL/l) and appears to be due *primarily* to immunoregulatory defects rather than to the direct effects of infectious agents [216]. (3) Although the overt manifestations of autoimmunity are often the same, they may be caused by quite different defects in regulation [216]. For instance, both NZB and MRL/l mice show spontaneously developing autoimmunity. In NZB mice this appears to be due to loss of the Ly-1$^+$, 23$^+$ (feedback suppressor) population [217]. in MRL/l mice there is an increase rather than a decrease in the Ly-1$^+$, 23$^+$ population, but Ly-1$^+$ cells in MRL mice are insensitive to suppressor signals generated by the Ly-1$^+$, 23$^+$ feedback suppressor cells [218]. Hence, in both situations there is loss of normal control of Ly-1 helper cells, resulting in the production of high levels of autoantibodies.

Although the nature of the regulatory defect(s) which leads to the development of autoimmunity in malaria have not been investigated, it is unlikely to be due to a lesion similar to that observed in the NZB, since mice infected with malaria show an increase rather than a decrease in suppressor T-cell activity and can in fact alleviate the spontaneously developing autoimmunity in NZB mice [215]. It is tempting to speculate on the possibility that the regulatory defect induced by infection may be more analogous to that observed in MRL/l mice, i.e., it may be due to increased activity in the Ly-1$^+$, 23$^+$ population and a loss of sensitivity of Ly-1 cells to suppressor signals. Such a model would explain the ability of malaria to induce autoimmunity on the one hand, and to favorably modify the spontaneous disease in the NZB mice on the other.

D. Bidirectional Effects of the Immune Response

The evidence we have considered so far indicates that the immune response in malaria contains both positive and negative components. Both components are often present simultaneously. Hence, in an infection or phase of an infection where effective immunity is being induced, there is presumably a balance in favor of those positive attributes of the host response, whereas in an infection where immunity is not induced, the negative effects of the immune response predominate. If this were the case, manipulations of the immune system which reduced the level of the immune response should have effects on host-parasite systems where effective immunity is induced (e.g., *P. yoelii* in mice) that are fundamentally different from their effects on those systems where effective immunity is not induced (e.g., *P. berghei* in mice). Examination of the effects of certain manipulations on malarial infections indeed strengthens the idea that the immune response does exert bidirectional effects.

1. T-Cell Depletion

Normal mice respond effectively to *P. yoelii* (17X). Partial or complete elimination of T cells results in a worsening of the disease (Section III.B). In contrast, normal mice do not elicit an effective response to *P. berghei*—the infections proving uniformly fatal. T-cell depletion (nudes) or ALS treatment results in a substantial prolongation of the survival time of these animals (Ref. 219 and Jayawardena, unpublished results). Similarly, neonatally thymectomized and ALS-treated hamsters infected with *P. berghei* survive significantly longer than nonthymectomized controls [220,221]. Hence, in situations where the immune response is not effective and may, in fact, be harmful, T-cell depletion leads to an improvement rather than a worsening of the disease. The precise manner in which T cells exert their negative effects in these systems has not been analyzed, but (1) activation of suppressor T cells, (2) polyclonal B-cell activation and its consequent effects, (3) enhancing antibodies, (4) autoantibodies with pathologic effects, and (5) other T-cell-dependent immunopathological responses could be involved.

2. Selective B-Cell Deficiencies

Plasmodium yoelii (17X) infections are more severe in mice with the CBA/N defect than in nondefective controls (see Section III.3). On the other hand, *P. berghei* (ANKA) infected CBA/N mice survive significantly longer than nondefective mice (Jayawardena and Kemp, in preparation). CBA/N mice appear particularly hyporesponsive in autoantibody production [222]. It has been suggested that the increased severity of *P. yoelii* (17X) infections in these mice is due to a deficiency in a "protective" autoantibody [79]. CBA/N mice infected with malaria also make less "pathologic" autoantibody (Kemp and Jayawardena, unpublished results). Hence, the increased survival of *P. berghei*-infected CBA/N mice may be due to a reduction in the latter type of antibody.

3. Cyclophosphamide

Pretreatment of mice with a large dose of cyclophosphamide (250 mg/kg) causes a marked increase in the severity of *P. yoelii* (17X) infections (Jayawardena, unpublished results). The same treatment has been reported to convert a normally fatal *P. yoelii* (17XL) infection to a nonfatal one [223]. The cyclophosphamide-treated *P. yoelii* (17XL)-infected mice showed increased DTH responses to malarial antigens, and the beneficial effects of cyclophosphamide were attributed to an abrogation of antibody production. However, cyclophosphamide is also known to inactivate suppressor T cells [224]. Hence, the beneficial effects of cyclophosphamide may in part be due to an inhibition of suppressor T-cell activity.

4. Splenectomy

Plasmodium inui infections follow a chronic course lasting several months in the Kra monkey. If monkeys are splenectomized *before* infection, the infections prove rapidly fatal. If, however, a chronically infected animal is splenectomized, the animal recovers [225]. Similarly, although splenectomy results in a worsening of *P. yoelii* (17X) infections, it appears to have a beneficial effect on fatal *P. berghei* (ANKA) infections (Jayawardena, unpublished). Hence, the spleen appears to play both host-protective and host-suppressive roles. The ability of the spleen to exert these different effects is very similar to that reported in tumor-bearing animals where splenectomy has been found to increase or decrease resistance depending on the immunogenicity of the tumor and the nature of the immune response elicited by the tumor [226]. The immunosuppressive effects of the spleen could be mediated by suppressor T cells and host inhibitory antibodies of various kinds.

VII. CONCLUDING REMARKS

It was suggested at the beginning of this article that the mammalian immune system could be regarded primarily as a device for maintaining homeostasis, and the immune responses generated in an infected host could be viewed as the efforts of the system, perturbed by infection, to reestablish a new level of equilibrium. Such a model is compatible with the host response observed in malaria and provides a useful framework in which to discuss the significance of many of the responses observed.

The establishment of a state of equilibrium between host and parasite is dependent on the activation of an effective host response. In a natural host-parasite association or one which simulates a "natural" association, e.g., *P. yoelii* (17X) in mice, there is rapid recruitment of a series of "protective" responses—involving NK cells, T cells, antibody, monocytes, and macrophages—which prevent the parasite from overwhelming the host. Independently, or more likely as a consequence of the activation of these responses, other responses which are concerned with regulating the nature and intensity of the host response (possibly involving feedback mechanisms) are activated. Responses which reflect a temporary loss of normal regulatory control (e.g., autoimmunity) are also seen. The end result in the case of *P. yoelii* (17X) infection is the achievement of a new level of equilibrium in which small numbers of the parasite persist, but the host develops resistance to reinfection. In contrast, in systems such as *P. berghei* in the mouse or *P. inui* in the Kra monkey, there appears to be less effective triggering of the "protective" responses, but comparable or greater triggering of "harmful" responses. The result in a normal animal is a failure to induce effective immunity. However, as manipulations such as splenectomy or cyclophosphamide treatment convert these chronic or fatal infections into nonfatal ones, the failure of these parasites to induce immunity cannot be attributed purely to reduced triggering of protective responses due to an intrinsic lack of immunogenicity, but rather implies that certain components of the host response actively interfere with the development of protective immunity.

The critical interactions between parasite and immune system which determine whether immunity is achieved or not are unclear. However, since the majority of both beneficial and harmful responses activated are thymus dependent, T cells play a central role in the "design" of these relationships. Understanding the mechanisms by which certain parasites immunize and others suppress or tolerize T cells, may permit manipulation of immunity in favor of the host.

ACKNOWLEDGMENTS

The author's research is supported by Research Career Development Award RF-78021 from the Rockefeller Foundation and by National Institutes of Health grant AI-13949.

REFERENCES

1.   Noguer, A., W. Wernsdorfer, R. Kouznetsov, and J. Hemple (1978). The malaria situation in 1976. *WHO Chron. 32:*9.

2. Cohen, S., and G. H. Mitchell (1978). Prospects for immunisation against malaria. *Curr. Top. Microbiol. Immunol. 80:*97.
3. Cohen, S. (1979). Immunity to malaria. *Proc. R. Soc. Lond. (Biol.) 203:* 323.
4. Lwinn, M., G. A. T. Targett, and M. J. Doenhoff (1979). Chemotherapy of malaria (*Plasmodium chabaudi*) infections in immunosuppressed mice. *Trans. R. Soc. Trop. Med. 73:*103.
5. Davies, A. J. S., R. L. Carter, and G. A. T. Targett (1977). Parasites as research models for cancer. In *Parasites: Their World and Ours.* A. M. Fallis, Ed.). Symposium of the Royal Society of Canada, Toronto, 1977.
6. Killick-Kendrick, R., and W. Peters, Eds. (1978). *Rodent Malaria.* Academic Press, New York.
7. Laveran, A., (1880). Note sur un nouveau parasite trouvé dans le sang de plusieurs malades atteints de fièvre palustre. *Bull. Acad. Natl. Med. (Paris) 9:*1235.
8. Garnham, P. C. C. (1966). *Malaria parasites and other Haemosporidia,* Blackwell Scientific Publications, Oxford.
9. Landau, I., and Y. Boulard (1978). Life cycles and morphology. In *Rodent Malaria,* (R. Killick-Kendrick and W. Peters, Eds.). Academic Press, New York, p. 53.
10. Corradetti, A. (1963). Acquired sterile immunity in experimental protozoal infections. In *Immunity to Protozoa,* (P. C. C. Garnham, A. E. Pierve, and I. M. Roitt, Eds.). Blackwell Scientific Publications, Oxford, p. 69.
11. Barker, L. R. (1971). Acquired immunity to *Plasmodium berghei yoelii* in mice. *Trans. R. Soc. Trop. Med. Hyg. 65:*586.
12. Jayawardena, A. N., G. A. T. Targett, R. L. Carter, E. Leuchars, and A. J. S. Davies (1977). The immunological response of CBA mice to *P. yoelii.* 1. General characteristics, the effects of T cell deprivation and reconstitution with thymus grafts. *Immunology 32:*849.
13. Sergent, E. (1963). Latent infection and premunition. Some definitions of microbiology and immunology. In *Immunity to Protozoa,* (P. C. C. Garnham, A. E. Pierce, and I. M. Roitt, Eds.). Blackwell Scientific Publications, Oxford, P. 39.
14. Gershon, R. K., R. L. Carter, and K. Kondo (1967). On concomitant immunity in tumour-bearing hamsters. *Nature (Lond.) 213:*674.
15. Miller, L. H., S. J. Manson, J. A. Dvorak, M. H. McGinnis, and I. K. Rothman (1975). Erythrocyte receptors for (*Plasmodium knowlesi*) malaria: the duffy blood group determinants. *Science 189:*561.
16. Craik, R. (1920). A note on the erythrocytes in malaria. *Lancet 1:*1110.
17. Allison, A. C. (1960). Glucose-6-phosphate dehydrogenase deficiency in red blood cells of East Africans. *Nature (Lond.) 186:*53.
18. Allison, A. C. (1954). Protection afforded by sickle-cell trait against subtertian malarial infection. *Br. Med. J. 1:*290.
19. Zuckerman, A. (1957). Blood loss and replacement in plasmodial infec-

tion. 1. *Plasmodium berghei* in untreated rats of varying age and in adult
rats with erythropoetic mechanisms manipulated before inoculation. *J. Infect. Dis. 100:*172.

20. Miller, L. H., and R. Carter (1976). Innate resistance in malaria. *Exp. Parasitol. 40:*132.

21. Luzzato, L. (1974). Genetic factors in malaria. *Bull. WHO 50:*195.

22. Greenberg, J., and L. P. Kendrick (1957). Parasitemia and survival in inbred strains of mice infected with *Plasmodium berghei. J. Parasitol. 43:*413.

23. Eugui, E. M., and A. C. Allison (1979). Malarial infections in different strains of mice and their correlation with natural killer cell activity. *Bull. WHO, 57*(Suppl. 1):231.

24. Borwell, P., G. Holmquist, A. Cattan, E. Ojo, E. Hakansson, L. G. Lundin, and H. Wigzell (1980). Murine malaria: Genetic resistance and humoral antibody specificity. *Proceedings of the Fourth International Congress of Immunology,* Paris, 1980 (Abstract 5.7.02).

25. Most. H., R. S. Nussenzweig, J. Vanderberg, R. Herman, and M. Yoelii (1966). Susceptibility of genetically standardised (JAX) mouse strains to sporozoite and blood-induced *Plasmodium berghei* infections. *Milit. Med. 121:*915 (Suppl.).

26. Brown, I. N., A. C. Allison, and R. B. Taylor (1968). *Plasmodium berghei* infection in thymectomized rats. *Nature (Lond.). 219:*292.

27. Stechschulte, D. J. (1969). Effect of thymectomy on *Plasmodium berghei* infected rats. *Proc. Soc. Exp. Biol. Med. 131:*748.

28. Clarke, I. A., and A. C. Allison (1974). *Babesia microti* and *Plasmodium berghei yoelii* infections in nude mice. *Nature (Lond.). 252:*328.

29. Roberts, D. W., R. G. Rank, W. P. Weindanz, and J. F. Finnerty (1978). Prevention of recrudescent malaria in nude mice by thymus grafting or by treatment with hyperimmune serum. *Infect. Immunol. 16:*821.

30. Sharkis, S. J., A. Ahmed, L. L. Sensenbrenner, W. W. Jedrzejczak, A. L. Goldstein, and K. W. Sell (1978). The regulation hematopoiesis: Effect of thymosin or thymocytes in diffusion chambers. In *Experimental Hematology Today,* (S. J. Baum and D. Ledney, Eds.). Springer-Verlag, New York.

31. Jayawardena, A. N., G. A. T. Targett, E. Leuchars, R. L. Carter, M. J. Doenhoff, and A. J. S. Davies (1975). T cell activation in murine malaria. *Nature (Lond.) 258:*149.

32. Freeman, R. R., and C. R. Parish (1978). Spleen cell changes during fatal and self-limiting malarial infections of mice. *Immunology 35:*479.

33. Weinbaum, F. I., C. B. Evans, and R. E. Tigelaar (1976). An in vitro assay for T cell immunity to malaria in mice. *J. Immunol. 116:*1280.

34. Phillips, R. S. (1970). *Plasmodium berghei:* Passive transfer of immunity by antisera and cells. *Exp. Parasitol. 27:*479.

35. Jayawardena, A. N., G. A. T. Targett, E. Leuchars, and A. J. S. Davies (1978). The immunological response of CBA mice to *P. yoelii.* II. The passive transfer of immunity with serum and cells. *Immunology 33:*157.

36. Gravely, S., and J. P. Kreier (1976). Adoptive transfer of immunity to
     Plasmodium berghei with immune T and B lymphocytes. *Inf. Immun. 14:*
     184.
37. Brown, K. N., W. Jarra, and L. A. Hills (1976). T cells and protective
     immunity to *Plasmodium berghei* in rats. *Inf. Immun. 14:858.*
38. Roberts, D. W., and W. P. Weidanz (1978). Splenomegaly, enchnced phago-
     cytosis, and anemia are thymus-dependent responses to malaria. *Inf. Im-
     Mun. 20:728.*
39. Whitelaw, A., J. F. A. P. Miller, and G. F. Mitchell (1977). Studies on im-
     mune responses to parasite antigens in mice. VI. Delayed type hypersen-
     sitivity to blood cells from *Plasmodium berghei* infected mice. *Cell. Im-
     munol. 32:216.*
40. Wyler, D. J., and J. I. Gallin (1977). Spleen-derived mononuclear cell
     chemotactic factor in malaria infections: A possible mechanism for splenic
     macrophage accumulation. *J. Immunol. 118:478.*
41. Rosenberg, Y. J. (1978). Autoimmune and polyclonal B cell responses
     during murine malaria. *Nature (Lond.) 274:170.*
42. Jayardena, A. N. (1977). T cell dependent effector and suppressor re-
     sponses in murine malaria. In *Proceedings of the Fifth International
     Congress of Protozoology,* (S. H. Hunter, Ed.), New York.
43. Jayawardena, A. N. (1975). Thymus dependency of the immune re-
     sponse in murine malaria. PhD. Diss., University of London, England.
     p.
44. Jayawardena, A. N., G. A. T. Targett, R. L. Carter, A. J. S. Davies, and E.
     Leuchars (1975). The T cell response in murine malaria. *Trans. R. Soc.
     Trop. Med. Hyg. 69:427.*
45. Cantor, H., and E. A. Boyse (1977). Regulation of cellular and humoral
     immunity by T cell subclasses. *Cold Spring Harbor Symp. Quart. Biol.
     41:23.*
46. Raff, M. C., and H. Cantor (1971). Subpopulations of thymus cells and
     thymus derived lymphocytes. In *Progress in Immunology,* (B. Amos, Ed.).
     Academic Press, New York, p. 83.
47. Boyse, E. A., M. Miyazawa, T. Aoki, and L. Y. Old (1968). Ly-A and Ly-
     B. Two systems of lymphocyte isoantigens in the mouse. *Proc. R. Soc.
     Lond. [Biol.] 170:175.*
48. Cantor, H., and E. A. Boyse (1975). Functional subclasses of T lympho-
     cytes bearing different Ly antigens. I. The generation of functionally dis-
     tinct T cell subclasses as a differentiative process independent of antigen.
     J. Exp. Med. 141:1376.
49. Stanton, T. H., and E. A. Boyse (1976). A new serologically defined locus,
     Qa-1, in the T 1a region of the mouse. *Immunogenetics 3:525.*
50. Flaherty, L. (1976). The T 1a region of the mouse: Identification of a
     new serologically defined locus. *Immunogenetics 3:533.*
51. Spira, D. T., P. H. Silverman, and C. Gaines (1970). Antithymocyte
     serum effects on *Plasmodium berghei* infections in rats. *Immunology 19:*
     759.

52. Brown, K. N. (1971). Protective immunity to malaria provides a model for the survival of cells in an immunolobically hostile environment. *Nature (Lond.) 230:*163.

53. Jayawardena, A. N., C. A. Janeway, J. D. Kemp, and R. K. Gershon (1980). Specific immunity to malaria: Identification of T and B cell subsets mediating resistance to *P. yoelii. Proceedings of the Fourth International Congress of Immunology,* Paris, 1980 (Abstract 12.8.13).

54. Coleman, R. M., N. J. Renricca, J. P. Stout, W. H. Brisette, and D. M. Smith (1975). Splenic mediated erythrocyte cytotoxicity in malaria. *Immunology 29:*49.

55. Freeman, T., S. R. Smithers, G. A. T. Targett, and P. J. Walker (1970). Specificity of immunoglobulin G in rhesus monkeys infected with *Schistosoma mansoni, Plasmodium knowlesi* and *Trypanosoma brucei. J. Infect. Dis. 121:*40.

56. Voller, A. (1964). Fluorescent antibody methods and their use in malarial research. *Bull. WHO 30:*343.

57. Eaton, M. D. (1938). The agglutination of *Plasmodium knowlesi* by immune serum. *J. Exp. Med. 67:*857.

58. Brown, K. N., and I. N. Brown (1965). Immunity to malaria: Antigenic variation in chronic infections of *Plasmodium knowlesi. Nature (Lond.) 208:*1286.

59. Desowitz, R. S., and B. Stein (1962). A tanned red cell haemagglutination test, using *P. berghei* antigen and homologous antisera. *Trans. R. Soc. Trop. Med. Hyg. 56:*257.

60. Voller, A., G. Huldt, C. Thors, and E. Engyall (1975). New serological test for malaria antibodies. *Br. Med. J. 1:*659.

61. Brown, I. N. (1969). Immunological aspects of malaria infection. *Adv. Immunology 11:*267.

62. McGregor, I. A. (1971). Immunity to plasmodial infections: Consideration of factors relevant to malaria in man. *Int. Rev. Trop. Med. 4:*1.

63. Tobie, J. E., D. C. Abele, G. J. Hill, P. G. Contacos, and C. B. Evans (1966). Fluorescent antibody studies on the immune response in sporozoite-induced and blood-induced *Vivax* malaria and the relationship of antibody production to parasitemia. *Am. J. Trop. Med. Hyg. 15:*676.

64. Targett, G. A. T. (1970). Antibody response to *Plasmodium falciparum* malaria. Comparisons of immunoglobulin concentrations, antibody titres and the antigenicity of different asexual forms of the parasite. *Clin. Exp. Immunol. 7:*501.

65. Cox, F. E. G., and S. A. Turner (1970). Antibody levels in mice infected with *Plasmodium berghei yoelii. Ann. Trop. Med. Parasitol. 64:*175.

66. Cox, F. E. G., C. A. Crandall, and S. A. Turner (1969). Antibody levels detected by the fluorescent antibody technique in mice infected with *Plasmodium vinckei* and *P. chabaudi. Bull. WHO 41:*251.

67. Cox, F. E. G. (1970). Protective immunity between malaria parasites and piroplasms in mice. *Bull. WHO 43:*325.

68. Abele, D. C., J. E. Tobie, G. J. Hill, P. G. Contacos, and C. B. Evans (1965).

Alterations in serum proteins and 19S antibody production during the course of induced malarial infections in man. *Am. J. Trop. Med. Hyg. 14:* 191.

69. Collins, W. E., and J. C. Skinner (1968). Fluorescent antibody techniques for malaria case detection. In *Eighth International Congress on Tropical Medicine and Malaria, Teheran, 1968.* Abstracts and Reviews, Teheran.

70. Targett, G. A. T., and A. Voller (1965). Studies on antibody levels during vaccination of rhesus monkeys against *Plasmodium knowlesi. Br. Med. J. 2:*1104.

71. Roberts, D. W., and W. P. Weindanz (1979). T cell immunity to malaria in the B cell deficient mouse. *Am. J. Trop. Med. Hyg. 28:*1.

72. Weinbaum, F. I., C. B. Evans, and R. E. Tigelaar (1976). Immunity to *Plasmodium berghei yoelii* in mice. I. The course of infection in T cell and B cell deficient mice. *J. Immunol. 117:*1999.

73. Janeway, C. A., R. A. Murgita, F. I. Weinbaum, R. Asofsky, and H. Wigzell (1977). Evidence for an immunoglobulin-dependent antigen-specific helper T cell. *Proc. Nat. Acad. Sci. U.S.A. 74:*4582.

74. Longenecker, B. M., R. P. Breitenbach, and J. N. Farmer (1966). The role of the bursa Fabricius, spleen and thymus in the control of a *Plasmodium lophurae* infection in the chicken. *J. Immunol. 97:*594.

75. Rank, R. G., and W. P. Weidanz (1976). Nonsterilizing immunity in avian malaria: An antibody-independent phenomenon. *Proc. Soc. Exp. Biol. Med. 151:*257.

76. Amsbaugh, D. F., C. T. Hansen, B. Prescott, P. W. Stashak, D. R. Barthold, and P. J. Baker (1973). Genetic control of the antibody response to type III pneumococcal polysaccharide in mice. I. Evidence that an X-linked gene plays a decisive role in determining responsiveness. *J. Exp. Med. 136:* 931.

77. Scher, I., M. M. Frantz, and A. D. Steinberg (1973). The genetics of the immune response to a synthetic double stranded RNA in a mutant CBA mouse strain. *J. Immunol. 110:*1396.

78. Mosier, D. E., I. Scher, H. Ruhl, P. L. Cohen, I. Zitron, and W. E. Paul (1975). Activation of normal and defective B lymphocytes by thymus independent antigens. In *Role of Mitogens in Immunobiology,* (J. J. Oppenheim and D. Rosenstreich, Eds.). Academic Press, New York, p. 313.

79. Jayawardena, A. N., C. A. Janeway, Jr., and J. D. Kemp (1979). Experimental malaria in the CBA/N mouse. *J. Immunol. 123:*2532.

80. Jayawardena, A. N., and J. D. Kemp (1979). Immunity to *Plasmodium yoelii* and *Babesia microti:* Modulation by the CBA/N X chromosome. *Bull. WHO 57*(Suppl.):255.

81. Phillips, R. S., and V. E. Jones (1972). Immunity to *Plasmodium berghei* in rats: Maximum levels of protective antibody activity are associated with eradication of the infection. *Parasitology 64:*117.

82. Coggeshall, L. T., and H. W. Kumm (1937). Demonstration of passive immunity in experimental monkey malaria. *J. Exp. Med. 66:*177.

83. Diggs, C. L., and A. G. Osler (1969). Humoral immunity in rodent malaria.
    II. Inhibition of parasitemia by serum antibody. *J. Immunol. 102:*298.

84. Brown, I. N., and R. S. Phillips (1974). Immunity to *Plasmodium berghei*
    in rats: Passive serum transfer and role of the spleen. *Inf. Immun. 10:*1213.

85. Stechschulte, D. J., N. T. Briggs, and B. T. Welde (1969). Characterization
    of protective antibodies produced in *Plasmodium berghei* infected rats.
    *Milit. Med. 134:*1140.

86. Cohen, S., and G. A. Butcher (1969). Comments on immunization. *Milit.
    Med. 134:*119.

87. Cohen, S., and I. A. McGregor (1963). Gammaglobulin and acquired im-
    munity to malaria. In *Immunity to Protozoa*, (P. C. C. Garnham, A. E.
    Pierce, and I. Roitt, Eds.). Blackwell Scientific Publications, Oxford, p. 123.

88. Cohen, S., G. A. Butcher, and R. B. Crandall (1969). Action of malarial
    antibody in vitro. *Nature (Lond.) 223:*368.

89. Cohen, S., and G. A. Butcher (1970). Properties of protective malarial
    antibody. *Immunology 19:*369.

90. Butcher, G. A., and S. Cohen (1972). Antigenic variation and protective
    immunity to *Plasmodium knowlesi* malaria. *Immunology 23:*503.

91. Miller, L. H., K. G. Powers, and T. Shiroishi (1977). *Plasmodium knowlesi:*
    Functional immunity and antimerozoite antibodies in rhesus monkeys after
    repeated infection. *Exp. Parasitol. 41:*105.

92. Butcher, G. A., G. H. Mitchell, and S. Cohen (1978). Antibody mediated
    mechanisms of immunity to malaria induced by vaccination with *Plasmo-
    dium knowlesi* merozoites. *Immunology 34:*77.

93. R. R. Freeman, A. T. Trejdosiewicz, and G. A. M. Cross (1980). Protec-
    tive monoclonal antibodies recognizing stage specific merozoite antigens of
    a rodent malaria parasite. *Nature (Lond.) 284:*366.

94. Brown, K. N., I. N. Brown, P. I. Trigg, R. S. Phillips, and L. A. Hills (1970).
    Immunity to malaria. II. Serological response of monkeys sensitised by
    drug-suppressed infection or by dead parasitised cells in Freund's complete
    adjuvant. *Exp. Parasitol. 28:*318.

95. Brown, K. N. (1976). Resistance to malaria. In *Immunology of Parasitic
    Infections*, (S. Cohen and E. H. Sadum, Eds.). Blackwell Scientific Publi-
    cations, Oxford, p. 268.

96. Kilejian, A., A. Abati, and W. Trager (1977). *Plasmodium falciparum* and
    Plasmodium coatneyi. Immunogenicity of knob like protrusions on infected
    erythrocyte membranes. *Exp. Parasitol. 42:*157.

97. Lustig, H. J., V. Nussenzweig, and R. S. Nussenzweig (1977). Erythrocyte
    membrane-associated immunoglobulins during malaria infection of mice.
    *J. Immunol. 119:*210.

98. Kreier, J. P., H. Shapiro, D. Dilley, I. P. Szilvassy, and M. Ristic (1966).
    Autoimmune reactions in rats with *Plasmodium berghei* infection. *Exp.
    Parasitol. 19:*155.

99. Barrett-Connor, E. (1967). *Plasmodium vivax* malaria and Coombs-posi-
    tive anemia. *Am. J. Trop. Med. Hyg. 16:*699.

100.   Rosenberg, E. B., G. T. Strickland, S. L. Yand, and G. Whalen (1973).
        IgM antibodies to red cells and autoimmune anemia in patients with
        malaria. *Am. J. Trop. Med. Hyg. 22:*146.
101.   Mitchell, G. F. (1980). Responses to infection with metazoan and pro-
        tozoan parasites in mice. *Adv. Immunol. 28:*451.
102.   Clark, I. A., A. C. Allison, and F. E. G. Cox (1976). Protection of mice
        against *Babesia* spp. and *Plasmodium* spp. with BCG. *Nature (Lond.) 259:*
        309.
103.   Clark, I. A., F. E. G. Cox, and A. C. Allison (1977). Protection of mice
        against *Babesia* spp. and *Plasmodium* spp. with killed *Corynebacterium
        parvum. Parasitology 74:*9.
104.   Nussenzweig, R. S. (1967). Increased nonspecific resistance to malaria
        produced by administration of killed *Corynebacterium parvum. Exp.
        Parasitol. 21:*224.
105.   Herod, E., I. A. Clark, and A. C. Allison (1978). Protection of mice
        against the haemoprotozoan *Babesia microti* with *Brucella abortus* strain
        19. *Clin. Exp. Immunol. 31:*518.
106.   Clark, I. A., (1979). Resistance to *Babesia* spp. and *Plasmodium* spp. in
        mice pretreated with an extract of *Coxiella burnetii. Inf. Immun. 24:*319.
107.   Schultz, W. W., K. Y. Huang, and F. B. Gordon (1968). Role of interfer-
        on on experimental mouse malaria. *Nature (Lond.) 220:*709.
108.   Jahiel, R. I., J. Vilcek, R. S. Nussenzweig, and J. Vanderberg (1968).
        Interferon inducers protect mice against *Plasmodium berghei* malaria.
        *Science 161:*802.
109.   Jahiel, R. I., R. S. Nussenzweig, J. Vanderberg, and J. Vilcek (1968).
        Antimalarial effect of interferon inducers at different stages of develop-
        ment of *Plasmodium berghei* in the mouse. *Nature (Lond.) 220:*710.
110.   Martin, L. K., A. Einheber, E. H. Sadum, and R. E. Wren (1967). Effect
        of bacterial endotoxin on the course of *Plasmodium berghei* infection.
        *Exp. Parasitol. 20:*186.
111.   MacGregor, R. R., J. N. Sheagren, and S. M. Wolff (1969). Endotoxin
        induced modification of *Plasmodium berghei* infection in mice. *J. Im-
        munol. 102:*131.
112.   Jerusalem, C. (1968). Active immunization against malaria (*Plasmodium
        berghei*). 1. Definition of antimalarial immunity. *Z. Tropenmed. Para-
        sitol. 19:*171.
113.   Clark, I. A., E. J. Wills, J. E. Richmond, and A. C. Allison (1977). Sup-
        pression of babesiosis in BCG-infected mice and its correlation with tumor
        inhibition. *Inf. Immun. 17:*430.
114.   Allison, A. C., and I. A. Clark (1977). Specific and non-specific immun-
        ity to haemoprotozoa. *Am. J. Trop. Med. Hyg. 26:*216.
115.   Moeller, G., Ed. (1979). Natural killer cells. *Immunol. Rev. 44:*
        Munksgaard, Copenhagen.
116.   Haller, O., M. Hansson, R. Kiessling, and H. Wigzell (1977). Role of non-
        conventional natural killer cells in resistance against syngenic tumour cells
        in vivo. *Nature (Lond.) 270:*609.

117.   Kiessling, R., E. Klein, and H. Wigzell (1975). "Natural" killer cells in
       the mouse. I. Cytotoxic cells with specificity for mouse Moloney leukemia
       cells. Specificity and distribution according to genotype. *Eur. J. Immunol.*
       *5:*112.
118.   Roder, J., and A. Duwe (1979). The beige mutation in the mouse selec-
       tively impairs natural killer cell function. *Nature (Lond.) 278:*451.
119.   Vassalli, J. D., A. Granelli-Piperno, C. Griscelli, and E. Reich (1978).
       Specific protease deficiency in polymorphonuclear leukocytes of Chediak-
       Higashi syndrome and Beige mice. *J. Exp. Med. 147:*1285.
120.   Johnson, K. J., J. Varnai, J. Oliver, and P. A. Ward (1979). Immuno-
       logical vasculitis in Beige mice with deficiency of leukocytic neutral pro-
       tease. *J. Immunol. 122:*1807.
121.   Gallin, J. I., J. A. Klimerman, G. A. Padgett, and S. M. Wolff (1975).
       Defective mononuclear leukocyte chemotaxis in the Chediak-Higashi syn-
       drome of humans, mink and cattle. *Blood 45:*863.
122.   Wolfe, S. A., D. E. Tracey, and C. S. Henney (1976). Induction of "natu-
       ral killer" cells by BCG. *Nature (Lond.) 262:*584.
123.   Ojo, E., O. Haller, A. Kimura, and H. Wigzell (1978). An analysis of
       conditions allowing *Corynebacterium parvum* to cause either augmenta-
       tion or inhibition of natural killer cell activity against tumor cells in mice.
       *Int. J. Cancer 21:*444.
124.   Gidlund, M., A. Orn, and H. Wigzell (1978). Enhanced NK cell activity
       in mice injected with interferon and interferon inducers. *Nature (Lond.)*
       *273:*759.
125.   Djeu, J. Y., J. A. Heinbaugh, H. T. Holden, and R. B. Herberman (1979).
       Augmentation of mouse natural killer cell activity by interferon and inter-
       feron inducers. *J. Immunol. 122:*175.
126.   Jahiel, R. I., J. Vilcek, and R. S. Nussenzweig (1970). Exogenous inter-
       feron protects mice against *Plasmodium berghei* malaria. *Nature (Lond.)*
       *227:*1350.
127.   Huang, K. Y., W. W. Schultz, and F. B. Gordon (1968). Interferon in-
       duced by *Plasmodium berghei. Science 162:*123.
128.   Kirchner, H., H. M. Hirt, H. Becker, and K. Munk (1977). Production
       of an antiviral factor by murine spleen cells after treatment with *Coryne-*
       *bacterium parvum. Cell. Immunol. 31:*172.
129.   Cannon, P. R., and W. H. Taliaferro (1931). Acquired immunity in avian
       malaria. III. Cellular reactions in infection and superinfection. *J. Pre-*
       *vent. Med. 5:*37.
130.   Taliaferro, W. H., and P. R. Cannon (1936). The cellular reactions during
       primary infections and superinfections of *Plasmodium brasilianum* in
       Panamian monkeys. *J. Infect. Dis. 59:*72.
131.   Shear, H. L., R. S. Nussenzweig, and C. Bianco (1979). Immune phago-
       cytosis in murine malaria. *J. Exp. Med. 149:*1288.
132.   Nougueira, N., S. Gordon, Z. A. Cohn (1977). *Trypanosoma cruzi:* The
       immunological induction of macrophage plasminogen activator requires
       thymus derived lymphocytes. *J. Exp. Med. 142:*172.

133. Clarke, I. A., E. J. Willis, J. E. Richmond, and A. C. Allison (1975). Immunity to intra-erythrocytic protozoa. *Lancet ii:*1128.

134. Cohen, S., G. A. Butcher, and G. H. Mitchell (1975). Immunization against erythrocytic forms of malaria. *Adv. Exp. Biol. Med. 93:*89.

135. Corradetti, A., F. Verolini, and A. Bucci (1966). Resistanza a *Plasmodium berghei* de parte di ratti albini precedentemente immunizati con *Plasmodium berghei* irradiato. *Parrassitologia 8:*133.

136. Wellde, B. G., and E. H. Sadun (1967). Resistance produced in rats and mice by exposure to irradiated *Plasmodium berghei. Exp. Parasitol. 21:* 310.

137. Wellde, B. G., R. A. Ward, and R. Voeka (1969). Aspects of immunity in mice inoculated with irradiated *Plasmodium berghei. Milit. Med. 134 (Spec. Iss.):*1153.

138. Wells, R. A., L. K. Martin, D. R. Stutz, and C. L. Diggs (1977). *Plasmodium yoelii:* An inbred model for protective immunisation against malaria in BALB/c mice. *Exp. Parasitol. 41:*472.

139. Playfair, J. H. L., J. B. DeSouza, and B. J. Cottrell (1977). Protection of mice against malaria by a killed vaccine: Differences in effectiveness against *P. yoelii* and *P. berghei. Immunology 33:*507.

140. Murphy, J. R., and M. J. Lefford (1978). Host defenses in murine malaria: Induction of a protected state of immunity with a formalin-killed *Plasmodium berghei* blood parasite vaccine. *Infect. Immun. 22:*798.

141. D'Antonio, L. E. (1972). *Plasmodium berghei:* Vaccination of mice against malaria with heat inactivated parasitised blood. *Exp. Parasitol. 31:*82.

142. Brown, K. N., I. N. Brown, and L. A. Hills (1970). Immunity to malaria. I. Protection against *Plasmodium knowlesi* shown by monkeys sensitized with drug suppressed infections or by dead parasites in Freund's adjuvant. *Exp. Parasitol. 28:*304.

143. Targett, G. A. T., and J. D. Fulton (1965). Immunisation of rhesus monkeys against *Plasmodium knowlesi* malaria. *Exp. Parasitol. 17:*180.

144. Mitchell, G. H., G. A. Butcher, and S. Cohen (1975). Merozoite vaccination against *P. knowlesi* malaria. *Immunology 29:*397.

145. Targett, G. A. T., and K. N. Mendis (1979). Immunisation against gametes and asexual erythrocytic stages of a rodent malaria parasite. *Nature (Lond.) 277:*389.

146. Kilejian, A. (1978). Histidine-rich protein as model malaria vaccine. *Science 201:*922.

147. Zinkernagel, R. M., and P. C. Doherty (1974). Restriction of in vitro T cell mediated cytotoxicity in lymphocytic choriomeningitis within a syngeneic or semi-allogeneic system. *Nature (Lond.) 248:*701.

148. Zinkernagel, R. M., and P. C. Doherty (1977). Major transplantation antigens, virus, and specificity of surveillance T cells. The altered self hypothesis. *Contemp. Top. Immunobiol. 7:*179.

149. Desowitz, R. S. (1975). Plasmodium berghei: Immunogenic enhancement of antigen by adjuvant addition. *Exp. Parasitol. 38:*6.

150. Murphy, J. R., and M. J. Lefford (1979). Vaccination against *Plasmodium berghei. Am. J. Trop. Med. Hyg. 28:4.*

151. Playfair, J. H. L., and J. B. DeSouza (1979). *Parasite Immunol. 1:197.*

152. Playfair, J. H. L. (1978). Effective and ineffective responses to parasites: Evidence from experimental models. *Curr. Top. Microbiol. Immunol. 80:37.*

153. Cottrell, B. J., J. H. L. Playfair, and J. B. DeSouza (1978). Cell mediated immunity in mice vaccinated against malaria. *Clin. Exp. Immunol. 34:147.*

154. Finerty, J. F., and E. P. Krehl (1977). Delayed immune reactions in mice immunized with malarial antigen. *Am. J. Trop. Med. Hyg. 26:377.*

155. Brown, K. N., L. A. Hills, and W. Jarra (1976). Preliminary studies of artificial immunization of rats against *Plasmodium berghei* and adoptive transfer of this immunity by splenic T and T+ B cells. *Bull. WHO 54:149.*

156. Nussenzweig, R. S., J. P. Vanderberg, Y. Sanabria, and H. Most (1972). *Plasmodium berghei:* Accelerated clearance of sporozoites from blood as part of the immune mechanism in mice. *Exp. Parasitol. 31:88.*

157. Garnham, P. C. C., and R. S. Bray (1956). The inference of immunity upon the tissue stages (including late exoerythrocytic schizonts) of mammalian malaria parasites. *Rev. Bras. Malariol. Doencas Trop. 8:151.*

158. Verhave, J. P. (1975). Immunisation with sporozoites. An experimental study of *Plasmodium berghei* malaria. PhD Diss., University of Nijmegen, The Netherlands.

159. Beaudoin, R. L., C. P. A. Strome, T. T. Palmer, and M. Bawden (1975). Immunogenecity of the sporozoites of the anka strain of *P. berghei* following different treatments. *Am. Soc. Parasitol. (Abstract) 231:98.*

160. Mulligan, H. W., P. F. Russel, and B. N. Mohan (1941). Active immunisation of fowls against *Plasmodium gallinaceum* by injections of killed homologous sporozoites. *J. Malariol. Inst. India 4:25.*

161. Spitalny, G. L., and R. S. Nussenzweig (1972). Effects of various routes of immunisation and methods of parasite alteration on the development of protection against sporozoite-induced rodent malaria. *Proc. Helminthol. Soc. Wash. 39:506.*

162. Nussenzweig, R. S., J. Vanderberg, H. Most, and C. Orton (1967). Protective immunity produced by the injection of x-irradiated sporozoites of *Plasmodium berghei. Nature (Lond.) 216:160.*

163. Nussenzweig, R. S., J. Vanderberg, G. Spitalny, C. I. O. Rivera, C. Orton, and H. Most (1972). Sporozoite induced immunity in mammalian malaria: A review. *Am. J. Trop. Med. Hyg. 21:722.*

164. Nussenzweig, R. S., A. H. Cochrane, and H. J. Lustig (1978). Immunological responses. In *Rodent Malaria,* (R. Killick-Kendrick and W. Peters, Eds.). Academic Press, New York, p. 247.

165. Nussenzweig, R. S., J. P. Vanderberg, and H. Most (1969). Protective immunity produced by the injection of x-irradiated sporozoites of *P. berghei.* Dose response, specificity and humoral immunity. *Milit. Med. 134:1176.*

166. Vanderberg, J., R. Nussenzweig, and H. Most (1969). Protective immu-
      nity produced by the injections of x-irradiated sporozoites of *Plasmodium
      berghei*. V. In vitro effects of immune serum on sporozoites. *Milit. Med.
      134* (Suppl.):1183.
167. Nardin, E., R. W. Gwadz, and R. S. Nussenzweig (1979). Characterisation
      of sporozoite surface antigens by indirect immunofluorescence. Detection
      of stage and species specific antimalarial antibodies. *Bull. WHO 57* (Suppl.),
      p. 211.
168. Nussenzweig, R. S., J. P. Vanderberg, H. Most, and C. Orton (1969). Spe-
      cificity of protective immunity produced by x-irradiated *Plasmodium
      berghei* sporozoites. *Nature (Lond.) 222:*488.
169. Nussenzweig, R. S., and D. Chen (1974). The antibody response to
      sporozoites of simian and human malaria parasites: Its stage and species
      specificity, and strain cross reactivity. *Bull. WHO 50:*293.
170. Cox, F. E. G., and A. Voller (1966). Cross immunity between malaria
      parasites of rodents. *Ann. Trop. Med. Parasitol. 60:*297.
171. Nussenzweig, R. S., M. Yoelii, and H. Most (1966). Studies on the pro-
      tective effect of *Plasmodium chabaudi* infection in mice upon a subse-
      quent infection with another rodent malarial species—*Plasmodium vinckei.
      Milit. Med. 131* (Suppl.):1237.
172. Vickerman, K. (1974). Antigenic variation in African trypanosomes. In
      Parasites in the Immunized Host: Mechanisms of Survival. Ciba Founda-
      tion Symposium, No. 25, North-Holland, Amsterdam, p. 53.
173. Cunningham, M. P. (1966). The preservation of viable metacyclic forms
      of *Trypanosoma rhodesiense* and some studies of the antigenicity of the
      organisms. *Trans. R. Soc. Trop. Med. Hyg. 60:*126.
174. Gray, A. R. (1965). Antigenic variation in a strain of *Trypanosoma
      brucei* transmitted by *Glossina morsitans* and *G. Palpalis. J. Gen. Micro-
      biol. 41:*195.
175. Yoshida, N., R. S. Nussenzweig, P. Potocnjak, V. Nussenzweig, and M.
      Aikawa (1980). Hybridoma produces protective antibodies directed
      against the sporozite stage of malaria parasite. *Science 207:*71.
176. Chen, D. E., R. Tigelaar, and F. I. Weinbaum (1977). Immunity to sporo-
      zoite induced malaria in mice. I. The effect of T and B cell deficiency in
      mice. *J. Immunol. 118:*1322.
177. Spitalny, G. L., J. P. Verhave, J. H. E. Meuwissen, and R. S. Nussenzweig
      (1977). *Plasmodium berghei:* T cell dependence of sporozoite-induced
      immunity in rodents. *Exp. Parasitol. 42:*73.
178. Spitalny, G. L., C. Rivera-Ortiz, and R. S. Nussenzweig (1976). *Plasmo-
      dium berghei:* The spleen in sporozoite-induced immunity in rodents.
      *Exp. Parasitol. 40:*179.
179. Smrkovski, L. L., and G. T. Strickland (1978). Rodent malaria: BCG-
      induced protection and immunosuppression. *J. Immunol. 121:*1257.
180. Potocnjak, P., N. Yoshida, R. S. Nussenzweig, and V. Nussenzweig (1980).
      Monovalent fragments (Fab) of monoclonal antibodies to a sporozoite
      surface antigen (Pb 44) protect mice against malarial infection. *J. Exp.
      Med. 151:*1504.

181. Jayawardena, A. N., G. A. T. Targett, A. J. S. Davies, E. Leuchars, and R. L. Carter (1975). Changes in PHA and LPS responsiveness in murine malaria. *Trans. R. Soc. Trop. Med. Hyg. 69:*426.

182. Weinbaum, F. I., J. Weintraub, F. K. Nkrumah, C. B. Evans, R. E. Tieglaar, and Y. J. Rosenberg (1978). Immunity to *Plasmodium berghei yoelii* in mice. II. Specific and nonspecific cellular and humoral responses during the course of infection. *J. Immunol. 121:*629.

183. Greenwood, B. M., J. H. L. Playfair, and G. Torrigiani (1971). Immuno-suppression in murine malaria. I. General characteristics. *Clin. Exp. Immunol. 8:*467.

184. McBride, J. S., and H. S. Micklem (1977). Immunosuppression in murine malaria. II. The primary response to bovine serum albumin. *Immunology 33:*253.

185. Wedderburn, N., and B. N. Dracott (1977). The immune response to type III pneumococcal polysaccharide in mice with malaria. *Clin. Exp. Immunol. 28:*130.

186. McBride, J. S., H. S. Micklem, and J. M. Ure (1977). Immunosuppression in murine malaria. I. Response to type III pneumococcal polysaccharide. *Immunology 32:*635.

187. Whitmore, D. B. (1974). The immune response to heterologous erythro-cytes in mice infected with malaria. Ph.D. Diss., University of St. Andrews, Scotland.

188. Sengers, R. C. A., C. R. Jerusalem, W. H. Doesburg (1971). Murine malaria. IV. Disturbed immunological responsiveness during *Plasmodium berghei* infection. *Exp. Parasitol. 30:*41.

189. Freeman, R. R. (1978). T cell function during fatal and self-limiting malarial infections of mice. *Cell. Immunol. 41:*373.

190. Krettli, A. U., and R. S. Nussenzweig (1974). Depletion of T and B lymphocytes during malarial infections. *Cell. Immunol. 13:*440.

191. Loose, L. D., J. A. Cook, and N. R. DiLuzio (1972). Malarial immuno-suppression. A macrophage mediated defect. *Proc. Soc. Wash. (Basic Res. Mal.) 39:*484.

192. Warren, H. S., and W. P. Weidanz (1976). Malarial immunodepression in vitro: Adherent spleen cells are functionally defective as accessory cells in the response to horse erythrocytes. *J. Immunol. 6:*816.

193. Greenwood, B. M., J. C. Brown, D. G. DeJesus, and E. J. Holbrow (1971). Immunosuppression in murine malaira. II. The effect of reticuloendothe-lial and germinal centre function. *Clin. Exp. Immunol. 9:*345.

194. Lucia, H. L., and R. S. Nussenzweig (1969). *Plasmodium chabaudi* and *Plasmodium vinckei:* Phagocytic activity of mouse reticuloendothelial system. *Exp. Parasitol. 25:*319.

195. A. N. Jayawardena and B. H. Waksman (1977). Suppressor cells in experimental trypanosomiasis. *Nature (Lond.) 265:*539.

196. Jayawardena, A. N., B. H. Waksman, and D. D. Eardley (1978). Activation of distinct helper and suppressor T cells in experimental trypanoso-miasis. *J. Immunol. 121:*622.

197. Wyler, D. J., H. G. Herod, and F. I. Weinbaum (1979). Response of sensitised and unsensitised human lymphocyte subpopulations to *P. falciparum* antigens. *Infect. Immunol. 24:*106.
198. Jandinski, J., H. Cantor, T. Tadakuma, D. L. Peavey, and C. W. Pierce (1976). Separation of helper T cells from suppressor T cells expressing different Ly components. I. Polyclonal activation: Suppressor and helper activities are inherent properties of distinct T cell subclasses. *J. Exp. Med. 146:*1169.
199. Pierce, C. W., and J. A. Kapp (1976). Regulation of immune responses by suppressor T cells. *Contemp. Top. Immunobiol. 5:*91.
200. Cohen, S., I. A. McGregor, and S. P. Carrington (1961). Gammaglobulin and acquired immunity to human malaria. *Nature (Lond.) 192:*733.
201. Mattern, P., R. Maseyeff, R. Michel, and P. Peretti (1961). Etude immunochimique de la B_2-macroglobulines des serums des malades atteints de trypanosomiase africaine a T. gambiense. *Ann. Inst. Pasteur (Paris) 101:* 382.
202. Greenwood, B. M. (1974). Possible role of a B cell mitogen in hypergammaglobulinaemia in malaria and trypanosomiasis. *Lancet i:*435.
203. Greenwood, B. M., and R. M. Vick (1975). Evidence for a malaria mitogen in human malaria. *Nature (Lond.) 257:*592.
204. Wyler, D. J. (1974). B cell mitogen in hypergammaglobulinemia in malaria and trypanosomiasis. *Lancet i:*742.
205. Freeman, R. R., and C. R. Parish (1978). Polyclonal B cell activation during rodent malarial infections. *Clin. Exp. Immunol. 32:*41.
206. Motika, E. J. (1975). Cellular basis and the nature of the hyperimmunoglobulinemia induced by antigen challenge. *Cell. Immunol. 19:*31.
207. Antoine, J. C., C. Petit, M. A. Bach, J. F. Bach, J. C. Salamon, and S. Ayrameas (1977). T cell dependence of cells synthesizing immunoglobulin without detectable antibody function induced after antigenic stimulation. *J. Immunol. 7:*336.
208. L'age-Stehr, J., H. Teichman, R. K. Gershon, and H. Cantor (1980). Stimulation of regulatory T cell circuits by Ig associated structures on activated B cells. *Eur. J. Immunol. 10:*21.
209. Zuckerman, A. (1964). Autoimmunization and other types of indirect damage to host cells as factors in certain protozoan diseases. *Exp. Parasitol. 15:*138.
210. Zuckerman, A. (1960). Autoantibody in rats with *Plasmodium berghei*. *Nature (Lond.) 185.*
211. Greenwood, B. M., E. M. Herrick, and E. J. Holborow (1970). Speckled anti-nuclear factor in African sera. *Clin. Exp. Immunol. 7:*75.
212. Houba, V., and A. C. Allison (1966). Antiglobulins (rheumatoid-factor like globulius) and other gammaglobulins in relation to tropical parasitic infections. *Lancet i:*848.
213. Shaper, A. G., M. H. Kaplan, N. J. Mody, and P. A. McIntyre (1968). Malarial antibodies and autoantibodies to heart and other tissues in the immigrant and indigenous peoples of Uganda. *Lancet i:*1342.

214. Greenwood, B. M., and A. Voller (1970). Suppression of autoimmune disease in New Zealand mice associated with infection with malaria. (NZB X NZW)F$_1$, hybrid mice. *Clin. Exp. Immunol. 7:*793.

215. Greenwood, B. M., and A. Voller (1970). Suppression of autoimmune disease in New Zealand mice associated with infection with malaria. II. NZB mice. *Clin. Exp. Immunol. 7:*805.

216. Cantor, H., and R. K. Gershon (1979). Immunological circuits: Cellular composition. *Fed. Proc. 38:*2058.

217. Cantor, H., L. McVay-Boudreau, J. Hugenberger, K. Naidorf, F. W. Shen, and R. K. Gershon (1978). Immunoregulatory circuits among T cell subsets: II. Physiologic role of feedback inhibition in vivo: Absence in NBZ mice. *J. Exp. Med. 147:*1116.

218. Gershon, R. K., M. Horowitz, J. D. Kemp, D. B. Murphy, and E. D. Murphy (1978). The cellular site of immunoregulatory breakdown in the lpr mutant mouse. In *Genetic Control of Autoimmune Disease* (N. R. Rose, P. E. Bigazzi, and N. L. Warner, Eds.). Elsevier North-Holland, Amsterdam, p. 223.

219. Sheagren, J. N., and A. P. Monaco (1968). Protective effect of anti-lymphocyte serum on mice infected with *Plasmodium berghei. Science 164:*1423.

220. Wright, D. H. (1968). The effect of neonatal thymectomy on the survival of golden hamsters infected with *P. berghei. Br. J. Exp. Pathol. 49:*379.

221. Wright, D. H., R. M. Masembe, and E. R. Bazira (1971). The effect of anti-thymocyte serum on golden hamsters and rats infected with *Plasmodium berghei. Br. J. Exp. Pathol. 52:*465.

222. Kemp. J. D., A. N. Jayawardena, B. Huber, and R. K. Gershon (1980). B cell subsets in autoimmunity. An autoimmune haemolytic response to mouse erythrocytes is modulated by the CBA/N defect and anti-Ly B 3 anti-sera. *Cell. Immunol. 53:*84.

223. Finerty, J. F., and E. P. Krehl (1976). Cyclophosphamide pretreatment and protection against malaria. *Inf. Immun. 14:*1103.

224. Askenase, P. W., B. J. Hayden, and R. K. Gershon (1975). Augmentation of delayed type hypersensitivity by doses of cyclophosphamide which do not affect antibody responses. *J. Exp. Med. 141:*697.

225. Wyler, D. J., L. H. Miller, and L. H. Schmidt (1977). Spleen functions in quartan malaria (due to *P. inui*): Evidence for both protective and suppressive roles in host defense. *J. Infect. Dis. 135:*86.

226. Nordlund, J. J., and R. K. Gershon (1975). Splenic regulation of the clinical appearance of small tumours. *J. Immunol. 114:*1486.

3

Immunology of *Trypanosoma cruzi* Infections

RAYMOND E. KUHN   Wake Forest University, Winston-Salem, North Carolina

I.	Introduction	138
	A. General Information on Chagas' Disease	138
	B. Biology of the Host-Parasite Relationship in Experimental Chagas' Disease	138
II.	Protective Immunologic Responses in Chagas' Disease	140
	A. General Considerations	140
	B. The Role of Macrophages	141
	C. B-Cell Responses to *Trypanosoma cruzi*	143
	D. The Role of Complement	144
	E. Opsonic/Cytophilic Antibody in Chagas' Disease	146
	F. Antibody-Dependent Cellular Cytotoxicity against *Trypanosoma cruzi*	147
	G. Cell-Mediated Immunity in Chagas' Disease	149
	H. Detection and Destruction of *Trypanosoma cruzi*-Infected Host Cells	151
	I. Autoantibodies in Chagas' Disease	152
III.	Immunosuppression in Chagas' Disease	153
IV.	Perspectives	158
	References	161

I. INTRODUCTION

A. General Information on Chagas' Disease

Trypanosoma cruzi is the obligate intracellular parasite which causes Chagas' disease, or South American trypanosomiasis. The parasite is transmitted by several species of reduviid bugs, and many species of mammals can act as reservoirs for this pathogenic protozoan. Chagas' disease is most prevalent in people occupying the lower socioeconomic classes in endemic areas of South and Central America, although it can occur as a congenital disease, and an alarming number of people are infected via contaminated blood as the result of transfusions. Recent estimates place the number of humans with Chagas' disease at 12-40 million. In some areas 40% or more of the population is serologically positive for the disease [1].

The parasite is transmitted to its definitive host in the feces of an infected bug. Trypanosomes in the feces usually enter the tissues of mammals through skin abrasions or the soft tissues of the face. Trypomastigotes can either immediately invade cells at the portal of entry, often inducing a "chagoma" which is diagnostically characteristic of a recent infection, or the parasites may be transported in the blood to another site prior to invading host cells. In general, different *T. cruzi* strains are reticulotropic or myotropic under experimental conditions but are characteristically found to reside predominately, although to varying degrees, in cardiac and skeletal musculature. The disease in humans may be clinically apparent or inapparent. Acute Chagas' disease is fatal in about 10% of all cases, with the highest mortality in children. Whereas parasites are often found in the peripheral circulation during the acute disease, they are much more difficult to detect in the blood of chronic chagasic patients. Chronic disease symptoms are varied but can include cardiomyopathies and enlargement of the hollow viscera, the latter condition presumably due to destruction of nervous tissue innervating the affected areas [2]. To date there is no effective treatment, and there are no effective vaccines for Chagas' disease.

B. Biology of the Host-Parasite Relationship in Experimental Chagas' Disease

Dvorak and his co-workers have reported results of several studies on the interaction of *Trypanosoma cruzi* (Ernestina strain) with mammalian cells under well-defined conditions in vitro. Blood-form trypomastigotes were found to invade bovine embryonic skeletal muscle cells within a few minutes of inoculation into the culture system [3]. Following invasion, parasites differentiated into amastigotes which then entered a "lag period" prior to division. It was not uncommon for more than one parasite to invade a single cell. Of interest was the observation that the intracellular amastigotes underwent nine divisions, a characteristic which was independent of host cell volume. Differentiation into trypomastigotes and escape from the host cell occurred rapidly, ending the intracellular cycle on an average of 6.5 days following initial invasion. Increased penetration, decreased lag time, and decreased doubling time of the parasite were found with increasing temperature from 29 to 38°C [4], and the conditions involved in penetration suggested a requirement for physiologic changes in the parasite during invasion [4]. The means by which *T. cruzi* invades mammalian cells has not been determined, although suggestions include phagocytosis by macrophages and "nonprofessional phagocytes" [5], fusion of parasite-host cell membranes [6], and mechanical penetration [3]. It is probable that various parasite strains and host cells would yield different times for completion of the intracellular cycle in vitro.

Studies in vivo have found that waves of increasing numbers of parasites in the blood occur at approximately 4-day intervals in sublethally irradiated rodents infected with *T. cruzi*. Howells and Chiari [7] used Y and MR strains of *T. cruzi* in irradiated Swiss mice and found waves of increasing parasitemia at 3-4 days, and Cover et al. [8] found much the same pattern in irradiated rats infected with the Sonya strain of parasite. These types of observations suggest that the intracellular cycle in vivo may be shorter than that reported by Dvorak and Hyde [3] using an in vitro system.

The course of parasitemia in experimental Chagas' disease and the capacity of experimental animals to survive the acute phase of infection are dependent on the virulence of the parasite strain and on the age, sex, and genetic composition of the host [9]. With highly virulent parasites, susceptible hosts generally exhibit rapidly increasing parasitemias and die with large numbers of parasites in the blood, whereas highly resistant mice tend to control the number of parasites in the blood and survive the acute phase [10]. In mice infected with the Brazil strain of *T. cruzi*, the number of parasites in the blood is reportedly indicative of the number of parasites in the tissues [11].

Cover et al. [8] found that in immunologically compromised rats infected with *T. cruzi*, amastigotes were first seen in the heart on day 8, with an increase in numbers through day 16 of infection. Parasites in the skeletal muscle appeared by day 11 and similarly increased in numbers to a peak on day 16. Thereafter, the numbers of parasites in these tissues (cardiac and skeletal muscle) decreased while the numbers of tryomastigotes increased dramatically in the blood. Cover et al. [8] suggested that the recovery of immunocompetence in these rats correlates with the diminution of parasites in the tissue.

Antigenic variation as characterized in African trypanosomiasis has not been shown to occur with *T. cruzi*, although two morphologic types of the parasite are present in early and late infections. A slender form of *T. cruzi* generally predominates in the blood initially, with a broad form appearing in large numbers later [7,8,12]. Slender forms are thought to be more invasive for mammalian cells, while the broad forms may be more adaptive to the insect vector [7].

Neither broad nor slender forms are thought capable of dividing as extracellular trypomastigote forms [13].

II. PROTECTIVE IMMUNOLOGIC RESPONSES IN CHAGAS' DISEASE

A. General Considerations

A number of studies have demonstrated that protective immunity to *T. cruzi* can be induced in experimental animals following various immunization procedures or infection with avirulent or attenuated parasites. Kagan and Normal [14] and Seah and Marsden [15] were able to elicit immunity in mice against highly virulent trypanosomes by first inoculating these mice with an avirulent strain of the parasite. The studies by Seah and Marsden confirmed an earlier report by Kagan and Normal [14] that the longer the exposure to avirulent parasites (14 days) the better the protection against challenge with virulent trypanosomes. Fernandez et al. [16] used antimetabolites to attenuate culture forms of *T. cruzi* and reported the induction of protective immunity with these attenuated parasites when vaccinated mice were challenged with virulent forms. Similarly, Hanson et al. [17] found that vaccination with x-irradiated trypomastigotes of the Brazil strain elicited strong protective responses in mice. Several investigations have also found that killed preparations of culture forms of *T. cruzi* can induce effective resistance against trypanosomes which would be lethal in nonimmunized mice. Gonzalez Cappa and co-workers [18] have reported excellent protection by immunizing mice with relatively large amounts of killed epimastigotes prior to challenge with the Tulahuen strain of *T. cruzi*. Recently, McHardy and Elphick [19] examined the possibility of inducing greater protective immunity in mice by immunization with up to five strains of killed culture-form parasites and then challenging with blood-form trypomastigotes of heterologous or homologous strains. However, multiple combinations of strains used for immunization were not more effective than immunization with single strains. Although significant protection was seen in most cases, immunization with two particular strains in combination (M and T strains) was less effective than either alone, and in no case was adequate protection induced against the Y strain of *T. cruzi*.

Manipulations which compromise the immunological status of experimental animals have shown that defects induced by radiation [7,8,10], blockade of the mononuclear phagocyte system (MPS) [10,20,21], thymectomy [22,23], and treatment with cortisone [24] cause an exacerbation of experimental Chagas' disease. There appears to be no single manifestation of the immune system which does not play a significant role in resistance to *T. cruzi*. Nonspecific effector cells such as macrophages and polymorphonuclear leucocytes, as well as specific T and B lymphocyte responses, have all been shown in in vitro and/or in vivo studies to participate in the rejection of these hemoflagellates.

B. The Role of Macrophages

Studies by Taliaferro and Pizzi [25] and Rubio [26] showed that macrophages could not only kill *T. cruzi* but also were parasitized by these organisms during the course of an infection. Both studies also determined that macrophages in previously immunized mice had a greater capacity to destroy parasites than did those in normal mice. Culture forms of *T. cruzi* were rarely found to infect macrophages in vivo but instead were readily destroyed. More recent in vivo and in vitro studies have attempted to determine the role of the macrophage in Chagas' disease, and the mechanism(s) by which macrophages are effective in killing the parasite.

Studies of *T. cruzi*-infected mice have attempted to evaluate the contribution of macrophages by injections of blocking agents or by nonspecific stimulation of macrophages to enhance their participation in phagocytic destruction of cellular antigens. Several studies have shown that blockade of the MPS results in an exacerbation of the infection with elevated parasitemias and mortality. Recent studies by Kierszenbaum et al. [21] and Trischmann et al. [10] employed mice injected with silica and infected with highly virulent parasites. It was found that blockaded mice exhibited reduced resistance to *T. cruzi.* Kierszenbaum et al. [21,27] also examined the effect of nonspecific suppression or stimulation of the MPS with diethylstilbestrol and nuramyl dipeptide, respectively, and noted that these treatments affected the resistance to the parasite with concomitant increase or reduction in parasitemia levels and mortality.

In vitro studies have determined the capacity of normal and activated macrophages to kill the parasite. Elegant studies by Dvorak and Schmunis [28] examined the interaction of trypomastigotes and culture forms of the Ernestina strain (myotropic) of *T. cruzi* with normal mouse macrophages. Under well-controlled culture conditions they found that trypomastigotes were commonly found in macrophages within 1 hr and that these parasites were killed in 1-4 hr, followed soon thereafter by death of the macrophage. They did not observe any trypomastigotes surviving within macrophages. Similarly, epimastigotes entered macrophages and were killed, although destruction of these culture forms took much longer than for trypomastigotes, and in some cases the macrophages did not die. Other studies have also shown that epimastigotes are engulfed and killed by macrophages, but trypomastigotes are often capable of surviving and reproducing within these phagocytes [5,37].

Activated macrophages have a greater capacity for killing both epimastigote and trypomastigote forms of *Trypanosoma cruzi* than do normal macrophages. Macrophages harvested from mice previously infected or immunized with BCG can control in vitro infection to a greater extent than can macrophages from normal mice [6,29-31]. Exposure of macrophages to increasing numbers of culture forms (epimastigotes) revealed that both normal and BCG-activated macrophages could effectively control infections when the parasite-to-phagocyte ratio was 1:1, but increasing the ratio to 10:1 overwhelmed the normal macrophages [6,39,30]. The BCG-activated macrophages, however, were shown to be effective in killing *T. cruzi* at a ratio of 10:1 but not 100:1. Williams and Remington [32] used human peripheral blood monocytes and similarly found that activation of human monocytes in vitro resulted in more effective killing than unstimulated monocytes of fibroblast-derived trypomastigotes.

The effectiveness of macrophages in killing *T. cruzi* appears related to the ability to contain the parasite within the phagocytic vacuole. It has been suggested by Nogueira and Cohen [5,33] and Kress et al. [30] and is inferred in other studies, that *T. cruzi* can escape the phagosome of macrophages and subsequently reside in the host cell's cytoplasm. The mechanism of escape is not known but is apparently less effective in activated macrophages than in normal macrophages. Studies by Kress et al. [30] have shown that fusion of secondary lysosomes with phagosomes containing parasites occurs in both activated and normal macrophages, but the activated macrophages contain a larger number of secondary lysosomes. This difference may result in the greater capacity to control in vitro infection by activated macrophages.

Further studies by Nogueira and co-workers have implicated spleen cell factors which enhance macrophage killing of *T. cruzi* [34,35]. It was reported that spleen cells from BCG- or *T. cruzi*-sensitized mice release factors when exposed to specific antigens in vitro which induce increased microbiocidal activity in resident and inflammatory macrophages [34]. Release of the factor(s) from sensitized spleen cells required the presence of T lymphocytes [35]. Activation of macrophages was correlated with plasminogen activator secretion and hydrogen peroxide production, which was thought to be related to enhanced killing of *T. cruzi* by macrophages [36].

There is some question regarding the mode of uptake of *T. cruzi* by macrophages. Nogueira [33] has reported that trypomastigotes purified from culture forms of *T. cruzi* are actively engulfed by macrophages and nonprofessional phagocytes, including HeLa and L cells. The evidence is based on the presence of membrane-bound trypanosomes within macrophages and other cells and on the inhibition of parasite uptake by cells pretreated with cytochalasin B. Kipnis et al. [37] later performed similar experiments using epimastigotes and blood-form trypomastigotes and reported that cytochalasin B blocked uptake of epimastigotes, but not trypomastigotes, into macrophages, suggesting that trypomastigotes could invade macrophages without being phagocytized. Tanowitz et al. [6] and Dvorak and his co-workers presented results which implicated phagocytosis as a mechanism of interiorization into macrophages [28] but also reported direct penetration of the parasite into other cell types [3]. Clearly, further studies are needed to resolve the nature of uptake of *T. cruzi* into mammalian cells and particularly the membrane-related events which allow parasites to cross host cell membranes, especially as these events relate to escape from phagolysosome destruction.

C. B-Cell Responses to *Trypanosoma cruzi*

Antibody may contribute to immunity against *T. cruzi* through complement-dependent cytolysis, as opsonic and/or cytophilic antibody for enhancement of phagocytosis, in antibody-dependent cellular cytotoxicity (ADCC) reactions against the parasite, and possibly, by interfering with physiologic processes of the parasite. Although it is known from several studies involving passive transfer of antiserum to *T. cruzi* that the humoral response is effective in resisting the parasite, the importance of antibody and the mode of action of its protective effect in vivo are not known. An ablastin-like (reproduction-inhibiting) antibody, as develops during *Trypanosoma lewisi* infections in rats, has not been found in serum of *T. cruzi*-infected mammals.

Studies on antibody responses in chagasic patients have primarily involved determination of anti-*T. cruzi* antibody levels as diagnostic indices and have utilized a number of procedures including direct and indirect agglutination, complement fixation, and ELISA (enzyme-linked immunosorbent assays). Results of studies on the appearance of antibody during Chagas' disease are varied. Lelchuk et al. [38] reported that acute patients have essentially normal levels of serum IgG, IgM, and IgA during the acute stage of disease with slightly elevated levels of IgG during the chronic stage. *T. cruzi*-specific IgM was regularly found in acute patients, followed later by the parasite-specific IgG and IgA. Marsden et al [39] could not find a correlation between complement-fixing antibody titers and elevated levels of serum IgG, IgA, or IgM, but there was an increase in IgG in chronic patients. Vattuone et al. [40] examined 11 acute and 12 chronic patients and concluded that IgM levels were higher than normal values in both acute and chronic persons. The study by Vattuone et al. [40] also compared several serodiagnostic methods including complement fixation, direct agglutination, indirect hemagglutination, and the indirect fluorescent antibody assay and concluded that direct agglutination and the indirect fluorescent antibody assays were of greatest utility in diagnosing Chagas' disease. Recently, Teixeira et al. [41] reported results of studies on immunodepression in chagasic patients and included information on immunoglobulin levels in acute patients. These workers found that total immunoglobulin levels were higher in acute patients than in uninfected volunteers with significant differences apparent only in the IgG, but not IgM or IgA, class of immunoglobulin.

Somewhat greater insight into the role of antibody in immunity against *T. cruzi* has been obtained with animal models. Kierszenbaum and Howard [42] compared low- and high-responder mice to examine whether or not animals with high antibody responsiveness were more resistant to *T. cruzi* than low responders. It was found that the Biozzi low responders were highly susceptible to *T. cruzi,* whereas the Biozzi high responders were resistant to the parasite. The Biozzi low responders produced low levels of anti-*T. cruzi* antibody and were not readily immunized with culture forms against subsequent challenge with virulent trypomastigotes. To ascertain the contribution of antibody in resistance to *T. cruzi,* these workers obtained antiserum to the parasite from immunized outbred mice and passively transferred 0.2 ml daily on days 2-17 into infected Biozzi low responders. The antiserum protected the low-responder recipients against lethal infection, with no mortality and reduced parasitemias resulting.

Krettki and Brener [43] also were able to transfer resistance with various antisera. However, pretreatment of Y and CL strains of *T. cruzi* with heterologous or homologous antiserum protected mice against infection with the Y strain but not the CL strain. Also, injection of 0.4 ml of either homologous or heterologous antiserum 1 hr prior to infection of mice with Y strain provided good protection.

The specific role of antibody in controlling *T. cruzi* infection in vivo, however, is enigmatic because of the continued existence of parasites in the blood of animals which have apparently developed a significant degree of immune resistance to the parasite. Indeed, it is possible to use antiserum from convalescent mice, which continue to harbor the parasite, to confer passive resistance to newly infected hosts [14,44]. Hanson [45] demonstrated that antiserum transferred to mice during the course of infection could reduce both the level of parasites in the blood and the numbers of parasites in the tissues of such passively immunized mice.

In earlier studies, Kagan and Norman [14], who showed protection by passive transfer of immune serum, investigated the possibility that persistence of *T. cruzi* in survivors of the acute infection was due to immune selection of a less virulent and, perhaps, antibody-insensitive parasite subpopulation. Mice which had been inoculated with an avirulent strain of *T. cruzi* and which had subsequently survived the acute phase of infection with the highly virulent Tulahuen strain were used as donors of infected blood. This blood was transferred to CFW mice and provided both the infection inoculum of parasites as well as any humoral products which could modify the course of infection. Blood from the survivors of this series of infections was then transferred to normal mice, the same process was repeated (i.e., T_1, T_2, T_3, T_4), and the mean death dates of the groups were compared. Although some differences were noted, in general it appeared that no significant change in the virulence of the Tulahuen strain occurred as a result of immune control of the infection. These very interesting observations suggest that a deficiency in the immune system exists to allow persistence of the parasite in the immune host (premunition phenomenon) and/or the parasite evokes mechanisms for evasion of immune destruction.

D. The Role of Complement

In contrast to earlier reports [46,47], Budzko et al. [48] and Kierszenbaum [49] have reported that trypomastigotes can be lysed with anti-*T. cruzi* antiserum and complement. This observation suggests that antibody-mediated complement-dependent lysis of *T. cruzi* could be an important mechanism of controlling infections in vivo. The experiments by Budzko et al. [48] determined that immune mouse or human serum could kill blood-form trypomastigotes in the presence of complement, and that this killing was inhibited if the complement was treated with cobra venom factor. In vivo treatment of mice with cobra venom factor on day 7 of infection with the Tulahuen strain of *T. cruzi* precipitated a rapid exacerbation of the disease, resulting in increased parasitemias and mortalities. It was concluded in these experiments that antibody and C-mediated lysis occurred by both the classic and alternative pathway was involved in lysis of the parasite with immune mouse serum. Similar results were reported by Kierszenbaum [49], suggesting that the importance of the complement is its resistance to *T. cruzi*. Furthermore, Kierszenbaum reported that antiserum raised in mice immunized with culture forms of the parasite and subsequently surviving challenge infection could kill trypomastigotes in the presence of complement in vitro.

Teixeira and Santos-Buch [47], could not demonstrate the lysis of trypomastigotes by specific antibody and complement. Anziano et al. [46] determined, however, that rabbit anti-*T. cruzi* antiserum and serum from chronic chagasic patients could lyse culture forms via the classical pathway, and that it appeared that C3 and C4 were bound to the surface of trypanosomes. Nogueira et al. [50] reexamined earlier reports that normal sera of several animal species could effect lysis of culture forms of *T. cruzi* and found that normal guinea pig serum lyses epimastigotes but not trypomastigotes of culture forms. The lysis of epimastigotes by guinea pig serum, followed by density gradient centrifugation, was used by Nogueira and co-workers [50] to obtain trypomastigotes and "transitional forms" for in vitro studies on the interaction of *T. cruzi* with various mammalian cell types.

Studies by Cunningham et al. [51] examined complement levels in mice during the course of experimental Chagas' disease. It was found that early in infection the levels of complement began to decrease and that the rate of decrease was similar in mice that are relatively resistant (C57BL/6), as well as in mice that are highly susceptible (C3H), to *T. cruzi* infections (Figure 1). Indeed, no correlation was found between the degree of hypocomplementemia and time of death of infected mice. C3H(He) mice died at a time when complement levels were about 40% of normal. C57BL/6 mice, on the other hand, exhibited a progressive loss of complement to 15% of normal and yet survived the acute phase of the disease. More recently it has been found that complement levels return to normal in C57BL/6 mice which survive beyond 3 months postinfection (Cunningham et al., unpublished observation).

Cunningham et al. [51] reported that intact trypanosomes (living and formalin-fixed), disrupted trypanosomes, and materials released into the medium

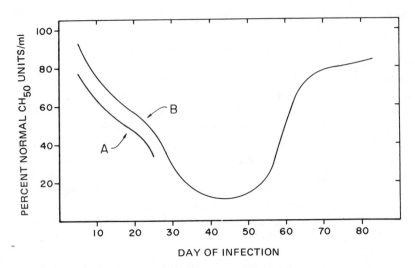

Figure 1 Complement levels during the course of *T. cruzi* infection in mice which differ in susceptibility to the parasite. The degree of hypocomplementemia in (A) susceptible versus (B) resistant mice does not appear to be correlated to survival of the acute disease. Complement levels return to normal at 2-3 months postinfection in resistant mice (B). (From Cunningham et al. [51] and Cunningham et al., unpublished observations.)

by cultured parasites could deplete complement in normal human, mouse, and guinea pig serum. The mechanism of decomplementation in vitro involved primarily the C1-dependent classic pathway. The significance of the soluble complement-activating factor released from living parasites and the direct decomplementation by trypanosomes during infection in vivo is not known. It is of interest, however, that the degree of complement depletion in vivo appears to be associated with the numbers of parasites in the blood, i.e., hypocomplementemia increases with increasing parasitemia and decreases later in infection as parasites become less abundant in the peripheral circulation (Cunningham et al., unpublished observation).

E. Opsonic/Cytophilic Antibody in Chagas' Disease

It was suggested by Rubio [26] that development of antibody during the course of infection with *Trypanosoma cruzi* facilitated phagocytic destruction of parasites in hamsters. Taliaferro and Pizzi [25] reported histologic observations which support the conclusions of Rubio [26]. Opsonic and cytophilic antibody may enhance phagocytosis of *T. cruzi* by macrophages by coating the parasite, thus making it more readily phagocytized, and by arming macrophages with specific antibody bound via Fc receptors. It is also possible that trypanosomes may be inhibited from escaping the phagosome if they are restricted by specific antibody.

Hoff [31] examined cytophilic antibody-*T. cruzi* macrophage interactions in vitro. Preincubation of normal or activated macrophages before exposure to *T. cruzi* culture forms revealed no increase in uptake by normal macrophages but a substantial increase of intracellular parasites in activated macrophages after 24 hr contact with *T. cruzi*. Cytophilic antibody did not seem to confer resistance to normal macrophages. Kipnis et al. [37] pretreated *T. cruzi* culture forms and blood-form trypomastigotes with antiserum prior to exposing them to macrophages in vitro. Opsonized culture forms were bound to macrophages more readily than untreated parasites, but enhanced binding of antibody-treated trypomastigotes to macrophages was not detected. Nevertheless, treated or untreated culture forms did not establish infections in macrophages, whereas opsonization of trypomastigotes increased the number of infected macrophages.

Based on these studies, it seems that antibody may increase the susceptibility of macrophages to infection rather than conferring greater destructive capabilities against *T. cruzi*. Before such conclusions are drawn, however, experiments similar to those by Hoff [31] and Kipnis et al. [37] should be done using the number of parasites killed rather than the number of macrophages infected as the index of macrophage effectiveness. It may be that *T. cruzi* antibody does mediate greater killing by macrophages, but that macrophages become saturated and essentially exhausted under these in vitro conditions.

F. Antibody-Dependent Cellular Cytotoxicity against *Trypanosoma cruzi*

It has been reported that anti-*T. cruzi* serum, the immunoglobulin fraction of specific antiserum, and serum from chagasic patients can mediate ADCC against *T. cruzi* and a similar parasite, *Trypanosoma dionisii*. Abrahamsohn and da Silva [52] found that normal mouse spleen cells, and particularly the nonadherent population, could induce destruction of *T. cruzi* in the presence of specific antiserum. These workers used a morphologic criterion (loss of motility) to assess killing of the parasite and correlated lack of motility with postassay growth of the surviving culture. Others workers have developed indirect, radioisotopic assays in attempts to measure parasite destruction. Mkwananzi et al. [53] studied ADCC as effected by normal human lymphoid cells against *Trypanosoma dionisii*, an intracellular parasite of bats, and proposed that these parasites can be used as a model for information on immunity to *T. cruzi*. *Trypanosoma dionisii* were labeled with technetium-99, and the amount of isotope released from parasites in the presence of antiserum and lymphoid cells was used as an index of ADCC. It was found that peripheral blood leukocytes, depleted of macrophages by prior treatment with carbonyl iron, could mediate release of ^{99}Tc to a much greater extent in the presence of rabbit anti-*T. dionisii* antiserum than in the absence of antiserum.

However, Sanderson et al. [54,55] studied ADCC against *T. cruzi* culture forms and found that rat polymorphonuclear leukocytes (especially eosinophil-rich preparations), not the lymphoid cells, were effector cells in ADCC. To measure ADCC, Sanderson and his co-workers developed isotope release assays [54] in which parasites were grown in the presence of tritium-labeled precursors of protein, RNA, and DNA; the subsequent release of ^{3}H macromolecules on lysis of the organisms was determined. It was found that [^{3}H] RNA was more readily released, and was released to a greater extent, than the other labeled constituents and was chosen as the labeled compound to monitor for estimates of cytotoxicity. Results of their studies showed that antiserum raised against epimastigotes or antiserum derived from rats infected with blood-form trypomastigotes for 14 days could mediate [^{3}H] RNA release from labeled epimastigotes when cocultured with normal rat spleen cells. Antiserum from infected rats was more effective than anti-epimastigote antiserum in causing release of [^{3}H] RNA in the ADCC assay.

Most recently, Olabuenaga et al. [56] have studied ADCC of *T. cruzi* culture forms with human peripheral blood leukocytes and used the [^{3}H] RNA release assay of Sanderson et al. [54] as the index of parasite destruction. Mononuclear and polymorphonuclear leukocytes were obtained by Ficoll-Hypaque gradient separation of blood from normal volunteers, and these cells were then tested for effectiveness in ADCC. It was found that only the polymorphonuclear cells were effective. Rabbit antiserum against *T. cruzi* culture forms, the immunoglobulin fraction of this antiserum, and serum from chronic chagasic patients could all effect ADCC with normal leukocytes. Preincubation of the trypanosomes or the leukocytes with antiserum showed that coating of the target cell, not the effector cell, was necessary for specific [^{3}H] RNA release. Olabuenaga et al. [56] also labeled the polymorphonuclear effectors with ^{51}CrO$_4$ to determine whether or not these cells were killed as a consequence of the ADCC reaction against *T. cruzi*. Their results suggest that the effector cells are not affected during the ADCC assay as determined by the observation that release of ^{51}Cr from polymorphonuclear leukocytes in the presence of *T. cruzi* was not different from the spontaneous release of the label in the absence of parasites.

As with the other possible roles of antibody in Chagas' disease, the importance of ADCC in immune control and/or rejection of *T. cruzi* has not yet been determined. It is important that further studies elucidate host cell-antibody-parasite interactions in Chagas' disease. If complement levels are reduced in patients with acute Chagas' disease (as is reported for mice), and if it is given that anti-*T. cruzi* antibody levels increase during Chagas' disease, then it is possible that ADCC and other antibody-host cell mechanisms are of primary importance in resistance to *T. cruzi.*

G. Cell-Mediated Immunity in Chagas' Disease

It has been found in studies using athymic mice and animals made T-cell-deficient by treatment with anti-thymocyte serum, or by thymectomy, that T-cell-mediated responses are necessary for development of immunity against *T. cruzi.* Vilches et al. [57] treated mice with the immunoglobulin fraction of rabbit anti-mouse thymocyte serum (ATS) and found that the disease was intensified as reflected by increased parasitemia and mortality in animals receiving relatively large inocula. Roberson et al. [22] studied the effect of neonatal thymectomy of rats and ATS treatment of mice on the course of experimental Chagas' disease and found, as did Vilches et al. [57], that these treatments caused an exacerbation of the disease. More dramatic were the results of studies reported by Trischmann et al. [10] and Kierszenbaum and Pienkowski [58] on the course of injection in athymic (nude) mice. Their studies showed an extremely rapid accumulation of parasites in the blood and early death in these T-deficient mice (Figure 2). The implanatation of the thymus gland from heterozygous (nu/+) mice into nude animals reverted these recipients to a state of resistance similar to that of the heterozygous donor [58]. Although it seems clear that T-cell responses are necessary for development of protection in Chagas' disease, the mechanism(s) by which this protection is manifested is not understood. To date, for instance, there is no evidence that *T. cruzi*-specific cytotoxic T lymphocytes develop during infection or can be induced experimentally to effect direct cytotoxicity against *T. cruzi.*

In addition to studies in mice, it is known that delayed-type hypersensitvity (DTH) to *T. cruzi* antigens develop in acute and chronic chagasic patients. Studies using peripheral blood leukocytes (PBL) of chagasic patients have shown positive in vitro correlates of cell-mediated immunity against antigens of *T. cruzi.* Yanovsky and Albano [59] found that 12 of 14 seropositive (IFA and C fixation) chagasic patients had PBL which, in the presence of *T. cruzi* antigens, demonstrated inhibition of leukocyte migration from capillary tubes. The two patients whose cells did not demonstrate migration inhibition were IFA positive but C fixation assay negative. Tschudi et al. [60] examined the ability of PBL of chagasic patients to respond to *T. cruzi* antigens and phytohemagglutinin (PHA) in vitro as well as determining whether or not these patients could develop DTH against a soluble antigen of the parasite. It was found that the patients responded to both the antigen and PHA (as measured by counting blast cells) and also developed a DTH response.

Lelchuk et al. [61] studied several characteristics of cell-mediated immunity in chagasic patients as these were affected by chemotherapy of the disease

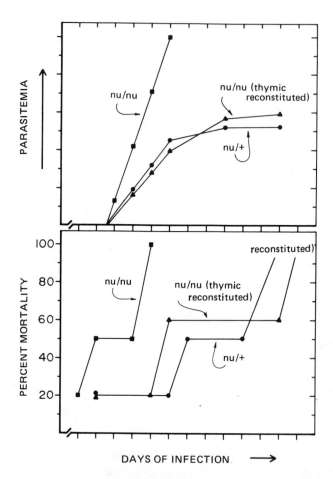

Figure 2 Parasitemia and mortality levels in *T. cruzi*-infected nude mice (nu/
nu; ■), heterozygous (nu/+; ●) normal mice, and nude mice reconstituted by
syngeneic thymic graft (▲). (Modified from Kierszenbaum and Pienkowski [58]
and Trischmann et al. [10].)

with nifurtimox. It was found that leukocytes of untreated patients demonstrated inhibition of migration in vitro in the presence of *T. cruzi* antigens. Using
an RBC-rosetting procedure, these workers determined that there was no difference in the percentage of T and B cells in the peripheral circulation of untreated
patients, normal controls and nifurtimox-treated individuals. PHA-induced blastogenesis and ADCC against sensitized chicken RBC were found to be at approximately the same levels of activity in all three groups tested.

H. Detection and Destruction of *Trypanosoma cruzi*-Infected Host Cells

In the mammalian host, *T. cruzi* resides much of the time within the host cells and at these times is somewhat inaccessible to the host immune system. However, studies have now shown that immune cells can detect intracellular trypanosomes and can mediate the destruction of infected host cells [62-64].

Studying acute experimental Chagas' disease in mice, Kuhn and Murnane [62] found that immune spleen cells of infected mice could mediate the release of ^{51}Cr from labeled, infected syngeneic fibroblasts in vitro. It was shown that cytotoxic spleen cells developed against infected host cells and exhibited increasing cytotoxic activity with increasing duration of infection. Immune spleen cells did not express cytotoxic activity when exposed to normal fibroblasts and, in experiments in which ^{51}Cr-labeled normal cells were cocultured with unlabeled infected cells, it was determined that no "innocent bystanders" were destroyed as a result of cytotoxic reactions. These observations suggest that killing results from direct lymphocyte-mediated cytotoxicity rather than by lymphotoxins, and that immune spleen cells from acute *T. cruzi* infections do not exhibit autoimmune activity against fibroblasts. In addition, it was reported that incubation of infected fibroblasts in the presence of anti-*T. cruzi* antiserum from infected mice had no effect on immune destruction of infected target cells, indicating that neither ADCC nor immunological enhancement occurred under these experimental conditions.

Santos-Buch and Teixeira [63] studied immunity against infected host cells in rabbits with experimental Chagas' disease. These workers found that both normal and *T. cruzi*-infected allogeneic heart cells were killed in vitro by PBL of rabbits immunized with the microsomal fraction of *T. cruzi* culture forms. It was determined as a part of these experiments, however, that autoimmune cytotoxic responses were not directed against allogeneic kidney cells, suggesting a degree of organ specificity in this autoimmunity. Cross-reactivity of *T. cruzi* antigens with heart antigens and/or exposure of "self antigens" by disrupted heart cells is presumably responsible for anti-heart cell autoimmunity.

More recently Teixeira et al. [64] have reported results of studies on immunity to infected host cells and autoimmunity in patients with Chagas' disease. It was found that both uninfected and infected allogeneic heart cells could be killed by T lymphocytes from chagasic patients. Autoimmune anti-heart responses were greater in acute patients than chronic patients and were also found in seropositive but clinically asymptomatic patients. Microsomal fractions of heart cells and *T. cruzi* were shown to effect in vitro inhibition of leukocytes from these patients, providing further evidence that some degree of cross-reactivity may exist between *T. cruzi* and heart cell constituents.

Ribeiro dos Santos, Hudson, and others recently presented results of their studies on immunity against the intracellular stage of *T. cruzi* (presented at the

International Congress on Chagas' Disease, July 23-28, 1979, Rio de Janeiro, Abstract No. K-5, pp. 184-185). These results showed that parasite antigens can bind to both infected and normal mammalian cells in vitro. The appearance of parasite antigens on host cells in vitro occurred only when large numbers of amastigotes were present in the extracellular environment. Addition of specifically sensitized T lymphocytes or antiserum from infected rabbits plus complement was shown to mediate the lysis of antigen-bound host cells. Furthermore, immunofluorescent studies revealed the presence of antigen surrounding infected cells in sections of muscle tissue. Autoimmune responses were reportedly found only in chronic infected animals.

Whereas it is possible that development of immunity to intracellular amastigotes could provide protection to the host early in Chagas' disease by destroying host cells (before massive infection) and rendering the intracellular parasite vulnerable to direct immunologic destruction, later consequences of destruction of large numbers of cells (either by the immune response or by the escape of mature parasites) with exposure of sequestered "self antigens" could lead to an exacerbation of the pathology of the disease in the chronic phase.

I. Autoantibodies in Chagas' Disease

Cossio et al. [65] reported that antibody in sera of chronic chagasic patients could selectively bind to endocardium, vascular structure, and interstitium of striated muscle (EVI antibodies). This antibody was not detected in normal serum or in serum from patients with non-chagasic cardiomyopathies, although it was present in 95% of patients with chagasic heart disease and 45% of asymptomatic chagasic patients. The EVI antibody could be removed from sera by absorption with several strains of *T. cruzi* culture forms and with blood forms of *Trypanosoma rhodesiense,* suggesting that a common antigen exists in these parasites which is cross-reactive with components of mammalian cardiac and skeletal muscle [66]. Szarfman et al. [67] examined sera of 60 patients from outside of areas endemic for Chagas' disease and having parasitic infections other than *T. cruzi* to determine the specificity of the EVI antibody. The EVI antibody is apparently quite specific for Chagas' disease with only two of the 60 non-chagasic sera being EVI positive: one from a patient with *Plasmodium falciparum* infection and one from a patient with leishmaniasis. Szarfman et al. [68] followed these experiments with a study of acute chagasic patients to examine the possibility that the antibody is induced early in infection, possibly against antigens of the parasite. Of 15 acute patients, 12 were found positive for EVI antibody, suggesting that the antibody is induced directly as a result of infection but still leaving open the possibility that it is induced against unmasked or altered self-antigens.

Schmunis et al. [69] examined the effect of treatment of acute patients with nifurtimox on EVI antibody. Nifurtimox treatment clears peripheral blood parasites and after treatment leaves the patient without significant anti-*T. cruzi* antibody titers. However, it was found that even though all of the patients became seronegative for antibodies against *T. cruzi,* 6 of 10 remained EVI positive. If EVI antibodies are indicative of pathologic problems, these results led Schmunis et al. [69] to question the effectiveness of "drug cure" in alleviating later chronic manifestations of Chagas' disease.

In addition to the EVI antibodies, it has been found that antibodies which react with mammalian neurons exist in the sera of chronic patients. Ribeiro dos Santos et al. [70] studied 230 chagasic sera and found 83% to be reactive to neurons of several mammalian species. Whereas 75% of the asymptomatic patients were positive, 100% of the patients with cardiomyopathies and/or mega syndrome had antineuronal antibodies in their sera. Unlike the EVI antibody, adsorption of sera with *T. cruzi* did not remove the anti-neuron antibody activity. Ribeiro dos Santos et al. [70] suggested that the anti-neuron antibody is not the primary mechanism of nervous tissue destruction in Chagas' disease but may function to perpetuate autoimmune mechanisms and contribute to an intensified chronic disease.

III.   IMMUNOSUPPRESSION IN CHAGAS' DISEASE

Immunosuppression develops during the course of many host-parasite relationships. To date, however, the significance of immunosuppression in terms of immunity to protozoan or metazoan parasites has not been determined. Immunosuppression is particularly enigmatic when one considers that the suppression phenomenon is expressed at a time when the host is developing immunity against its parasite. Also, some parasite-infected hosts become completely unresponsive to heterologous antigens and yet do not apparently succumb to resident or newly acquired bacterial, fungal, or viral infections. It is possible that many parasites have evolved characteristics which can induce immunosuppression in mammals, resulting, perhaps, in a reduced ability of the host to reject the parasite.

As has been reported with other protozoans, *Trypanosoma cruzi* is known to cause depressed immunological responsiveness in humans and experimental animals. Information on immunosuppression in chagasic patients was reported by Teixeira et al. [41]. These workers examined 12 seropositive children from Bahia, Brazil, to determine their immune responsiveness. Six children presented clinical symptoms of acute Chagas' disease, while the other six were designated clinically inapparent; the latter group was diagnosed as chagasic as a result of the appearance of anti-*T. cruzi* antibody while these children were being routinely monitored. Children with clinical symptoms had strong delayed-type hypersensitivity reactions to a *T. cruzi* antigen preparation and to 2,4-dinitrochlorobenzene; their cells also exhibited positive leucocyte inhibition in vitro in the pres-

ence of a microsomal antigen from *T. cruzi*. The asymptomatic children showed
no responses under these same conditions. Teixeira et al. [41] concluded from
these results that the clinically inapparent children had alterations in thymus-
dependent responses.

Immunosuppression resulting from *T. cruzi* infections has been studied
much more extensively in experimental Chagas' disease. Reed et al. [71] have
investigated the ability of mice to develop and express delayed hypersensitivity
to oxazolone during *T. cruzi* infections. Their studies revealed that mice have
depressed cellular responses in vivo to oxazolone if sensitized and challenged
after initiation of *T. cruzi* infection or if sensitized prior to infection and challenged during the course of the disease. Sensitivity to tuberculoprotein after
sensitization with complete Freund's adjuvant and challenge during infection
was also suppressed. However, immunization of mice with attenuated culture-
forms of *T. cruzi* followed by infection with virulent trypomastigotes abrogated
the suppression of delayed hypersensitivity in mice to oxazalone. In later studies
these same workers further investigated immunosuppression of cellular responses
in experimental Chagas' disease [72] and found that when spleen or lymph node
cells from suppressed mice were transferred to normal syngeneic recipients they
could confer adoptive immunity even though the donors were suppressed. Also,
transfer of adherent peritoneal exudate cells from normal mice to oxazolone-
sensitized *T. cruzi*-infected mice could partially restore responses in these suppressed recipients, which suggests that macrophages may play a role in *T. cruzi*-
induced immunosuppression.

Rowland and Kuhn [73] and Ramos et al. [74] have examined the ability
of lymphoid cells from *T. cruzi*-infected mice to exhibit blastogenic responses to
mitogens and other antigens in vitro. Rowland and Kuhn [73] found suppression of blastogenic responses to PHA and an antigen extract of *T. cruzi* culture
forms early in the course of the disease in both relatively resistant (C57BL/6) and
highly susceptible (C3H) mice and also, as Reed et al. [71] reported, suppression
of anamnestic responses to PPD [75]. In addition, Rowland and Kuhn found
that delayed hypersensitivity responses to *T. cruzi* antigens, as measured by ear
induration, was suppressed.

Recently, Ramos et al. [74] have reported results of their studies on suppression of blastogenic responses during experimental Chagas' diseases. These
workers found suppressed spleen cell responses to ConA and LPS beginning on
day 14 of infection. Spleen cells from mice infected with *T. cruzi* could suppress
ConA and LPS responses of normal spleen cells in vitro, and good evidence was
presented that *T. cruzi* did not, in itself, effect suppression of spleen cell blastogenic responses. Rowland and Kuhn [75] and Ramos et al. [74] reported that
suppressor cells could be detected in lymph nodes and spleens, respectively,
when cells from these organs were cocultured with normal lymphoid cells. Ramos
et al. [74] reported that the suppressor cells in spleens of *T. cruzi*-infected

C57BL/10 mice were not adherent cells. Also, treatment of spleen cells with anti-Thy-1 antiserum plus complement could abrogate suppressor activity; however, the T-cell-depleted spleen cells remained unresponsiveness to LPS, suggesting that a defect exists in the splenic B-cell population as well. Rowland and Kuhn [73] claimed that the suppressor cell in lymph nodes in mice with experimental Chagas' disease was adherent and did not possess Thy-1 antigens.

Humoral immune responses to heterologous antigens have also been shown to be suppressed in animals infected with *T. cruzi.* Clinton et al. [76] found a progressive decrease in the ability of infected mice to develop direct and indirect plaque-forming cells to burro erythrocytes with depressed responses beginning on days 11 and 15 for IgM and IgG responses, respectively. Cunningham et al. [77] found similar results when comparing the ability of C57BL/6 and C3H(He) mice to respond to sheep erythrocytes during the course of experimental Chagas' disease. No meaningful differences to account for the differential susceptibilities of these mice were apparent in either onset or degree of suppressed responses during the acute infection (Figure 3). Ramos et al. [78] reported that in vivo responses to T-dependent (burrow erythrocytes and aggregated human gamma-globulin) and T-independent (LPS and DNP-Ficoll) antigens are suppressed during infections with depression evident on day 20 for T-dependent responses and on day 15 for T-independent responses. Cunningham and Kuhn (unpublished observation) have examined in vitro responses of spleen and lymph node cells of

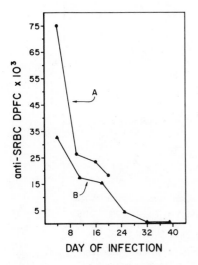

Figure 3   Anti-SRBC responses during the course of experimental Chagas' disease in mice (A) highly susceptible and (B) relatively resistant to *T. cruzi.* (From Cunningham et al. [77].)

T. cruzi-infected C57BL/6 mice to T-dependent and T-independent antigens.
Using a Mishell-Dutton culture system, it was found that spleen cells are suppressed earlier in infection than lymph node cells, but that these cell types become unresponsive to both T-dependent and T-independent antigens. Detection of immunosuppression in in vitro studies eliminates, to a large degree, the
problem of possible effects of antigenic competition (with parasite antigens)
in in vivo studies of immunosuppression.

Cunningham et al. [77] reported that mice infected with *T. cruzi* accumulate a substance in their sera which passively suppresses the humoral immune responses of syngeneic recipients. This passive suppression was shown to be transient and dependent upon administration of the serum from an infected animal
prior to attempts to immunize against sheep erythrocytes. The suppressor sub-
stance(s) in the serum of infected mice increases in activity with the duration of
infection for the first 40-50 days (Figure 4). However, after this time, suppressor activity begins to decrease even though the donors of the sera remain incapable of mounting a response (Cunningham and Kuhn, unpublished observation).

Recent studies have revealed that the suppressor substance is effective in
inhibiting the induction, but not the expression, of humoral responses of spleen
and lymph node cells in vitro (Cunningham and Kuhn, submitted for publication). Addition of suppressive serum to Mishell-Dutton cultures at the time of

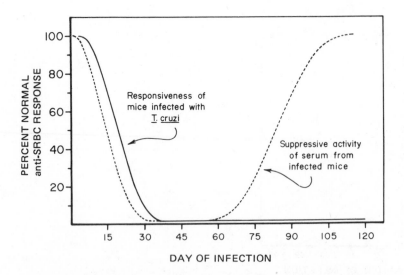

Figure 4   Relationship of suppressed humoral responses and presence of suppressor substance in mice infected with *T. cruzi*. (From Cunningham et al. [77] and
Cunningham and Kuhn, unpublished observations.)

initial antigen-lymphoid cell interaction, or during the first 36 hr of culture, will suppress responses. However, the addition of the suppressive serum at times after 36 hr has no effect on expression of the lymphoid cell responses.

Some molecular characteristics of this suppressor substance have been determined. The material has a molecular weight of 196,000-210,000, is trypsin sensitive, is not acid dissociable, does not bind to an anti-mouse Ig affinity column, cannot be removed by adsorption with *T. cruzi* culture forms, allogeneic spleen cells, or sheep erythrocytes, but does bind to normal syngeneic spleen cells (Cunningham and Kuhn, submitted for publication).

Whereas Ramos et al. [74] have determined that the spleens of *T. cruzi*-infected mice contain a Thy-1-bearing nonadherent suppressor cell which will inhibit cell-mediated response of normal cells in vitro, Cunningham and Kuhn (manuscript submitted for publication) have identified a non-Thy-1-bearing adherent suppressor cell in spleens which can actively suppress humoral responses to both T-dependent and T-independent antigens in vitro. The plastic adherent population of infected spleen cells (94-97% of which are nonspecific esterase positive) will suppress normal spleen cell humoral responses in vitro by 90% at a ratio of 1 infected cell to 300 normal spleen cells. Treatment of the suppressor spleen cells with either anti-brain-associated theta anti-serum or anti-mouse Ig plus complement does not abrogate the suppressive activity. By every criterion examined, the splenic suppressor cell of *T. cruzi*-infected mice which is involved in suppression of humoral responses of normal cells is a macrophage. Furthermore, the nonadherent population of spleen cells of infected mice, if incubated with normal adherent cells, are fully responsive.

Ramos et al. [78] and Clinton et al. [76] presented evidence that macrophage function in infected mice is not detectably different from normal macrophages in binding and processing ^{131}I human serum albumin or burro erythrocytes [78], or in in vivo ability to clear colloidal carbon [76]. However, these functions of the macrophage may be independent of any immunoregulatory manifestations. Also, it is conceivable that there are splenic thymus-derived suppressor cells for regulation of blastogenic responses while macrophages play an active role in *T. cruzi*-induced suppression of humoral responses. Recent studies by Cunningham and Kuhn (unpublished observation) show that lymph node cells from *T. cruzi*-infected mice, though unresponsive in Mishell-Dutton anti-sheep erythrocyte cultures, do not possess a detectable suppressor cell population capable of affecting humoral responses of normal lymphoid cells.

There is clearly much information needed on immunosuppression in Chagas' disease, mechanisms by which suppression is manifested, and the significance of suppression on development of protective immunity against *T. cruzi*.

It is puzzling that *T. cruzi*-infected mice develop states of almost complete unresponsiveness to heterologous antigens yet appear capable of resisting infections of common environmental pathogens or of responding to *T. cruzi*.

However, it could be hypothesized that, concomitant with parasite-induced immunosuppression, there is an extensive nonspecific polyclonal activation of memory cells which would provide protection of the host against pathogens to which the animal has previously been exposed. In this way the more diverse the experience of the host's immune system at the time of infection with *T. cruzi,* the greater the heterogeneity of memory cells and, therefore, the less the likelihood of encountering new pathogens to which the host does not have resident memory cells.

IV. PERSPECTIVES

Although cellular and humoral immune responses, as well as phagocytic mechanisms, are known to be important and functional in immunity to *Trypanosoma cruzi,* it is not understood how specific immune functions operate in vivo to control the parasite, or why it does not seem possible to develop sterile immunity against *T. cruzi.* During the acute phase of the disease the immune system responds, in most cases, and reduces the number of parasites in the blood and tissues; yet the host harbors the parasite in the chronic period and apparently for the life of the host. These observations suggest that *T. cruzi* has evolved mechanisms by which it can avoid immune destruction and/or that infection with *T. cruzi* yields the host immunodeficient in its ability to effect complete elimination of the parasite.

Information on mechanisms of evasion of immune destruction by *T. cruzi* is sparse. The parasite may have some resistance to antibody-mediated immunity by an ability to cap immunoglobulin bound to its surface [79]. Antibody-mediated complement-dependent lysis may be limited further because of reduced complement levels during the acute infection. It has been found that *T. cruzi* culture forms can decomplement serum, and that a factor released from cultured parasites can inactivate complement [51]. It also has been suggested that these trypanosomes can bind C3 and C4 [46]. In addition, it is reported that there are *T. cruzi* antigens in the peripheral circulation of infected animals, some of which are associated with parasite membranes [80,81]. Released parasite antigens would result in some immune reactions occurring away from the parasite.

As an intracellular parasite, *T. cruzi* spends much of its time protected from the host's immune products by a host cell membrane. However host lymphocytes are capable of destroying infected cells, releasing intracellular forms of *T. cruzi* into the extracellular environment where they are more vulnerable. Unfortunately, mammalian hosts apparently also become sensitized to self antigens, perhaps as a result of cross-reacting antigens of the parasite or of exposure of sequestered self-antigens on rupture of infected host cells. EVI antibodies, antineuronal antibodies, and the cell-mediated immune destruction of cell components may participate in the development of severe chronic conditions in patients.

Considerable research is required in this area to determine the antigens responsible for responses to infected cells, the stimulus for autoimmune activities, and the role of autoimmunity in the pathology of Chagas' disease.

The significance of parasite-induced immunosuppression in Chagas' disease has not been elucidated. Both cellular and humoral immune responses to heterologous antigens are suppressed early in *T. cruzi* infections, and the degree of suppression increases with duration of infection. At the same time, however, both cellular and humoral immunity are developing against *T. cruzi*, and these responses are sufficient in most cases to control the acute infection. There are several possible explanations for this seemingly paradoxical situation. The onset of immunosuppression may occur after the immune system has become sensitized to *T. cruzi* antigens, and the expression of this immunity may not be suppressed. *Trypanosoma cruzi*-induced immunosuppression may be accompanied by polyclonal activation, and clones of cells sensitized to *T. cruzi* early in infection, or immunocytes previously sensitized to antigens cross-reactive with *T. cruzi* (i.e., bacterial or viral antigens), could be mobilized to resist the parasite as well as to provide protection against previously encountered pathogens. Although anti-*T. cruzi* immunity develops in infected mammals, it is possible that the full expression of the immune system is inhibited. Some parasite antigens may be in undetectably low concentrations early in infection and do not increase to potentially immunogenic levels until after the onset of immunosuppression. A host may, therefore, have full responsiveness to only a part of the antigens expressed by *T. cruzi* during the acute and chronic phases of the disease. If immunosuppression inhibits a host from developing as effective an immune response as it is capable of mounting, then manipulations which would abrogate immunosuppression may allow greater anti-*T. cruzi* immunity and perhaps earlier control of the acute infection. However, it is also possible that abrogation of immunosuppression would enhance autoimmunity in Chagas' disease and could intensify problems in the chronic phase of the disease. Clearly, a more thorough understanding of autoimmunity and immunosuppression in Chagas' disease is required.

Another area in which little is known and which requires considerable research is the genetic basis of resistance against *T. cruzi*. It is known that age, sex, species, and strain of host have an influence on the course of infection in experimental Chagas' disease [9]. However, the physiologic and/or immunological traits of hosts which render them more resistant or susceptible than other hosts are not known. It was shown by Trischmann et al. [10] that there is no apparent relationship between resistance to *T. cruzi* and the H-2 haplotype of mice. As seen in Table 1, C57BL/10 (H-2^b) mice are relatively resistant to *T. cruzi*, whereas C3H mice (H-2^k) are highly susceptible. Congenic mice which are H-2^k but with C57BL/10 background genes (B10.Br), however, are as resistant to *T. cruzi* as are C57BL/10 (H-2^b). Because some immune response genes are located in the major histocompatibility complex, and because these are not entirely responsible

Table 1 Differential Resistance of Several Strains of Mice to *Trypanosoma cruzi*

Strain of Mouse	H-2 Haplotype	Background Genes of Congenic Mice	Relative Susceptibility*
C57BL/10	H-2^b	—	Resistant
C3H(He)	H-2^k	—	Susceptible
B10.Br	H-2^k	C57BL/10	Resistant
C3H.SW	H-2^b	C3H	Susceptible
A	H-2^a	—	Susceptible
A.By	H-2^b	A	Susceptible
DBA/2	H-2^d	—	Susceptible
BALB/c	H-2^d	—	Intermediate
CBA	H-2^k	—	Intermediate

*Susceptibility or resistance was assessed as the ability of mice to survive the acute phase of the disease.
Source: Trischmann et al. [10].

for resistance to *T. cruzi,* the capacity of an animal to resist *T. cruzi* is apparently a polygenic phenomenon. (Neva et al. [personal communication] recently examined patients in Brazil with chronic Chagas' disease to determine whether or not any HL-A characteristics could be correlated with development of chagasic heart disease. However, no relationship was found to suggest that a particular allele [or alleles] is associated with susceptibility for severe chronic manifestations.)

The likelihood of development of an effective vaccine against *T. cruzi* in the near future is remote. Numerous descriptive studies have been reported on antigen analysis of various fractions of *T. cruzi.* However, tests with experimental vaccines in animals have primarily used reduced parasitemia and mortality and survival of the acute phase as indices of vaccine effectiveness. The possible problems of vaccines alone stimulating autoimmunity, and the efficacy of vaccines in sufficiently controlling the disease to avoid chronic conditions, must be thoroughly understood before human testing can be initiated. It will be necessary, therefore, to develop animal models which reflect similar conditions of human Chagas' disease for both the acute and chronic phases. Existing animal models for acute Chagas' disease seem appropriate, although a good, well-documented model system for studies on chronic Chagas' disease does not exist. Figueiredo et al. reported recently that rabbits with chronic Chagas' disease present megacolon and typical chagasic cardiomyopathies (presented at International Congress on Chagas' Disease, July 23-28, 1979, Rio de Janeiro, Abstract No. 18). Rabbits therefore, may prove to be acceptable experimental animals for studying Chagas' disease. However, other systems should be explored, particularly small primates, and thorough histopathological studies should be done on all models proposed for studying immunity to *T. cruzi.*

Finally, it must be remembered that Chagas' disease is primarily a disease of poor people. It exists in large populations of South Americans because their dwellings provide an optimal habitat for the insect vector. Even the most effective vaccines and drugs may not have the beneficial effects of improved housing, education, and nutrition for people in endemic areas. Concomitant with the willingness of governments to fund biomedical research on Chagas' disease (as well as other socioeconomically oriented diseases of developing countries), there must be a concerted effort to improve the basic quality of life of these peoples.

REFERENCES

1. Marinkelle, C. J. (1976). Epidemiology of Chagas' disease in Colombia. In *American Trypanosomiasis Research.* PAHO Sci. Pub. No. 318, 340 pp.
2. Koberle, F. (1968). Chagas' disease and Chagas' syndromes: The pathology of American trypanosomiasis. *Adv. Parasitol. 6:*63.
3. Dvorak, J. A., and T. P. Hyde (1973). *Trypanosoma cruzi:* Interaction with vertebrate cells in vitro: Individual interaction at the cellular and subcellular levels. *Exp. Parasitol. 34:*268.
4. Dvorak, J. A., and C. M. Poore (1974). *Trypanosoma cruzi:* Interaction with vertebrate cells in vitro. IV. Environmental temperature effects. *Exp. Parasitol. 36:*150.
5. Nogueira, N., and Z. Cohn (1976). *Trypanosoma cruzi:* Mechanism of entry and intracellular fate in mammalian cells. *J. Exp. Med. 143:*1402.
6. Tanowitz, H., M. Wittner, Y. Kress, and B. Bloom (1975). Studies of in vitro infection by *Trypanosoma cruzi.* I. Ultrastructural studies on the invasion of macrophages and L-cells. *Am. J. Trop. Med. Hyg. 14:*25.
7. Howells, R. E., and C. A. Chiari (1975). Observations in two strains of *Trypanosoma cruzi* in laboratory mice. *Ann. Trop. Med. Parasitol. 69:*435.
8. Cover, B., W. E. Gutteridge, and F. P. Wharton (1978). The course of infection of *Trypanosoma cruzi* in gamma-irradiated rats. *Trans. R. Soc. Trop. Med. Hyg. 72:*596.
9. Goble, F. (1970). In *Immunity to Parasitic Animals.* (G. J. Jackson, R. Herman, and I. Singer, Eds.). Appleton-Century-Crofts, New York, 597 pp.
10. Trischmann, T., H. Tanowitz, M. Wittner, and B. Bloom (1978). *Trypanosoma cruzi:* Role of the immune response in natural resistance of inbred strains of mice. *Exp. Parasitol. 45:*160.
11. Hanson, W. L., and E. L. Roberson (1974). Density of parasites in various organs and the relation to numbers of trypomastigotes in the blood during acute infections of *Trypanosoma cruzi* in mice. *J. Protozool. 21:*512.

12.   Brener, Z. (1969). The behavior of slender and stout forms of *Trypano-soma cruzi* in the blood stream of normal and immune mice. *Ann. Trop. Med. Parasitol. 63:*215.

13.   Gutteridge, W. E., B. Cover, and M. Gaborak (1978). Isolation of blood and intracellular forms of *Trypanosoma cruzi* from rats and other rodents and preliminary studies of their metabolism. *Parasitology 76:*159.

14.   Kagan, I. G., and L. Norman (1962). Immunologic studies on *Trypano-soma cruzi:* IV. Serial transfer of organisms from immune to non-immune mice. *J. Parasitol. 48:*584.

15.   Seah, S., and P. D. Marsden (1969). The protection of mice against a virulent strain of *Trypanosoma cruzi* by previous inoculations with an avirulent strain. *Ann. Trop. Med. Parasitol. 63:*211.

16.   Fernandez, J. F., M. Halsman, and O. Castellani (1966). Effect of mito-mycin C, Actinomycin D, and pyrimidine analogs on the growth rate, pro-tein and nucleic acid synthesis, and on the viability of *Trypanosoma cruzi. Exp. Parasitol. 18:*203.

17.   Hanson, W. L., W. L. Chapman, Jr., and V. B. Waits (1976). Immunization of mice with irradiated *Trypanosoma cruzi* grown in cell culture. Relation of numbers of parasites, immunizing injections, and route of immunization to resistance. *Int. J. Parasitol. 6:*341.

18.   Gonzalez Cappa, S. M., U. J. Pesce, A. I. Cantarella, and G. A. Schmunis (1974). *Trypanosoma cruzi:* Protection of mice with epimastigote anti-gens from immunologically different parasite strains. *Exp. Parasitol. 35:*179.

19.   McHardy, N., and J. P. Elphick (1978). Immunization of mice against in-fection with *Trypanosoma cruzi:* Cross-immunization between five strains of the parasite using freeze-thawed vaccines containing epimastigotes of up to five strains. *Int. J. Parasitol. 8:*25.

20.   Goble, F. C., and J. L. Boyd (1962). Reticulo-endothelial blockade in ex-perimental Chagas' disease. *J. Parasitol. 48:*223.

21.   Kierszenbaum, F., E. Knecht, D. B. Budzko, and M. C. Pizzimenti (1974). Phagocytosis: A defense mechanism against infection with *Trypanosoma cruzi. J. Immunol. 112:*1839.

22.   Roberson, E. L., W. L. Hanson, and W. L. Chapman, Jr. (1973). *Trypano-soma cruzi:* Effects of anti-thymocyte serum in mice and neonatal thy-mectomy in rats. *Exp. Parasitol. 34:*168.

23.   Schmunis, G. A., S. M. Gonzalez Cappa, O. C. Traversa, and J. F. Janovsky (1971). The effect of immuno-depression due to neonatal thymectomy on infections with *Trypanosoma cruzi* in mice. *Trans. R. Soc. Trop. Med. Hyg. 65:*89.

24.   Pizzi, T., and J. Chemke (1955). Accion de la cortisona sobre la infec-cion experimental de la rata por *Trypanosoma cruzi. Biologica 21:*31.

25.   Taliaferro, W. H., and T. Pizzi (1955). Connective tissue reactions in nor-mal and immunized mice to a reticulotrophic strain of *Trypanosoma cruzi. J. Infect. Kis. 96:*199.

26.   Rubio, M. (1959). Natural and acquired immunity against *Trypanosoma cruzi* in the hamster (*Cricitus auratus*). *Biologica 27:*95.

27. Kierszenbaum, F., and R. W. Ferraresi (1979). Enhancement of host resistance against *T. cruzi* infection by the immunoregulatory agent muramyl dipeptide. *Inf. Immun. 25:*273.

28. Dvorak, J. A., and G. A. Schmunis (1972). *Trypanosoma cruzi:* Interaction with mouse peritoneal macrophages. *Exp. Parasitol. 32:*289.

29. Kress, Y., B. Bloom, M. Wittner, A. Rowen, and H. Tanowitz (1975). Resistance of *Trypanosoma cruzi* to killing by macrophages. *Nature (Lond.) 257:*394.

30. Kress, Y., H. Tanowitz, B. Bloom, and M. Wittner (1977). *Trypanosoma cruzi:* Infection of normal activated macrophages. *Exp. Parasitol. 41:*385.

31. Hoff, R. (1975). Killing in vitro of *Trypanosoma cruzi* by macrophages from mice immunized with *T. cruzi* or BCG, and absence of cross-immunity on challenge in vivo. *J. Exp. Med. 142:*299.

32. Williams, D. M., and J. S. Remington (1977). Effect of human monocytes and macrophages on *Trypanosoma cruzi. Immunology 32:*19.

33. Nogueira, N. (1974). The escape of *T. cruzi* from the vacuolar system of macrophages. *J. Cell. Biol. 63:*246.

34. Nogueira, N., and Z. A. Cohn (1978). *Trypanosoma cruzi:* in vitro induction of macrophage microbicidal activity. *J. Exp. Med. 148:*288.

35. Nogueira, N., S. Gordon, and Z. Cohn (1977). *Trypanosoma cruzi:* The immunological induction of macrophage plasminogen activator requires thymus-derived lymphocytes. *J. Exp. Med. 146:*172.

36. Nathan, C., N. Nogueira, C. Juangbhanich, J. Ellis, and Z. Cohn (1979). Activation of macrophages in vivo and in vitro: Correlation between hydrogen peroxide release and killing of *Trypanosoma cruzi. J. Exp. Med. 149:*1956.

37. Kipnis, T. L., V. L. G. Calich, and W. Dias da Silva (1979). Active entry of bloodstream forms of *Trypanosoma cruzi* into macrophages. *Parasitology 78:*89.

38. Lelchuk, R., A. P. Dalmasso, C. L. Inglesini, M. Alvarez, and J. A. Cerisola (1970). Immunoglobulin studies in serum of patients with American trypanosomiasis (Chagas' disease). *Clin. Exp. Immunol. 6:*547.

39. Marsden, P. D., S. K. K. Seah, K. E. Mott, A. Prata, and H. Platt (1970). Immunoglobulins in Chagas' disease. *J. Trop. Med. Hyg. 73:*157.

40. Vattuone, N. H., A. Szarfman, and S. M. Gonzalez Cappa (1973). Antibody response and immunoglobulin levels in humans with acute or chronic *Trypanosoma cruzi* infections (Chagas' disease). *Am. J. Trop. Med. Hyg. 76:*45.

41. Teixeira, A. R. L., G. Teixeira, V. Macedo, and A. Prata (1978). Acquired cell-mediated immunodepression in acute Chagas' disease. *J. Clin. Invest. 62:*1132.

42. Kierszenbaum, F., and J. G. Howard (1976). Mechanisms of resistance against experimental *Trypanosoma cruzi* infection: The importance of antibodies and antibody forming capacity in the Biozzi high and low responder mice. *J. Immunol. 116:*1208.

43. Krettli, A. W., and Z. Brener (1976). Protectige effects of specific antibodies in *Trypanosoma cruzi* infections. *J. Immunol. 116:*755.

44. Culbertson, J. T., and M. H. Kolodny (1938). Acquired immunity in rats against *Trypanosoma cruzi. J. Parasitol. 24:*83.

45. Hanson, W. L. (1976). Immunology of American trypanosomiasis (Chagas' disease). In *Immunology of Parasitic Infections.* (S. Cohen and E. Sadun, Eds.). Blackwell Scientific Publications, Oxofrd, 222 pp.

46. Anziano, D. F., A. P. Dalmasso, R. Lelchuk, and C. Vasquez (1972). Role of complement in immune lysis of *Trypanosoma cruzi. Infect. Immun. 6:* 860.

47. Teixeira, A. R. L., and C. A. Santos Buch (1974). The immunology of experimental Chagas' disease. I. Preparation of *Trypanosoma cruzi* antigens and humoral antibody response to these antigens. *J. Immunol. 113:* 859.

48. Budzko, D. B., M. C. Pizzimente, and F. Kierszenbaum (1975). Effects of complement depletion in experimental Chagas' disease: Immune lysis of virulent blood-forms of *Trypanosoma cruzi. Inf. Immun. 11:*86.

49. Kierszenbaum, F. (1976). Cross-reactivity of lytic antibodies against blood forms of *Trypanosoma cruzi. J. Parasitol. 62:*134.

50. Nogueira, N., C. Bianco, and Z. Cohn (1975). Studies on the selective lysis and purification of *Trypanosoma cruzi. J. Exp. Med. 142:*224.

51. Cunningham, D. S., W. H. Craig, and R. E. Kuhn (1978). Reduction of complement levels in mice infected with *Trypanosoma cruzi. J. Parasitol. 64:*1044.

52. Abrahamsohn, I. A., and W. D. da Silva (1977). Antibody-dependent cell-mediated cytotoxicity against *Trypanosoma cruzi. Parasitology 75:*317.

53. Mkwananzi, J. B., D. Franks, and J. R. Baker (1976). Cytotoxicity of antibody-coated trypanosomes by normal human lymphoid cells. *Nature (Lond.) 259:*403.

54. Sanderson, C. J., M. M. Bunn-Moreno, and J. F. Lopez (1978). Antibody-dependent cell-mediated cytotoxicity of *Trypanosoma cruzi:* The release of tritium-labelled RNA, DNA and protein. *Parasitology 76:*299.

55. Sanderson, C. J., A. J. Lozez, and M. M. Bunn-Moreno (1977). Eosinophils and not lymphoid K cells kill *Trypanosoma cruzi. Nature (Lond.) 268:*340.

56. Olabuenaga, S. E., R. L. Cardoni, E. L. Segura, N. E. Riera, and M. M. E. de Bracco (1979). Antibody-dependent cytolysis of *Trypanosoma cruzi* by human polymorphonuclear leucocytes. *Cell. Immunol. 45:*85.

57. Vilches, A. M., A. Katzin, H. Golfera, and G. A. Schmunis (1973). The effect of heterologous anti-thymocyte serum upon the course of infection with *Trypanosoma cruzi* in mice. *Z. Tropenmed. Parasitol. 24:*279.

58. Kierszenbaum, F., and M. M. Pienkowski (1979). Thymus-dependent control of host defense mechanisms against *Trypanosoma cruzi* infection. *Inf. Immun. 24:*117.

59. Yanovsky, J. F., and E. Albado (1972). Humoral and cellular responses to *Trypanosoma cruzi* infection. *J. Immunol. 109:*1159.

60. Tschudi, E. I., D. F. Anziano, and A. P. Dalmasso (1972). Lymphocyte transformation in Chagas' disease. *Inf. Immun. 6:*905.

61. Lelchuk, R., R. L. Cardoni, and A. S. Fuks (1977). Cell-mediated immunity in Chagas' Disease. Alterations induced by treatment with a tryanocidal drug (nifurtimox). *Clin. Exp. Immunol. 30:*434.

62. Kuhn, R. E., and J. E. Murnane (1977). *Trypansoma cruzi:* Immune destruction of parasitized fibroblasts in vitro. *Exp. Parasitol. 41:*66.

63. Santos-Buch, C. A., and A. R. L. Teixeira (1974). The immunology of experimental Chagas' disease. III. Rejection of allogeneic heart cells in vitro. *J. Exp. Med. 140:*38.

64. Teixeira, A. R. L., G. Teixeira, V. Macedo, and A. Prata (1978). *Trypanosoma cruzi*-sensitized T-lymphocyte mediated ^{51}Cr release from human heart cells in Chagas' disease. *Am. J. Trop. Med. Hyg. 27:*1097.

65. Cossio, P. M., C. Diez, A. Szarfman, E. Kreutzer, B. Candiolo, and R. M. Arana (1974). Chagasic cardiopathy: Demonstration of a serum gamma globulin factor which reacts with endocardium and vascular structures. *Circulation 49:*13.

66. Szarfman, A., P. M. Cossio, C. Diez, R. M. Arana, and E. Sadun (1974). Antibodies against endocardium, vascular structures, and interstitium of striated muscle that cross-react with *T. cruzi* and *T. rhodisiense. J. Parasitol. 60:*1024.

67. Szarfman, A., E. L. Khoury, P. M. Cossio, R. M. Arana, and I. G. Kagan (1975). Investigation of the EVI antibody in parasitic diseases other than American trypanosomiasis. An anti-skeletal muscle antibody in leishmaniasis. *Am. J. Trop. Med. Hyg. 24:*19.

68. Szarfman, A., P. M. Cossio, G. A. Schmunis, and R. M. Arana (1977). The EVI antibody in acute Chagas' disease. *J. Parasitol. 63:*149.

69. Schmunis, G. A., P. M. Cossio, A. Szarfman, L. Coarasa, and R. M. Arana (1978). Tissue reacting antibodies (EVI antibodies) in nifurtimox-treated patients with Chagas' disease. *J. Infect. Dis. 138:*401.

70. Ribeiro dos Santos, R., J. O. Marquez, C. C. Von Gal Furtado, J. C. Ramos de Oliveira, A. R. Martins, F. Koberle (1979). Antibodies against neurons in chronic Chagas' disease. *Z. Tropenmed. Parasitol. 30:*19.

71. Reed, S. G., C. L. Larson, and C. A. Speer (1977). Suppression of cell-mediated immunity in experimental Chagas' disease. *Z. Parasitekd. 52:*11.

72. Reed, S. G., C. L. Larson, and C. A. Speer (1978). Contact sensitivity responses in mice infected with *Trypanosoma cruzi. Inf. Immun. 22:*548.

73. Rowland, E. C., and R. E. Kuhn (1978). Suppression of cellular responses in mice during *Trypanosoma cruzi* infections. *Inf. Immun. 20:*393.

74. Ramos, C., I. Schadtler-Siwon, and L. Ortiz-Ortiz (1979). Suppressor cells present in the spleens of *Trypanosoma cruzi*-infected mice. *J. Immunol. 122:*1243.

75. Rowland, E. C., and R. E. Kuhn (1978). Suppression of anamnestic cellular responses during experimental American trypanosomiasis. *J. Parasitol. 64:*741.

76. Clinton, B. A., Ortiz-Ortiz, W. Garcia, T. Martinez, and R. Capin (1975).

Trypanosoma cruzi: Early immune responses in infected mice. *Exp. Parasitol. 37:*417.

77. Cunningham, D. S., R. E. Kuhn, and E. C. Rowland (1978). Suppression of humoral responses during *Trypanosoma cruzi* infections in mice. *Inf. Immun. 22:*155.

78. Ramos, C., E. Lamoyl, M. Feoli, M. Rodriguez, M. Perez, and L. Ortiz-Ortiz (1978). *Trypanosoma cruzi:* Immunosuppressed response to different antigens in the infected mouse. *Exp. Parasitol. 45:*190.

79. Schmunis, G. A., A. Szarfman, T. Langembach, and W. de Souza (1978). Induction of capping in blood-stage trypomastigotes of *Trypanosoma cruzi* by human anti-*Trypanosoma cruzi* antibodies. *Inf. Immun. 20:*567.

80. Gottlieb, M. (1977). A carbohydrate-containing antigen from *Trypanosoma cruzi* and its detection in the circulation of infected mice. *J. Immunol. 119:*465.

81. Gottlieb, M. (1978). *Trypansoma cruzi:* Identification of a cell surface polysaccharide. *Exp. Parasitol. 45:*200.

4

Immunology and Immunopathology of African Trypanosomiasis

JOHN M. MANSFIELD School of Medicine, University of Louisville, Louisville, Kentucky

I.   Introduction   167
     A. Course of Infection   168
     B. Immunopathology   169
II. The Immune Responses to Trypanosomes   177
     A. Parasite Antigens   178
     B. The Protective Immune Response   184
     C. Genetics of Resistance   190
III. Immunomodulation   192
     A. Immunosuppression   192
     B. Mechanism of Suppression   199
     C. Immunotherapy   207
IV. Conclusions and Suggestions   207
     References   210

I. INTRODUCTION

African trypanosomiasis is a protozoan disease of medical and veterinary importance. This infectious disease, perhaps more than any other parasitic disease endemic in Africa, has had a marked impact upon the colonization and economic development of the continent. It is because of trypanosomiasis that much of the area comprising sub-Saharan West, Central, and East Africa cannot effectively be settled or used for agriculture and pasturage [1-4]. In the regions of Africa where trypanosomes are endemic, overt disease flares up whenever humans and their animals move into areas where the vectors (tsetse fly) and wild animals that transmit or harbor the parasites live. In addition, drug-resistant strains of trypanosomes are constantly arising in areas where chemotherapy programs have been used to keep outbreaks of trypanosomiasis under control. The current political instability in regions of Africa where land use and game animal control programs have reduced the incidence of trypanosomiasis has also led to a recrudescence of disease. Goodwin [5] compares African trypanosomiasis with a dragon that "sometimes slumbers and smoulders quietly for long periods but at any moment it may awaken and cause widespread loss of life to man and his animals."

Species of *Trypanosoma* that causes disease in humans are *T. gambiense* and *T. rhodesiense* (both are considered to be subspecies of *T. brucei*), and the important pathogens of domestic animals are *T. brucei, T. congolense, T. simiae,* and *T. vivax.* (The host specificities, geographical ranges, morphological characteristics, and life cycles of these parasites have been detailed elsewhere [6-10] and will not be considered further in this review.) Infection of humans and their domestic animals with the African trypanosomes typically results in disease that is marked by numerous aberrations in function of the immune system. The focus of this chapter will be on the immunology of the host-parasite relationship specifically as it relates to histopathology of disease, control of parasitemia, and immunomodulation. It is unfortunate in trypanosomiasis, in which the immune system plays such a paramount role in the progression of the disease process, that more current relevant information on the clinical immunology is not available. Much of the information on the immunobiology of African trypanosomiasis has been derived from experimental studies. Nevertheless, comparisons and contrasts between the available clinical information and the experimental studies will be made where possible.

A. Course of Infection

Infections are initiated when metacyclic trypomastigote forms of *Trypanosoma* spp. are transmitted to the mammalian host by the bite of tsetse flies (*Glossina* spp.). The inoculated organisms transform into the larger trypomastigote forms (those forms typically seen in infected blood smears) and replicate at the site of inoculation. A chancre usually develops at this site which is characterized, histologically, by mononuclear cell infiltration [11]. Trypanosomes subsequently spread from the chancre via the blood and lymphatic vessels to other tissues of the body. When trypanosomes appear in the blood during infection, their numbers fluctuate in a cyclical manner; this intermittent parasitemia is typical in mammals infected with the African trypanosomes and reflects not only the antigenic variation that African trypanosomes undergo in the host but also the ability of the host to mount an antibody response to these variants which results in temporal elimination of organisms from blood and other tissues [12-17]. Eventually, however, trypanosomes may enter the cerebrospinal fluid and brain; these events signal the impending death of the host.

The symptoms of infection in humans and cattle are not specific for trypansomiasis and are quite variable from one individual or animal to another [12-14]. The earliest symptoms in humans may be a recurring fever and headache, which are closely associated with the appearance of trypanosomes in the blood. Another early development is that superficial lymph nodes and the nodes draining the chancre become markedly enlarged. Concurrently, facial edema, large circular erythematous skin rashes, pruritus, arthralgia, tachycardia, emaciation, and deep hyperesthesia (Kerandel's sign) develop. Subsequently, a marked lassitude and other symptoms of central nervous system (CNS) involvement may appear: ataxia, hand and limb tremors, mental changes, and daytime somnolence progressing to coma. As in infected humans, infected cattle exhibit febrile changes associated with the appearance (or elimination) of trypanosomes in blood, and superficial lymph nodes are grossly enlarged. Chronic wasting leading to extreme emaciation develops, and a terminal weakness and recumbency occur.

The severity and duration of the disease process depend largely upon the host species as well as the species (and strain) of the infecting trypanosome [13, 14,18,19]. For example, untreated *T. gambiense* infections of humans are chronic in nature, with death occurring after a period of a year or more; *T. rhodesiense* infections of humans, however, are more acute, with death occurring within a period of weeks to months. In *T. congolense*-infected cattle, different strains of the parasite have been shown to produce disease ranging from that with a favorable long-term survival rate and low parasitemias to that with less favorable short-term survival characteristics and high parasitemias.

B. Immunopathology

Numerous lesions have been found in the tissues of trypanosome-infected humans or animals. However, none of these lesions has been shown to be pathognomonic of the disease caused by a particular species of *Trypanosoma* or, indeed, by trypanosomes in general [12,19-21]. Many of the lesions may have an immunological etiology. For example, inflammatory foci are frequently detectable in liver, lung, heart, skeletal muscle, skin, and kidney, as well as in the brain tissues of humans and domestic animals with trypanosomiasis [12-14,19,20,22-25]. These lesions are most likely due to the host's immune responses to parasites present in the vasculature and the extravascular spaces of various organs.

1. Role of Immune Complexes

During the course of disease, there is, as mentioned above, a series of trypanosome antigenic variants arising in the host to which the host responds by mounting antibody responses in order to clear the variants from the body. Host tissues are periodically exposed to massive amounts of trypanosome antigens (both the variant-specific surface coat antigens—VSSA—and the invariant membrane, cytoplasmic, and nuclear antigens) as well as antibodies specific for these trypanosome antigens. Thus, immune complexes of trypanosome antigens and parasite-specific IgM or IgG plus complement (C) are formed and deposited in the vasculature and extravascular spaces of tissues. The composition of immune complexes formed would range, temporally, from those with an antigen excess (when large numbers of parasites are destroyed by a VSSA-specific antibody response and subsequently release antigens in quantity) to those with an antibody excess (as antigen is cleared but antibody continues to be synthesized prior to the emergence of a new variant-specific population). The resulting pathology is characteristic of the inflammatory changes occurring in Arthus lesions and in acute and chronic immune complex disease: split C components (or vasoactive substances such as kinins and the amines released from basophils and platelets) orchestrate a series of reactions ranging from increased vascular permeability and edema to cellular infiltration and necrosis. In fact, much of the nonneurologic symptomatology and pathology of African trypanosomiasis in humans (e.g., edema, arthralgia, skin rash, endocarditis, glomerulonephritis) is reminiscent of the classic serum sickness reaction.

The indirect and direct evidence for involvement of host immune responses in the pathogenesis of African trypanosomiasis is considerable. The observations of Boreham [26,27] and Boreham and Goodwin [28] on the elevation of kinin levels in sera of infected humans and animals were among the first clues that immune complexes were perhaps involved in the pathology of the disease. Additional indirect evidence was provided by the experimental studies of Tizard and Soltys [29] and Mansfield and Kreier [30] in which infected animals were skin-tested with trypanosome antigens and subsequently were shown to develop severe lesions of the Arthus type. Direct evidence for immune complex involvement came not only with the observations on depressed levels of C system proteins (C1q, C1, C3, C4, factor B) associated with a rise of parasite antibody and elimination of parasites from the circulation of infected humans and animals [31-36], but also with the detection of immune complexes and C in infected tissues, including brain, heart, skeletal muscle, and kidney [33,37-39].

Studies of Ig eluted from tissues with detectable immune complexes have shown specificity of the antibody for trypanosomal antigens [37,38]. It is probable that much of the pathology observed is due to complexes composed of antibody specific for invariant trypanosome antigens, which are released in large amounts into the circulation and tissues whenever destruction of trypanosomes occurs due to a VSSA-specific B-cell response. These invariant antigens, in contrast to unique VSSA, repeatedly saturate the host's immune system, resulting in greater antibody production for such antigens as well as the persistent formation of immune complexes. Thus, as the infected host attempts to control parasitemia, at least superficially (see Section II.B), by mounting antibody responses to the succession of trypanosomes arising with distinct VSSA within its blood and other tissues, it ultimately paves the way for extensive immune-complex-mediated damage to tissues. The site of localization and severity of such immune-complex-mediated lesions may vary not only with the host species but also with the species or strain of trypanosome. Experimentally this can readily be shown by infecting rabbits and mice with African trypanosomes. For example, the rabbits will develop a chronic disease characterized by glomerulonephritis and severe necrotic Arthus-like lesions appearing in the skin, predominantly around the ears, face, and genitalia; mice (depending upon the strains of parasites used) will undergo either an acute fulminating infection characterized only by a high parasitemia, or a more chronic infection characterized by intermittent parasitemia and microscopic lesions appearing in muscle, kidney, and, perhaps, the brain. Clinically, it has long been known that the pathology seen in infected humans or animals may vary with the parasite species and strain, as well as with the individual [9,12,13,19]. The reasons for these differences are not fully understood but depend, in part, not only on the genetic constitution of the host but also on the genetic constitution of the infecting variant trypanosome (see Section II.C).

Although immune complexes are implicated in the histopathology of trypanosomiasis, there are no reports on the quantitation of immune complexes in the sera of infected humans or domestic animals during infection. In one experimental study, Galvao-Castro et al. [38] report that complexes are detectable in the sera of mice infected for 2 weeks with *T. brucei*. In this same study it was demonstrated that T-cell-deficient mice, although harboring large numbers of parasites in the tissues, did not exhibit the histopathology evident in immunocompetent control mice; the histopathology could be restored by passive transfer of immune serum or T cells. Thus, a strong relationship between a T-dependent immune response (IgG?) to parasite antigens and the appearance of histopathology was established (also see Section II.B.1).

Anemia is consistently found in infected humans, domestic animals, and in some laboratory animals [12,14,19,40-44]. Immune complexes have been implicated in the development of anemia, as well as in the ontogeny of tissue lesions. Kobayashi et al. [44] demonstrated the presence of parasite-specific antibody in eluates of complexes from the erythrocytes of infected cattle. They suggest that the uptake of immune complexes from serum by erythrocytes, or the coating of erythrocytes by trypanosome antigens followed by antibody binding [45-47], results in their removal by cells of the mononuclear phagocyte system (MPS). Alternative suggestions may include C fixation by such complex-sensitized cells, resulting in lysis, or erythrocyte destruction by autoantibody [48,49] (see Section I.B.3).

Although recent studies stress the importance of the immune response in the pathological developments of trypanosomiasis [38], there is emerging evidence that the trypanosomes may directly induce certain pathological changes. For example, parasite extracts or autolysates have been shown to possess various biologically active substances (Refs. 50 and 51; also see Section III.B.1). One factor has been implicated in the anemia of trypanosomiasis: phospholipase liberated by dying parasites, which results in free fatty acid formation [52-55]. These substances lyse erythrocytes in vitro, and perhaps also in vivo when large numbers of parasites are destroyed by the host's antibody response. Further studies are needed, however, to assign any physiological significance to such factors derived from parasite extracts or autolysates in vitro.

Trypanosomes may be able to activate serum C proteins directly. Suggestive evidence was derived from the study of Nagle et al. [33] in which not only antibody and C deposits were detected in the kidneys of *T. rhodesiense*-infected rhesus monkeys, but also properdin deposits were found which led the authors to suggest that some trypanosome-associated C activation was involved in disease. Nielsen et al. [36] also demonstrated in infected cattle that properdin levels fluctuated with the numbers of parasites in blood, and that early C components were depleted. They suggested that parasites may directly and continuously activate C during infection. Musoke and Barbet [56] provided the first direct evidence for African trypanosome activation of C by C1-dependent and independent pathways. They demonstrated that a *T. brucei* VSSA preparation activated C via a C1-dependent pathway, whereas a parasite-derived particulate fraction activated the C1-independent pathway. Host immunoglobulins (e.g., immune complexes) apparently were not involved in the C activation observed. Nielsen et al. [57] have provided additional in vitro evidence that trypanosome products are capable of directly activating C system proteins; no evidence was provided, however, for involvement of a C1-independent pathway. Even though there is the in vitro evidence mentioned above for direct parasite activation of C components, it has not been established that the parasites contribute significantly to direct depletion of C levels in vivo or that such C activation contributes to the pathology. There are other mechanisms that may account for C activation independently of immune complexes or trypanosomes. For example C-reactive protein interacts with components of the complement system, and Thomasson et al. [58] have reported that C-reactive protein levels in serum are elevated during trypanosome infections. Furthermore, it is not unreasonable to suspect that the interaction of C system components with elements of the clotting and fibrinolytic systems also may be involved.

It is not known if T cells contribute significantly to the histopathology of disease. Mononuclear cell infiltration of tissues is often seen in clinical and experimental African trypanosomiasis. For example, cellular infiltration of the meninges of patients with Gambian trypanosomiasis and prominent perivascular "cuffing" of cells around cerebral vessels are often observed [12,13,23-25,59]; the cells involved are primarily lymphocytes and their progeny, as well as cells of the MPS. Mononuclear cells are also found in the cerebrospinal fluid of these patients [60,61]. Whether these are T cells and macrophages accumulating in response to parasite antigens present in such tissues (e.g., typical T-cell-mediated, delayed-type hypersensitivity reactions) or to autoantigens (see Section I.B.3), or whether they merely represent evidence of advanced inflammatory responses initiated by immune complexes or parasite products, is not clear. Clinical studies by Greenwood et al. [60] on the mononuclear cells in cerebrospinal fluid of *T. gambiense*-infected patients revealed that the majority of cells present were B cells or their progeny. They suggested that these cells are representative of those found in the brain tissue and, therefore, that the cellular response in the brain does not represent a T-cell response to trypanosome antigens.

The questions of whether T-cell responses to parasite antigens occur at all in infected animals (also see Section II.B.2) and whether these responses contribute to histopathology have been addressed primarily in experimental systems. Tizard and Soltys [29] skin-tested *T. brucei*- and *T. rhodesiense*-infected rabbits with trypanosome antigens; the cutaneous lesions that developed were of the antibody-mediated type (Arthus) as well as the cell-mediated type. In contrast, Mansfield and Kreier [30] skin-tested *T. congolense*-infected rabbits with trypanosome antigens and demonstrated that only antibody-mediated lesions of the Arthus type appeared. It is not known if the differences observed in the two studies were due to differences in tissue invasiveness shown by the organisms used (e.g., *T. congolense* is primarily an intravascular parasite, whereas with *T. brucei* and *T. rhodesiense* there is extensive tissue involvement) and, therefore, in the degree of T-cell sensitization, or to other factors. It is noteworthy that the cell-mediated reactions to trypanosome antigens observed by Tizard and Soltys [29] were transient in nature, detectable only by 3 weeks of infection and declined markedly in the terminal phase of disease several weeks later. There is no information available as to whether such T-cell responses were directed against VSSA or the invariant antigens. In a clinical study, De Raadt et al. [62] skin-tested *T. rhodesiense*-infected humans with trypanosome antigens but failed to elicit significant skin reactions.

2. Alterations in Lymphoid Organ Structure

A consistent finding in clinical and experimental African trypanosomiasis is that the size of lymphoid organs is altered. In most cases splenomegaly, enlargement of lymph nodes, and thymus atrophy occur [12-14,19,20,63-67].

In infected humans, domestic animals, and laboratory animals, the spleen enlarges shortly after infection to a size that may be greater than 20-30 times normal, especially in laboratory animals; this change is temporally associated with onset of anemia in some studies. Histologically it can be seen that splenic enlargement is due primarily to hypertrophy of lymphoid cells and cells of the MPS [13,19,20,63-65,68]; germinal centers are grossly expanded and plasma cells and macrophages are found in great numbers throughout splenic tissue, even in the periarteriolar sheath regions (areas normally occupied by small lymphocytes of the T-cell lineage) and red pulp. Only recently have studies documented by immunochemical means the relative changes in lymphoid cell populations in infected spleens. Mansfield and Bagasra [66] showed in *T. rho-desiense*-infected mice that macrophages increased the most in terms of absolute numbers and proportion of total cells, that B cells and plasma cells also increased in numbers and proportion, but that T lymphocytes increased minimally in absolute numbers with the result that the proportion of such cells dramatically decreased. Thus, T cells were diluted in infected spleen tissues by disproportionate increases in the numbers of macrophages and B cells. Similar findings have been made in other experimental systems [69-71]. Although the histologic picture suggests that similar changes occur in spleens of infected humans and domestic animals, specific information on changes in T, B, and macrophage cell populations is currently unavailable.

Lymph node enlargement occurs clinically and experimentally, but the size increase is less than that observed with the spleen [12-14,19,20,65,68]. In some infected humans the lymph node enlargement may be less obvious in advanced stages of the disease, during which time the nodes become smaller and harder as fibrotic changes occur [12,13]. Histologically it is seen in enlarged nodes that the B-dependent areas of the cortex are expanded, with well-developed germinal centers evident. Plasma cells and macrophages are also present within the classically T-dependent regions (the inter- and subfollicular areas of the paracortex), and numerous plasma cells and macrophages are evident in the medullary cords. Immunological enumeration of T, B, and macrophage cells in experimental studies revealed that the dilutional effect for T cells occurs less rapidly and to a lesser extent than in the spleen [72]. No clinical information is yet available on the cell populations of infected lymph nodes.

Another observation on lymphoid tissues, primarily in experimental trypanosomiasis, is that involution and degeneration of the thymus occurs [20,65,66,68]. The most consistent feature is a marked loss of corticomedullary distinction accompanying a loss of thymocytes; occasionally, germinal centers are detected within the thymic tissue, as are increased numbers of macrophages.

3. Changes in Immunoglobulins

A hallmark of clinical and experimental infections with the African trypanosomes has been that IgM levels in serum are grossly elevated over normal values [34,36,73-82]. Elevated IgM levels accompany the histologic expansion of the B-cell compartment of spleen and lymph nodes [69]. In endemic areas of Africa, elevated serum IgM is sometimes used as a diagnostic indicator of clinical infection in the absence of detectable parasitemia [75,83].

Values for IgM rise soon after infection to levels that may be as high as 20 times normal and remain elevated throughout infection. IgM may also appear in high concentration in cerebrospinal fluid [61,74,75]. Other immunoglobulin classes are not consistently elevated during disease. For example, IgM levels may be several times normal, IgG levels unchanged, and IgA and IgE levels depressed in *T. congolense*-infected cattle [36]; a relationship was noted, in this study, between elevated IgM levels and parasite burden. In another study of *T. congolense*-infected cattle it was determined that hypercatabolism of all Ig classes occurs [35]; thus, elevated IgM levels do not represent a decline in the catabolism of IgM or changes in the plasma volume, but represent a greatly elevated synthesis of these proteins by plasma cells.

There has been considerable supposition, but little hard evidence, that the major portion of the increase in IgM is non-parasite-specific antibody. Such estimates were derived primarily from the experimental studies of Houba et al. [77] and Freeman et al. [84] in which absorption of infected sera with trypanosome antigen in vitro (or in vivo) failed to significantly reduce IgM (or IgG) levels. Corsini et al. [69], in an examination of Ig secreted in vitro by spleen cells from trypanosome-infected mice, concluded that less than 10% of the antibody present was specific for the trypanosome antigens. In a clinical study of IgM in cerebrospinal fluid of infected patients, Greenwood and Whittle [61] also state that absorptions with parasite antigen had no detectable effect on the IgM content. None of these studies, however, take into account the different variant-specific trypanosomes that may have resulted in such elevated IgM levels. Nevertheless, based upon these reports and related work [85], it is considered that IgM increases are not due to parasite antigen stimulation directly. Additional clinical information is unavailable.

The current viewpoint concerning elevated IgM levels is that polyclonal B-cell stimulation occurs during infection which results in some antigen-nonspecific activation of host B cells (also see Section III.B.1). Much of the evidence in support of this contention has been obtained through the measurement of spontaneous increases in antibody or plaque-forming cell (PFC) activity directed against non-parasite-specific antigens. An early observation was that the serum of infected patients contained heterophile antibody specific for antigens such as sheep erythrocytes and guinea pig kidney [86,87]. Houba et al. [77] subsequently showed that serum from experimentally infected monkeys contained antibodies for heterophile antigens, and that these antibodies rose in titer as IgM levels became elevated; the heterophile antibodies were shown to be IgM. Interestingly, Houba et al. [77] demonstrated that while absorption of sera with trypanosomes failed to significantly reduce IgM levels the absorptions removed antibody activity for the trypanosomes as well as for the heterophile antigens;

thus, cross-reactivity of parasite antigen with antigens present on heterologous cells was shown. Heterophile antibody activity has been reported in other experimental trypanosome infections [49,88]. The occurrence of such antibody has been shown to be unrelated to any T-cell influence of trypanosomes or to B-cell stimulation by endogenous gram-negative bacteria [49]. Tests for determinants shared between the trypanosomes and the heterophile antigens were not performed in the latter studies.

Related evidence supportive of abnormal B-cell stimulation in clinical African trypanosomiasis is found in the work of Greenwood and Whittle [61] on the production of Ig light chains. They describe the presence of free Ig light chains in the cerebrospinal fluid and urine (but not serum) of *T. gambiense*-infected patients; mononuclear cells taken from cerebrospinal fluid also were positive for IgM and κ and λ light chains, which they suggest is evidence for local (e.g., CNS) production of IgM and free light chain molecules.

Further evidence for polyclonal B-cell activation in clinical and experimental trypanosomiasis is the appearance of rheumatoid-factor-like antibodies. In most studies these have been shown to be IgM antibodies with specificity for homologous and/or heterologous IgG [77,78,87-89]. Again, correlations were made between the elevation of IgM levels in serum and the appearance of rheumatoid-factor antibody; as with the heterophile antibodies, titers rose rapidly after infection. Rheumatoid-factor antibody production has not been reproducible in some experimental systems, however [78,90]. Parasite absorption studies have not been reported in clinical or experimental studies of rheumatoid-factor antibody in trypanosomiasis.

The appearance of autoantibody in the sera of infected animals is probably another facet of polyclonal B-cell activation. Although rheumatoid-factor antibody production certainly may be considered as an autoimmune response, the first clue that autoantibodies specific for tissue antigens occur in trypanosomiasis came from the study of Muschel et al. [31]. They demonstrated that serum from *T. gambiense-* and *T. rhodesiense*-infected rabbits contained complement-fixing antibody reactive with allogeneic rabbit liver and xenogeneic thymus tissue. Subsequently, Seed and Gam [91] reported the presence of antibody in *T. gambiense*-infected rabbit serum specific for allogeneic and autologous rabbit liver; they demonstrated that this antibody appears rapidly during infection and does not arise due to any detectable cross-reactivity between trypanosomes and tissue antigens. Similarly, Mansfield and Kreier [92] showed that *T. congolense*-infected animals developed high titers of autoantibody for autologous or allogeneic brain, liver, heart, and kidney tissue antigens; parasite cross-reactivity was shown not to occur. Additionally, they found that the autoantibody was exclusively of the IgM class. No evidence for a T-cell-mediated autoimmune response was found. In fact, an earlier study revealed that experimental T-cell-mediated autoimmune responses to CNS tissue could be depressed by infection with the African trypanosomes [93] (see Section III.A.2).

Autoantibodies reactive with a wide variety of normal tissue antigens or subcellular constituents have been subsequently reported. MacKenzie and Boreham [94] and others [90] confirmed that autoantibodies specific for tissue antigens were IgM antibodies in experimental trypanosome infections. Lindsley et al. [95] demonstrated the presence of autoantibodies in *T. rhodensiense*-infected rhesus monkey sera and *T. gambiense*-infected human sera which reacted with nucleic acids prepared from human cells; the monkey antibody classes involved were both IgM and IgG, however. Antibodies to fibrin/fibrinogen, C3b, erythrocytes, and thymocyte antigens have also been reported in trypanosome infections [49,96-98]. It has not yet been established to what extent the appearance of various autoantibodies may reflect a response to common tissue/molecular determinants.

There is no clear evidence which shows that autoantibodies play a significant role in the pathogenesis of disease. Mansfield and Kreier [92] could show no gross pathological effects following passive transfer of autoimmune serum to normal animals. Although others [49,95,98] have suggested that autoantibodies, or immune complexes containing autoantibody, may play a role in the development of anemia, glomerulonephritis, or immunosuppression (see Section III.A) of trypanosomiasis, the critical experiments establishing such a relationship have not been performed. In summary, the most likely explanation for the elevated IgM levels, the appearance of various heterophile antibodies, and appearance of autoantibodies is that they are incident to a more generalized phenomenon in African trypanosomiasis, namely, the histologic expansion of the B-cell compartment as the result of some polyclonal B-cell stimulus. The nature of the stimulus has not yet been resolved (see Section III.B.1 for a discussion of polyclonal B-cell activation by trypanosomes or their products).

II. THE IMMUNE RESPONSES TO TRYPANOSOMES

Humans and domestic animals infected with pathogenic African trypanosomes normally do not survive infection, even though immune responses are mounted against parasite antigens. One of the primary reasons for the inability of the immune system to produce a sterile immunity in infected hosts is that African trypanosomes have the ability to change their variant-specific surface coat antigens. New antigenic variants arise within the antigenically predominant trypanosome population of the blood and, perhaps, other tissues. As an immune response to the antigenically predominant population destroys those parasites, the variant parasites expressing distinct VSSA are spared and subsequently reproduce to become the next antigenically predominant population of the blood and tissues. Thus, the apparent consequences of trypanosome antigenic variation and host VSSA-specific immune responses are that selection for new variants occurs and that parasitemia is controlled only superficially. This cycle of antigenic variation and immunoselection may continue until the host dies.

In Section I, evidence was presented for parasite-specific immune responses contributing to the histopathology of disease. In this section the nature and extent of immune responses to trypanosome antigens will be detailed, and the significance of such responses in terms of controlling parasitemia will be discussed.

A. Parasite Antigens

Trypanosomes present the host immune system with a multitude of antigens during the course of infection. These antigens include not only a series of VSSA but also an array of invariant membrane, cytoplasmic, and nuclear antigens.

1. Variant-Specific Surface Antigen

The early electron photomicrography of Vickerman [99] revealed that the plasma membrane of African trypanosomes was covered by a 12-15 nm thick surface coat. This coat was subsequently shown to be glycoprotein in nature and, in fact, was the external antigen, VSSA, to which infected hosts respond in order to control parasitemia [100-102]. The VSSA completely covers the outer plasma membrane as a dense molecular monolayer and represents approximately 10% of all trypanosome cellular protein. The glycoprotein surface coat is found only on trypomastigotes and on metacyclic forms, being absent from all other stages such as some culture forms and the epimastigotes present in tsetse flies [99,104-106]. A correlation between virulence and VSSA expression has been made, since those forms without VSSA are not infective [107].

Recent studies have revealed much concerning VSSA composition and expression in the African trypanosomes. Purified VSSA from antigenically homogeneous or cloned trypanosomes are glycoproteins with a molecular weight of approximately 65,000 [108-110]. These molecules are single polypeptide chains which are composed of about 600 amino acids and up to 20 carbohydrate residues; the C-terminus portion of the VSSA molecule is tenuously anchored in the plasma membrane of trypanosomes [17,103]. The VSSA-associated carbohydrate determinants, which do not appear to be major immunological determinants, consist of different amounts of glucose, galactose, glucosamine, and mannose; they are located primarily within the C-terminus at sites proximal to the plasma membrane [110-112]. The carbohydrate determinants in the C-terminus are covered by the N-terminus amino acid residues and, apparently, are not accessible to antibody or lectin binding in undenatured native VSSA [103]. The precise nature of VSSA attachment to the plasma membrane is not known yet [256].

When the primary structures of serologically distinct VSSA are compared, there is considerable N-terminus amino acid heterogeneity found. Bridgen et al. [113] examined the N-terminus amino acid sequences of four distinct VSSA and found that there was no homology through the first 30 residues, which represented approximately 5% of the VSSA molecule. Detailed information on the residual amino acid sequences of VSSA has not yet been presented. Although no secondary structural homology was found in the N-terminus of VSSA molecules [17], there is evidence for some three-dimensional structural homology in the N-termini and C-termini of VSSA molecules. There are small C-terminus tryptic fragments of about 150 amino acids that are readily dissociated from larger more trypsin-resistant N-terminus VSSA fragments [103,114]. On the basis of trypsin cleavage studies it has been suggested that conformationally independent N-terminus and C-terminus domains exist in VSSA; however, the trypsin-sensitive cleavage points in different VSSA do not seem to be in the same position on the molecule [114]. Whether or not the VSSA domains elucidated thus far are analogous to the V-region and C-region domains of mammalian Ig molecules is a highly speculative but nonetheless interesting question.

VSSA molecules may be readily released by trypanosomes into host tissues. Weitz [115,116] described the existance of a trypanosomal "exoantigen" in the blood of infected animals. Recent studies have shown that the exoantigen is, in fact, soluble VSSA [100,117]. The mechanism(s) involved in VSSA release are not known but may include the release from dead or dying parasites as well as active cleavage [256]. The release of soluble VSSA may provide some degree of protection for the parasites by combining with antibody at anatomical sites remote from the surface coat. Such effects would be analogous to the blocking effects observed in tumor-bearing animals in which soluble tumor-specific antigen circulates. Such an event would also contribute to immune complex disease.

Purified VSSA are immunogenic. The immunization of animals with one VSSA will result in protection against infection with trypanosomes expressing that, but not any other, VSSA [16,17,103,108,109,118]. Although most serologic studies show that antiserum prepared to one VSSA will not cross-react with heterologous VSSA or with trypanosomes expressing heterologous VSSA, the radioimmunoassay studies of Barbet and McGuire [119] demonstrated serological cross-reactivity of VSSA derived from different trypanosome clones. Johnson and Cross [114] suggest that this cross-reactivity may be due to shared amino acid determinants and/or three-dimensional structural similarity primarily within the tryptic C-domains of heterologous VSSA. More recently, Cross [103, 120] presents convincing evidence to support this hypothesis. His radioimmunoassay and immunoprecipitation studies show that N-terminus tryptic fragments of VSSA neither cross-react with heterologous antisera nor induce antibody that cross-reacts with other VSSA. In contrast, a C-terminus tryptic fragment reacted with heterologous antisera and was an efficient inhibitor of cross-reactivity between heterologous antisera and VSSA. It can be anticipated that more specific and sensitive serologic probes of the N-termini and C-termini of VSSA molecules will reveal much concerning their structure. VSSA-specific hybridoma antibody studies currently underway [257,258] are resulting in such appropriately specific antisera. (A note of caution regarding the VSSA studies is necessary, however. Many of the biochemical and serologic studies of purified VSSA have been performed with *T. brucei*. There may be significant differences found in VSSA composition in terms of primary, secondary, and tertiary structure when other African trypanosome species are studied in more detail. The preliminary studies of Rovis et al. [121] and Reinwald et al. [122] on *T. congolense,* Cross [123] on *Trypanosoma evansi,* and Baltz et al. [118] on *Trypanosoma equiperdum* reveal some dissimilarity in VSSA characteristics.)

Thus, it is generally agreed that different antigenic variants arise during infection which are characterized by the expression of biochemically and serologically unique VSSA (unique, at least, within the exposed N-terminus of the molecules). An immune response to VSSA determinants may rid the host of variants expressing that antigen but provides no protection against future variants that may appear with different VSSA. From the limited number of studies performed to date, one fact emerges: there is no known limit to the number of different variants that may arise in an infected host. The only apparent limitation on antigenic variation is the demise of the host.

Antigenic variation has inhibited the development of any meaningful vaccination program. Current studies of VSSA are aimed at preventing or altering antigenic variation by perhaps interfering with trypanosome VSSA gene expression, although the changes in the trypanosome genome responsible for the appearance of distinct VSSA are not yet understood. Two major questions concerning the genetic bases of antigenic variation are the following. First, is the sequence of VSSA expression in the infected host a constant for any trypanosomal genetic strain (e.g., clone)? Second, what is the inducer for the gene switch from one VSSA type to another? Neither question has been answered yet with any degree of certainty due to technical problems and limitations in producing non-cross-reacting antiserum to the many different variants that may arise in an infection and in detecting small numbers of variants that may exist within a particular trypanosome population. There have been several recent reviews concerning the proposed mechanism(s) of antigenic variation by trypanosomes [15-17,124]; thus, it will serve no useful purpose to review again the literature on this subject, especially since there is little hard evidence available. However, a few summary statements concerning the current findings of workers relative to the questions above are appropriate.

It is not yet known if the VSSA sequence expressed by a genetic strain of trypanosomes is predictable or if VSSA expression is entirely random. There is evidence that cyclical (tsetse fly) transmission of parasites from a host originally infected with cloned trypanosomes will give rise to metacyclic trypomastigotes with similar, if not identical, VSSA determinants (e.g., reversion to some basic antigenic type occurs in the tsetse fly, regardless of the antigenic type of the populations ingested by the flies) [15,17,125-129]. However, there is also evidence that the metacyclic population of a tsetse fly is antigenically heterogeneous with respect to VSSA [130-132]. Earlier evidence, some derived from studies employing uncloned trypanosomes, suggested that a definite sequence of identifiable variants arose in an infected host [125,126,129,133-135]. More recent studies, however, show that the sequence of appearance of VSSA does not appear to be entirely predictable, even though certain VSSA types can be detected in different animals infected with the same clone [15,17,128,136-138]. And, there is indirect (serologic) evidence for the reappearance of a variant type in an infected host [139]. A problem with interpretation of data can be anticipated since it seems clear that the antigenic variants comprising the relapse populations of infected hosts are not composed entirely of one VSSA type, but rather may be composed of one major type with numerous minor types present in varying percentages [136,137,140]. A further complication may be that the antigenic variants present in the blood of an infected animal are not representative of variants in other tissues. For example, Seed and Effron [141] demonstrated the existance of numerous different variant trypanosome populations in the brains of infected mice. And, Galvao-Castro et al. [38] note serologic evidence for a delay in the antigenic variation of trypanosomes in extravascular tissue sites.

Although there seems to be no question that the immune response *selects* for antigenic variants present in a population of trypanosomes, there is a question as to whether or not antibody to VSSA may also *induce* the genetic switch which results in expression of a different VSSA. Cross [17] reviews evidence which shows that high concentrations of VSSA-specific IgM killed homologous trypanosome clones, but that intermediate concentrations of IgM not only killed but also induced a change in the VSSA expression of surviving trypanosomes. Takayanagi and Enriquez [142] presented similar results using strain-specific (but not clone-specific) antisera. Although recent evidence demonstrates that limited antigenic variation of *T. brucei* occurs in vitro [259], the rate of variation is not as great as that occurring in vivo.

Capping of VSSA by antiserum has recently been observed with *T. brucei* [143]. Since capping has been considered to be involved in the "triggering" of mammalian lymphocytes, it has been suggested that trypanosomal VSSA capping may occur in infected hosts and result in the triggering of trypanosomes to express new VSSA (e.g., antibody acts as the genetic inducer by causing capping). Barry [143] has shown, however, that such an event probably does not occur in the infected host. VSSA capping only resulted when a *bilayer* of antibody was present on the trypanosome surface in an indirect immunofluorescence procedure; a single layer of antibody, as would be found on trypanosomes in antibody-producing hosts, was not sufficient to induce capping. Also, trypanosomes taken from infected mice and examined for the presence of mouse Ig on the parasite membrane exhibited no evidence of capping in vivo. Furthermore, Barry [143] demonstrated that, once capping occurred in vitro, the parasites remained "nude" with respect to VSSA expression for a brief period, followed by reexpression of the *same* VSSA type. Thus, antibody-induced capping of VSSA does not seem to be the stimulus for expression of distinct VSSA.

The possible involvement of C or immune complexes on the trypanosome surface as the inducer for antigenic variation is raised by the work of Balber et al. [144]. They demonstrate not only that antibody-coated parasites shed or inactivate the immune complexes, but also that survivors of antibody- and C-mediated cytolysis expressed new variant antigens. Although antibody has been implicated as an inducer of antigenic variation, the possibility exists, then, that C components may actually be more directly involved in such variation. It is interesting to recall (see Section I.B.1) that trypanosomes can activate C independently of antibody.

There was earlier speculation that mutation in a common trypanosomal VSSA structural gene was involved in the appearance of new VSSA [145-147]. However, there is considerable (albeit indirect) evidence which suggests that some kind of induction mechanism (such as those discussed above), and not mutation, is involved. The evidence reviewed by Cross [17], Doyle [15], Vickerman [16], and by others [124,260], is that (1) the structural heterogeneity of different VSSA N-termini is too great to be ascribed to mutations; (2) the frequency of appearance of new variants in a population is high, approximately 1 in 10^4 organisms; (3) reversion to a basic antigenic type occurs upon cyclical transmission; and, (4) identical VSSA-expressing trypanosomes may be found in different animals infected with the same trypanosome clone. Although recently published evidence from recombinant DNA studies [261, 262] supports the concept of trypanosomes possessing multiple VSSA genes, the exact mechanism of gene induction and switching has not been elucidated.

2. Invariant Antigens

We have considered above the biochemistry, serology, and genetics of VSSA expression on the trypanosome membrane. The *invariant*, or common, antigens of trypanosomes are those that do not change from one variant type to another during the course of infection. (It is perhaps premature to classify VSSA C-domains as invariant antigens.)

There is serologic evidence for the existence of numerous common antigens within and between trypanosome strains and species [15,148-152]. The invariant antigens are not exposed on viable trypanosomes and consist of plasma membrane determinants (normally covered by the VSSA monolayer) and internal cytoplasmic and nuclear determinants; nearly 30 different common antigens may be detected serologically in trypanosome extracts [149]. These common antigens also can be detected in the serum of infected animals or humans as the result of parasite destruction [151] and probably play a significant role in the etiology of immune complex disease, as discussed in Section I.B.1. That there have been no definitive biochemical or serologic studies of such antigens reflects the lack of evidence that host immune responses to the antigens provide any degree of protection. Defined serologic assays either for common antigens or for antibody to such antigens have been used in order to develop diagnostic tests for *Trypanosoma* invections [116,152], and such assays are being tested in field trials.

Although little is known about the antigenic character of the plasma membrane underlying the VSSA monolayer, there is experimental evidence for the accretion of extrinsic molecules onto the membrane. The nonspecific uptake of host plasma proteins by trypanosomes was suggested in the early studies of Vickerman [153] and Seed [148]. The more recent work of Diffley and Honigberg [154,155] and Bogucki and Seed [156] confirm that a variety of host proteins are bound to the trypanosome surface. It has been shown in acute and subacute rodent infections with *T. brucei, T. congolense, T. gambiense,* and *T. rhodesiense* that host IgM, IgG, albumin, and C3 are bound to the parasite surface [154-157]. With *T. congolense* as a possible exception [157], all species accrete the same amounts of these proteins. Trypanosomes harvested from immunosuppressed rodents acquired the host proteins as well [155,157]. Thus, an immune response to VSSA determinants appears not to be involved in Ig uptake, although host antibody specific for VSSA can be detected on trypanosomes harvested from immunocompetent animals at appropriate times [143,157].

Although C3 uptake may be related to the ability of VSSA to activate the C system (see Section I.B.1), the uptake of Ig molecules in a nonspecific manner may be due to the presence of membrane-associated Fc receptors. Bogucki and Seed [156] demonstrated that the host Ig molecules were attached to the parasite membrane in such a manner as to leave Fab portions of the molecules exposed. Fc fragment inhibition and $F(ab')_2$ fragment uptake studies were not performed, however, to confirm the existence of an Fc receptor.

It is not known why trypanosomes acquire host proteins in this manner. Cross [17] suggests that the host materials may mask areas of the plasma membrane where VSSA density is low and where exposure of common antigens might occur. That the plasma membrane is involved in host protein binding is only inferred, since purified VSSA have not been reported to possess binding properties for these types of protein (C3 is, perhaps, an exception). One point should be made regarding this phenomenon, however: there is no evidence for clinical trypanosome isolates possessing this protein-binding ability. Indeed, it has been reported that recent field isolates accumulate less host Ig than do rodent adapted strains causing acute infections [156,263].

B. The Protective Immune Response

Because of antigenic variation, absolute recovery from trypanosomiasis is not provided by the host's immune system, and death is the usual outcome. Despite the inability of the immune system to provide a sterile immunity, there is no question that host B-lymphocyte responses to trypanosome antigens, specifically VSSA, are critically important in terms of protection against overwhelming sepsis by each particular antigenic variant that arises. In other words, whereas natural recovery from the *disease* does not occur, immunologic recovery from infection by a *specific variant type* does occur. The evidence for the temporal protective ability of the host's B-cell response is quite extensive and includes clinical and experimental studies. In this section, selected findings will be cited in order to illuminate points relative to the role of B cells in protection.

1. B-Cell Responses

The association of parasite-specific antibody responses with fluctuations in parasite numbers has been noted in infected humans, domestic animals, and laboratory animals [18,73,138,139,158-163]. Typically, serologic evidence has been presented which shows that antibody levels rise in serum accompanying the decline in numbers of parasites reactive with that antibody. These types of studies on infected animals, however, are few compared with the studies performed on immunized animals.

Vaccination studies with virulent isolates or rodent-adapted laboratory strains of *Trypanosoma* spp. were attempted many years ago but without success [164]; the animals simply became infected. More recent attempts at vaccination have employed active immunization with purified VSSA, trypanosome extracts, irradiated trypanosomes, or the actual infection of animals with virulent organisms followed by drug cure [108,114,118,165-183]. Although several active immunization studies did not reveal the immunological basis for the protection observed [174,178,183], others did. For example, Duxbury and Sadun [173] immunized rats and mice with irradiated *T. rhodesiense* and demonstrated not only that the animals were resistant to challenge with the homologous virulent organisms, but also that specific antibody was produced in such animals. Weitz [115] and Miller [184] immunized mice with *T. brucei* exoantigen (see Section II.A.1) and demonstrated homologous variant-specific protection by the resultant antibody response. Cross [108] protected mice against infection with specific variants of *T. brucei* by inducing antibody responses to purified VSSA. Seed [163] produced *T. gambiense* and *T. equiperdum* strain-specific protection in mice after immunization with surface antigen. Fulton and Lourie [185] demonstrated that drug-cured mice resisted reinfection with homologous *T. congolense* and *T. rhodesiense*. Duxbury et al. [186] noted the apparent lack of correlation between laboratory rodent and domestic animal vaccination trials. They showed that although mice could be protected by immunization with irradiated *T. congolense*, dogs and cattle could not be protected against homologous challenge infections. In contrast, Wellde et al. [178] provided cattle with long-lasting protection against the homologous variant by immunizing with irradiated *T. rhodesiense*. From all of these types of studies several general observations emerge: (1) any protection afforded by active immunization is variant specific and provides no protection against heterologous variants; (2) methods of antigen preparation, dose, route, and timing are critical; (3) viable irradiated trypanosomes (motile but nonreproducing) often provide significantly greater protection than nonviable organisms or their subcellular components; and, (4) it may be relatively easier to produce strong and long-lasting immunity in immunized laboratory animals than in cattle.

Additional evidence for the variant-specific protective effects of B-cell responses has been derived from passive immunization. In these types of studies the transfer of immune serum from previously infected or immunized animals, or the transfer of parasites sensitized with antibody, to other animals provided protection against homologous challenge infection [142,146,147,161,163,169, 187-189]. For example, Seed and Gam [147] transferred antiserum from *T. gambiense*-immunized animals to rabbits and mice in order to confer homologous protection. Takayanagi and Enriquez [142] and Takayanagi et al. [161] demonstrated passive protection of mice against *T. gambiense* with variant-specific antiserum. Also, protection against *T. rhodesiense* infection was provided by the passive transfer of variant-specific antibody to mice in the study of Campbell and Phillips [190]. From these and other related studies it is generally evident that only transfer of antibody against the surface coat antigens (VSSA) was protective, and that such passive protection was transient and required the injection of relatively high titer antiserum.

Studies on the nature of the protective antibody response in infected or immunized animals have shown that although both IgM and IgG parasite-specific antibody may be raised, the IgM response not only occurred earlier, but was more efficient in terms of both in vitro reactivity (e.g., agglutination) and in vivo protection [73,142,160-163,189]. The question of what happens to antibody-sensitized trypanosomes in vivo, in the infected host, has not been answered yet with any degree of clarity; most information on the effects of antibody has been derived from in vitro studies. For example, antibody-mediated lysis of trypanosomes in the presence of C has been shown in a number of experimental approaches [132,140,144,181,185,192,193]. It may be anticipated that an IgM response would be the most efficient in terms of C activation, as a single IgM molecule fulfills C1q divalency requirements for activation of C1. However, the recent results of Flemmings and Diggs [193] suggest that the cytotoxicity of antiserum and C for *T. rhodesiense* [181] proceeds by an antibody-dependent activation of the alternative C pathway (e.g., activation is Ig Fc and C1,4 independent). Other studies have reported antibody-mediated lysis of trypanosomes in the absence of C [138,192]; however, the mechanism(s) of such lysis is not known. Still other investigators report no evidence of any cytotoxic activity of antibody and C for the parasites even though antibody was present on the parasite surface as evidenced by trypanosome agglutination [194].

The significance of studies showing antibody- and C-mediated lysis of trypanosomes in vitro must be tempered by the realization that infected humans, domestic animals, and laboratory rodents are hypocomplementemic (see Section I.B.1) as the result of immune complexes formation and/or direct activation of C components by the trypanosomes. Thus, disposal of antibody-sensitized trypanosomes from the blood and other tissues may occur primarily via interaction with the phagocytic cells of the MPS. There is in vitro evidence for attachment and phagocytosis of trypanosomes by macrophages. Takayanagi et al.[191,195] showed that antibody to *T. gambiense* surface antigens enabled rat macrophages to take up the parasites and ingest them, and that macrophages from normal or immune mice were equally capable of trypanosome uptake. They could not show any enhancement of uptake in the presence of C via the macrophage C3b receptor [195]. The more recent study of Takayanagi and Nakatake [196] confirms the importance of the macrophage membrane Fc receptor for IgG in the uptake of antibody-sensitized *T. gambiense;* they show that F(ab')₂ fragments of the antibody agglutinated the parasites but did not result in their attachment to macrophages.

In vivo evidence supportive of the role of the MPS in removal of antibody-coated trypanosomes is not extensive. Fiennes [18] discussed the possible role for the MPS in protection of *T. congolense*-infected cattle (in fact, evidence is cited concerning the spontaneous recovery of several cattle from disease in the apparent absence of an antibody response). Holmes et al. [197] injected radio-labeled *T. brucei* into normal and immune mice and showed that, although parasites were not removed from the circulation of normal mice, the liver of immune mice rapidly cleared most of the parasites from the blood. It was not determined whether vascular sequestration or cellular uptake occurred in such mice. Stevens and Moulton [194] studied parasite uptake in vitro with antiserum, C, and macrophages from *T. brucei*-infected mice. Their results suggest that infected mouse peritoneal macrophages were activated and could phagocytize parasites in vitro in the absence of added antiserum. The inclusion of antibody resulted in enhanced uptake; inactivation of C by prior heat treatment of antisera resulted in reduced uptake. Normal mouse peritoneal macrophages were minimally phagocytic, even in the presence of antibody and C. An important observation in the study of Stevens and Moulton [194] was that macrophages harvested from mice after several weeks of infection were depressed with respect to their ability to phagocytize trypanosomes; the cause was not determined.

The latter observation of Stevens and Moulton [194] perhaps underscores the possibility that in vitro studies or studies on immunized animals may not be representative of macrophage function in infected animals with respect to MPS ability to clear antibody-sensitized trypanosomes from the body (also see Section III.A). Although Young et al. [198] report evidence for trypanosomes having been phagocytized by blood monocytes of infected African buffalo, to date there are no published studies on the mechanism(s) of trypanosome destruction by cells of the MPS in infected animals. It is important to point out that, although macrophages are implicated as important effector cells in terms of trypanosome disposal in infected hosts, macrophages alone are not capable of resisting or controlling parasitemia. The best evidence is that immunodeficient animals such as irradiated mice—which have unaltered macrophage function [199]—succumb to a fulminating parasitemia. Whether other cells in an antibody-dependent manner play a significant role in the removal and destruction of African trypanosomes is not known. For example, polymorphonuclear neutrophils and K cells may contribute to phagocytosis or killing (antibody-dependent cellular cytotoxicity), respectively, through immune adherence via membrane Fc receptors for Ig molecules.

The foregoing evidence implicates antibody as the major immunological factor involved in protection of animals from overwhelming parasitemia with any one trypanosome variant. As is clear, however, the actual mechanisms(s) involved in antibody-mediated destruction and/or removal of parasites from infected hosts are not completely understood yet. An important question regarding protective B-lymphocyte responses in trypanosomiasis is to what extent B cells must interact with accessory cells such as helper T lymphocytes. The experimental cell transfer and immunodeficiency studies cited below generally suggest that protective B-cell responses are helper T cell independent.

The early cell transfer studies of Takayanagi et al. [161] showed that immune mouse spleen cells and antibody could transfer complete protection to T. gambiense-challenged recipients; later experiments located the protective cell type in the glass-adherent fraction of immune spleen cells [200]. Although the specific identity of the transplanted protective cell was not determined in these studies, it was presumed to be the plasma cell. A more recent experiment by Takayanagi and Nakatake [201] purports to show that T lymphocytes are responsible for protection. Thymectomized, lethally irradiated mice were injected with trypanosome antigen and thymocytes from normal or immunized donors and subsequently challenged with T. gambiense. Protection occurred in mice administered antigen and T cells from immune donors. However, such protection was associated with the production of parasite-specific antibody. Thus, these results suggest, at best, that radioresistant B cells (or B cells present as a contaminant of the T-cell inoculum) were capable of producing VSSA-specific antibody in the presence of T cells.

Since parasite-specific IgG can be elicited in immunized or infected animals, it seems self-evident that helper T-cell-dependent B-cell responses can occur to trypanosome antigens [142,160,189]. However, that does not constitute proof that such IgG responses are involved in protection. It has already been noted that IgM specific for surface antigen seems to be more effective in protection. More formal evidence for a T-independent protective B-cell IgM response is found in the following studies. Campbell and Phillips [190] passively transferred *T. rhodesiense* variant-specific resistance to syngeneic recipient mice with serum, spleen cells, or B-cell-enriched spleen cells from immune donors; spleen cells enriched for T cells from immune donors provided no protection. Campbell et al. [202] subsequently demonstrated that not only could B-cell-deficient mice (B-cell maturation was suppressed from birth by administration of anti-μ chain serum) not recover from growth of the first variant population inoculated, but also could not be actively immunized against a homologous challenge infection. Jayawardena and Waksman [203] first noted that T-cell-deficient, congenitally athymic nude (nu/nu) mice were not more susceptible to *T. brucei* infection than were thymus-intact control mice and exhibited lower parasitemias than did controls. Similarly, Campbell et al. [204] showed that T-cell-deficient nu/nu mice not only survived infection for a longer period with lower parasitemias than thymus-reconstituted nu/nu mice or thymus-intact nu/+ littermates, but also produced higher levels of IgM antibody. They also showed that nu/nu mice were resistant to homologous challenge after immunization or infection and drug cure. That parasite burdens were lower in nu/nu than in thymus-intact mice in these studies is an intriguing finding. It may have been that higher levels of parasite-specific IgM were the result of an absence of suppressor T-cell influence, that thymus-dependent IgG responses in thymus-intact mice selected for (or induced) more virulent variant-specific types, or that IgG responses favored the development of immunopathology.

A study of *T. congolense* infections in nu/nu mice by Morrison et al. [70] revealed a different pattern of resistance. Their results showed that the nude mice had higher parasitemias than thymus-intact non-littermate control mice after 2 weeks of infection, and that nude mice subsequently survived for a shorter period of time. Interestingly, Morrison et al. [70] made the observation that there was a marked increase in the number of *T cells* detectable in infected nu/nu spleens at the time when parasitemias in these mice became significantly higher than controls. The immunological and/or pathological bases for their findings were not elucidated.

Askonas et al. [205] studied *T. brucei* infections of T-deprived mice (thymectomized, lethally irradiated, fetal liver cell reconstituted) and noted that, although the T-deprived mice died earlier, the course of parasitemia for the first 2 weeks was similar to controls. Clayton et al. [206] had mixed results with *T. brucei*-infected outbred nu/nu mice. They found that some of the animals failed to control the first peak of parasitemia, but that others controlled parasitemia better than the control thymus-intact mice. The bases of resistance or susceptibility in these two studies were not studied.

The evidence, especially that of Jayawardena and Waksman [203] and Campbell et al. [204], can also be interpreted to suggest that trypanosome VSSA molecules are helper T-cell-independent antigens. Indeed, the spatial arrangement of VSSA on the trypanosome membrane (e.g., high epitope density of N-terminus determinants, aligned in a monolayer) would seem to fulfill one criterion for antigens capable of stimulating certain B-cell subsets in the absence of helper T cells [207]. The nonspecific B-cell mitogenic effects associated with trypanosomes may fulfill another criterion for T-independent antigens (see Section III.B). An important related consideration from the study of Mansfield and Bagasra [66] is that trypanosome-infected animals are capable of mounting helper T-cell-independent B-cell responses even though they may be unable to mount B-cell responses to T-dependent antigens (see Section III). However, the early deaths of T-deprived mice after several weeks of infection in some studies [70,205,206] hints either that T-dependent (IgG) responses are more important for protection later in infection for certain strains of mice, or that antigenic variants may arise later in infection in some hosts which express a more T-dependent VSSA arrangement. Comparative studies of different parasite species and variants and T-deprived mice with various genetic backgrounds will perhaps shed some light on this matter.

In summary, IgM-secreting B cells may be of primary importance in protection against trypanosomes. Whether the experimental studies cited predominantly in this section in support of the protective role for such B-cell responses will find any correlation in clinical studies remains to be determined. As stated in the introduction to this chapter, there is a dearth of current clinical immunological information on infected humans and cattle.

2. T-Cell Responses

The appearance of VSSA-specific IgG antibody in immunized or infected animals is indirect evidence for participation of helper T-cells in the response. However, there are no clinical or experimental studies which clearly demonstrate, in vivo or in vitro, that T-cell responses occur to VSSA in infected hosts. In fact, few studies demonstrate any T-cell responsiveness to trypanosome antigens.

Tizard and Soltys [29] first demonstrated that rabbits infected with *T. brucei* and *T. rhodesiense* exhibited typical delayed-type hypersensitivity skin test responses to undefined trypanosome antigens. These responses could not be elicited earlier than 3 weeks postinfection and declined at about 5 weeks. It was reported that the cell-mediated response could be passively transferred to uninfected allogeneic recipients with infected rabbit spleen cells. Also, it was noted by Tizard and Soltys [29] that marked cross-reactivity occurred, since rabbits infected with *T. rhodesiense* exhibited delayed skin-test responses to *T. brucei* antigens and vice-versa. Thus, in this study it appears that cell-mediated immune skin reactions to trypanosomes are temporal in infected rabbits, and that the reactions probably occurred to common antigens of the parasites. In contrast, Mansfield and Kreier [30] tested *T. congolense*-infected rabbits and could not demonstrate any such T-cell responses by skin test or in vitro tests for lymphokine production by infected rabbit spleen or peritoneal exudate cells. It may be that the temporal T-cell responses observed in infected rabbits by Tizard and Soltys [29], and the lack of such responses detected in the study of Mansfield and Kreier [30], are attributable to the generalized depression of T-cell function observed in such animals by Mansfield and Wallace [208] (also see Section III).

One study has been reported, by Finerty et al. [209], in which mice immunized with formaldehyde-killed *T. rhodesiense* subsequently were shown to mount delayed-type hypersensitivity reactions to injection with an undefined trypanosome extract. When mice were immunized with formaldehyde-killed organisms and boosted with trypanosome extract, resistance to homologous challenge occurred. As neither antibody responses nor T-cell responses to defined parasite antigens were measured in this study, the exact nature of the protective response cannot be determined. Nevertheless, it was demonstrated that trypanosome antigens can elicit a T-cell response following an appropriate immunization regimen.

The skin-test responses to trypanosome antigens measured by Tizard and Soltys [29] and Finerty et al. [209] are mediated primarily by helper T cells and their products. Cytotoxic T-cell and suppressor T-cell responses to trypanosomes have not been reported, although infection may alter markedly such T-cell responses to parasite-unrelated antigens (see Section III). In summary, then, there is no clear evidence (other than indirect) for T-cell responses to VSSA or for T cells playing a protective role during infection.

C. Genetics of Resistance

It has been observed for many years that wild animals may harbor trypanosomes that are virulent for domestic animals and humans without evidence of extensive pathology or premature death. It is also known that certain breeds of cattle such as the longhorn N'dama and West African shorthorn Mutura seem to be much more resistant to the overt symptomology and pathology caused by trypanosomes than are Zebu and European breeds of cattle [1,3,4]. In some cases, susceptible cattle (or their offspring) maintained in tsetse endemic areas under repeated chemotherapy tend to become more resistant to reinfection or more "tolerant" of the infection—associated pathology [14,182,210,211]. The cellular and molecular bases of these types of relationships have not yet been elucidated. Experimental studies have begun on the genetics and/or immunogenetics of resistance to trypanosome infections in hopes of revealing some of the mechanisms of effective resistance to, or control of, trypanosomiasis.

Role of the Major Histocompatibility Complex

It is well established that major histocompatibility complex (MHC) linked immune response (Ir) genes influence the quality of immune responses to a variety of antigens [212]. Also, it is apparent that there is an association between H-2 or HLA type and susceptibility to certain diseases [213]. The question of linkage of the MHC to susceptibility or resistance to trypanosomiasis has been addressed only in experimental systems.

Morrison et al. [70] and Morrison and Murray [214] found marked differences in the susceptibility of inbred strains of mice to *T. congolense* infection. For example, A/J mice (H-2^a) displayed shorter periods of time between infection and appearance of the first parasitemia, higher mean parasitemias, and shorter survival times when compared with the less susceptible C57BL/6J mice (H-2^b); mouse strains (H-$2^{d,-k,-q}$) intermediate in their parasite burdens and survival times were also described. The infection of B6·A/F1 hybrid mice (H-2^b × H-2^a), derived from the resistant × susceptible parent crosses, showed that resistance was a dominant trait since these mice survived for a period of time compatible with the resistant parent. In the more recent study [214], survival times were measured in H-2 congenic resistant mice. Infected C57BL/10 mice (H-2^b) were compared with mice with different H-2 haplotypes (H-$2^{a,-d,-k}$) inserted in the B10 genetic background. All mice, regardless of H-2 haplotype, survived for a similar period of time. Thus, it appears that non-MHC-associated genes are associated with survival characteristics, and that Ir genes do not play a role in resistance to *T. congolense*. Similar findings were made by Levine and Mansfield [215] with *T. rhodesiense* infections of H-2 congenic resistant mouse strains.

The immunological and pathological changes occurring in the mouse strains exhibiting resistance or susceptibility have not been measured yet. The genetic bases for the differences, even though not H-2 linked, are probably quite complex. For example, Morrison and Murray [214] infected mice derived from backcrosses between resistant F_1 hybrids and susceptible parents (e.g., B6·A/F_1 × A/J) or resistant parents (B6·A/F_1 × C57BL/6J). The results, which were not entirely consistent, suggest multigenic control of susceptibility: the (B6·A/F_1

X A/J) backcrosses showed mixed susceptibility, with 25% surviving like the A/J mice, 50% surviving for an intermediate period, and 25% surviving for a period like the C57BL/6 mice; in contrast, survival patterns of the (B6·A/F₁ × C57BL/6J) backcrosses were much more heterogeneous. Also, F₁ hybrids between mice with intermediate susceptibility and resistant mice displayed earlier deaths than the resistant parent. Thus, at best it may be said that susceptibility to *T. congolense* infection in mice is under some complex multigenic control which is not associated with the MHC locus.

In studies similar to those described above, but in which *H-2* congenic resistant mouse strains were not used, Clayton [216] found that resistance apparently was not associated with *H-2* haplotype in *T. brucei*-infected mice. In addition, however, it was discovered that the course of infection depended not only on the host strain but also upon the strain of parasite used. Differences in the virulence of different antigenic types of *T. brucei* have also been reported by others [140,217]. It may be that differences in the virulence of trypanosome antigenic types are attributable to factors such as VSSA density or hyperinducible VSSA genes, formation of potent biologically active factors, or ability to induce generalized immunosuppression [264]. These and other possibilities seem ripe for study. Nevertheless, the genetics of the trypanosome is an additional variable in any study on the genetic bases of host resistance.

III. IMMUNOMODULATION

The African trypanosomes not only evade host immunological defense mechanisms by undergoing antigenic variation, they also are able to alter markedly the quality and quantity of host immune responses to a variety of antigens including, perhaps, the VSSA. In this section the level, nature, and proposed causes of generalized immunosuppression occurring in clinical and experimental trypanosomiasis are discussed.

A. Immunosuppression

Clinically it has been recognized for many years that infected humans and cattle are extremely susceptible to secondary infections. For example, Mott [23], in a 1906 presentation on the meningoencephalopathy occurring in patients with Gambian sleeping sickness, noted that 80% of his patients exhibited a terminal "diplostreptococcal" infection. Terminal complications of pneumonia or septicemia also have been noted by others in infected humans [5,151] and in cattle with advanced disease [14,18,218]. Although these clinical findings are suggestive of generally depressed immunocompetence, there was no formal clinical or experimental evidence for this until recently.

1. Depressed B-Lymphocyte Function

Goodwin et al. [219] first demonstrated that B-cell function was depressed in experimental African trypanosomiasis. In their study, *T. brucei*-infected mice and rabbits were immunized with sheep erythrocytes (SRBC), and the magnitude of the subsequent antibody response was measured. All infected animals displayed significantly lower hemagglutinin titers; and, in those animals with spontaneously elevated heterophile agglutinins (see Section I.B.3), the SRBC agglutinin levels declined upon specific immunization with SRBC. Confirmation of depressed B-cell function was reported by Urquhart et al. [220] in a study of *T. brucei*-infected rats and mice. They presented evidence for depressed IgG and IgE antibody production in vivo to *Nippostrongylus brasiliensis* parasites, which were used to superinfect *T. brucei*-infected animals.

Subsequently, a number of other studies were published which further elucidated the extent of depressed B-cell function in experimental African trypanosomiasis. Murray et al. [64] showed that *T. brucei*-infected mice failed to mount normal splenic IgM and IgG plaque-forming cell responses in vivo to SRBC, or IgM responses to bacterial lipopolysaccharide (LPS), a helper T-cell-independent antigen. A remarkable finding was that trypanocidal chemotherapy restored immunocompetence to SRBC within 48 hr. Ackerman and Seed [221] demonstrated that voles infected with *T. gambiense* made lower levels of serum antibody to human RBC and bovine serum albumin. Infection, however, did not depress such B-cell responses when immunization preceded infection. Ackerman and Seed [221] also found that trypanocidal drug therapy restored immunocompetence rapidly, within 3 days of treatment. Hudson et al. [88] confirmed the suppressive effect of *T. brucei* on the in vivo splenic PFC response to SRBC in mice, but also noted that, when SRBC were administered within 1-4 days of infection, enhancement of the PFC response occurred. Deer mice infected with *T. equiperdum* were shown by Moulton and Coleman [68] to have not only depressed in vivo splenic PFC responses to SRBC, but also depressed in vitro spleen blastogenic responses to LPS, which serves as a B-cell mitogen. Interestingly, they showed that control mice injected with multiple doses of irradiated trypanosomes mounted elevated PFC responses to SRBC. The in vitro studies of Jayawardena and Waksman [203] and Corsini et al. [69] also revealed that the proliferative response of B cells from infected mice to LPS was markedly depressed.

Mansfield and Bagasra [66] examined the primary in vivo splenic PFC responses and serum antibody levels in *T. rhodesiense*-infected mice to helper T-cell-dependent and independent antigens. They provided the first evidence that helper T-cell-independent B-cell function, as assessed by responses to pneumococcal polysaccharide type III (SIII) or polyvinylpyrrolidone (PVP), was normal or elevated until the terminal phase of infection when it became depressed. This was the first indication that infected animals could make a sufficiently normal antibody response to any antigen other than trypanosome VSSA or common antigens. These investigators also showed that responses to T-dependent antigens (SRBC, TNP-KLH) were completely depressed after a brief period of enhancement that occurred if trypanosomes and antigen were administered on the same day. Interestingly, however, B-cell responses to T-dependent antigen (TNP-KLH) could be completely restored in mice, in the nonterminal stage of infection, if the mice had been carrier (KLH) primed prior to infection; this effect was carrier-specific. On the basis of their findings, Mansfield and Bagasra [66] suggested that intrinsic B-cell function was intact through much of the infection but that helper T-cell-dependent B-cell responses were depressed due to irregularities in accessory cell function. Similarly, Terry [222] cites unpublished evidence that SIII antibody responses in *T. brucei*-infected mice are normal until late in infection when they become depressed. In contrast to these findings, Eardley and Jayawardena [223] demonstrated that *T. brucei*-infected mouse spleen cell cultures were depressed in their ability to make primary in vitro PFC responses to either T-dependent (SRBC) or T-independent (DNP-Ficoll) antigen. Also, Assoku et al. [224] showed recently that *T. congolense*-infected mice were unable to make normal SIII antibody responses.

Whereas the experimental evidence for loss of B-cell function is extensive, the clinical evidence is not nearly so comprehensive. Greenwood et al. [225] studied the antibody responses of *T. gambiense*-infected patients to *Salmonella typhi* vaccine. Although not as many patients as controls responded to *S. typhi* H antigen, there was no difference in patients versus controls in terms of an antibody response to O antigen. Similarly, a depression in antibody titer to H antigen in infected responder patients was noted, but no difference in the antibody response of infected responder patients to O antigen was noted. Thus, B-cell responses were only marginally depressed in this clinical study. It should be noted, however, that all patients received melarsoprol treatment during the immunization period and that such treatment may have had some effect on responsiveness. In a more recent study, Greenwood et al. [60] found that pokeweed mitogen stimulation of lymphocytes from Gambian sleeping sickness patients' cerebrospinal fluid was weak compared with stimulation of peripheral blood lymphocytes from controls. Since pokeweed mitogen stimulates human T and B cells, and since the majority of the lymphocytes in patient cerebrospinal fluid were B cells (see Section I.B.1), it seems probable that this is additional evidence for depressed B-lymphocyte function in human disease. No other clinical studies of infected humans are currently available.

Evidence for immunosuppression at the level of the B cell in infected cattle is somewhat mixed. Holmes et al. [226] found that secondary antibody responses in *T. congolense*-infected cattle to a clostridial vaccine were depressed. Scott et al. [227] subsequently found that only a mild depression of the serum antibody response to foot-and-mouth disease vaccine occurred in infected cattle. Results of a study by Whitelaw et al. [228] on louping-ill vaccine in cattle were supportive of depressed B-cell responses.

Several more recent and comprehensive studies do not completely resolve the question of generalized B-lymphocyte dysfunction in infected cattle. For example, Sollod and Frank [229] examined the primary and secondary serum antibody responses of acutely infected (*T. congolense*) cattle to a variety of defined antigens and also measured blood lymphocyte responses to pokeweed mitogen in vitro. Primary antibody responses to DNP-OVA or PI-3 virus in infected animals were only slightly lower, with delayed peak titers. Secondary responses to DNP were also slightly lower than control responses. Similary, the secondary antibody responses to the virus in infected cattle that had been primed before infection were only slightly lower than controls. Although total peripheral blood lymphocyte counts were markedly reduced during disease, the blastogenic responses of the lymphocytes to pokeweed mitogen were not significantly depressed. In contrast to these findings, Rurangirwa et al. [230] revealed that chronically infected (*T. congolense* and *T. vivax*) cattle mounted significantly lower serum antibody responses to viable *Leptospira biflexa* or *Brucella abortus* vaccines than did control cattle; *T. congolense*-infected cattle appeared to be more immunosuppressed than *T. vivax*-infected cattle. Although the antibody classes involved were not measured, the authors suggest that the antibody response kinetics may reveal a preferential suppressive effect on the IgG response. In addition, these investigators demonstrated measurable recovery of immunocompetence when Berenil, a trypanocidal drug, was administered with the vaccines. They suggest, therefore, that depressed B-cell responses in chronically infected cattle are maintained by the presence of viable trypanosomes. No other studies of infected cattle are available at this writing.

In summary, it can be seen that immunosuppression at the level of the B cell can readily be demonstrated to a variety of antigens in experimental model systems of African trypanosomiasis, but perhaps not so conclusively demonstrated in clinical forms of the disease. One fact should be kept firmly in mind concerning B-cell suppression in African trypanosomiasis: both naturally and experimentally infected hosts are capable of mounting protective B-cell responses, primarily IgM in nature, to the VSSA of trypanosomes in order to control parasitemia. Whether such parasite-specific responses are quantitatively or qualitatively as strong or protective as they could be in an infected individual is currently the subject of intense study in several laboratories.

2. Depressed T-Lymphocyte Function

Perhaps the first clue that African trypanosomes may depress T-lymphocyte function came from the experimental studies of Allt et al. [93] on *T. brucei-*

infected rabbits. They demonstrated that the induction of experimental allergic neuritis, an autoimmune response mediated by T lymphocytes, was depressed in infected animals. Subsequently, however, Urquhart et al. [220] and Murray et al. [64] were unable to demonstrate any marked depression of cell-mediated immunity in *T. brucei*-infected mice as evidenced by skin test responses to oxazolone or by cellular proliferation in regional lymph nodes to oxazolone. Murray et al. [64] did find a slight depression of cell-mediated immunity in mice infected for a prolonged period of time.

Definitive evidence for immunosuppression at the level of the T cell was first provided by Mansfield and Wallace [208] in a study on *T. congolense*-infected rabbits. In this study, tuberculin-sensitized animals were skin-tested with PPD; peripheral blood lymphocyte blastogenic responses in vitro to PPD were also measured. They found that infected rabbits mounted only weak delayed-type hypersensitivity skin test responses to PPD, and that lymphocyte proliferative responses to PPD were also markedly depressed. In addition, Mansfield and Wallace [208] documented the facts that the infected rabbit lymphocyte response in vitro to PHA, a T-cell mitogen, was also depressed, and that lymphokine (migration inhibition factor, MIF) production by antigen-stimulated lymphocyte cultures was impaired. It was shown also that immunosuppression occurred only in infected rabbits, since injection of nonviable organisms failed to cause the observed changes. Subsequently, others have confirmed that depressed T-lymphocyte responses occur in experimentally infected animals. For example, Ackerman and Seed [221] showed that *T. gambiense*-infected voles had depressed cell-mediated skin responses to oxazolone. Moulton and Coleman [68] described the depressed in vitro blastogenic responses of spleen cells from *T. equiperdum*-infected mice to the T-cell mitogens ConA and PHA. Similarly, Jayawardena and Waksman [230] and Corsini et al. [69] found that depressed in vitro spleen cell responses to ConA and/or PHA occurred rapidly after infection of mice with *T. brucei*. And, others have documented depressed T-cell responses in vivo and in vitro to mitogens, allogeneic cells, or antigens in *T-congolense*-infected mice [231,232].

Many of the observations on depressed T-cell responses in experimental African trypanosomiasis reflect a loss of helper T-cell function. Several studies reveal that cytotoxic T-cell function is also depressed. Perhaps the first indirect evidence was found in the study of Ackerman and Seed [233] in which *T. gambiense*-infected voles were shown to be susceptible to the growth of an allogeneic tumor; the immunological basis for this phenomenon was not elucidated. In contrast, Landolfo et al. [232] showed that *T. congolense*-infected mice, even though markedly immunosuppressed (at the B- and T-cell level), exhibited a delay in tumor-take and a lower tumor mass with a syngeneic adenocarcinoma; the tumor-specific immune response was not measured, however.

Direct evidence for depressed cytotoxic T-lymphocyte (CTL) function was first reported by Pearson et al. [231] for *T. congolense*-infected mice. They showed that CTL were not generated in a mixed lymphocyte culture (MLC) system with infected spleen responder cells and allogeneic stimulator cells. Delayed skin allograft rejection was also reported. Confirmation of depressed CTL function in *T. rhodesiense*-infected mice was provided by Mansfield et al. [72]. In their MLC studies, CTL function was lost first within the spleen cell population and subsequently, in the terminal phase of infection, in the lymph node cell populations. No clinical studies of CTL function are available.

Although evidence has been presented for loss of helper and cytotoxic T-cell function in experimental trypanosomiasis, there is only one report in which the induction of suppressor T-cell function in infected hosts was tested. Mansfield and Bagasra [66], employing the *T. rhodesiense* model system in which mice are capable of mounting helper T-cell-independent B-cell responses for a substantial period of infection, attempted to prime antigen-specific suppressor T cells in vivo by a low-dose priming regimen. Their results suggest that SIII-specific suppressor T cells could not be stimulated in low-dose-primed infected mouse spleens; the resultant PFC responses to SIII were not significantly depressed in comparison with unprimed infected controls, and the uninfected control mice which were low-dose primed with SIII exhibited marked suppression of the PFC response to an immunogenic dose of SIII. There are no other reports on the ability of infected animals to mount antigen-specific or antigen-nonspecific suppressor T-cell responses to appropriate stimuli. However, as discussed below (Section III.B), there is evidence for the *spontaneous* appearance of antigen-nonspecific suppressor T cells in the spleens of infected mice.

There are few clinical correlates to the experimental studies of T-cell function in infected hosts. Greenwood et al. [225] found that delayed-type skin test responses to PPD, *Candida,* and streptococcal antigens in *T. gambiense*-infected patients were significantly less than in control responses. Also, following sensitization with dinitrochlorobenzene (DNCB), fewer infected patients responded to a DNCB challenge dose than did controls. However, because patients received melarsoprol treatment during the course of DNCB sensitization, an effect of this drug on the DNCB skin tests response cannot be discounted. The depressed skin test responses to the microbial antigens were observed before any such trypanocidal chemotherapy was instituted. More recently, Greenwood and Whittle [61] examined the in vitro proliferative response of cerebrospinal fluid lymphocytes from infected patients to PHA. Although these responses were depressed, most of the cells present were B cells. No other studies of infected human T-cell function have been reported.

Relatively less work has been done with infected cattle. Sollod and Frank [229] examined the PHA and MLC responses of *T. congolense*-infected cattle lymphocytes. They found no significant differences in the lymphocyte blastogenic responses over a 5 week period when control comparisons were made. No other studies of infected cattle are currently available.

In summary then it is seen that there is much experimental, but limited clinical, evidence for depression of helper T-cell function in African trypanosomiasis. Experimental, but not clinical, evidence is available on depressed cytotoxic and suppressor T-cell function during disease. Since T lymphocytes represent a major protective as well as regulatory cell system in mammals, and since a defect in one or more T-cell subpopulations may have dramatic effects on the ability of an infected host to resist other pathogens or to regulate its own immune system, it is imperative that more clinical studies be initiated.

3. Macrophage Function

The importance of the MPS and its resident cells, the macrophages, in aiding immune elimination of trypanosomes has been discussed above (Section II. B.1). The relative ability of these cells to function normally in infected animals is a question that has not been adequately addressed.

Only one report, the experimental study of Murray et al. [63], addresses macrophage function in infected animals. These investigators found that *T. brucei*-infected mice were able to clear labeled SRBC from the circulation more rapidly than uninfected control mice; the increased clearance rate was attributed to increased hepatic, but not splenic, uptake. In infected spleens the total amount of label removed from the circulation was comparable with control spleens. However, it should be noted that infected spleens were up to 30 times larger than control spleens, so that less labeled material actually was removed from the circulation per milligram spleen tissue than in the controls. This is an important consideration since hypertrophy of the MPS accounts for much of the splenomegaly observed in infected animals (see Section I.B.2). Murray et al. [63] also demonstrated that peritoneal macrophages harvested from infected mice were able to ingest SRBC in vitro and passively transfer an immunogenic signal upon injection into uninfected mice. Thus, they suggest that the immunosuppression observed in their system [64] is not related to macrophage uptake or processing of antigen.

The only other published report on infected macrophages comes from the study of Stevens and Moulton [194]. They found that peritoneal macrophages from chronically infected mice were depressed in their ability to phagocytize trypanosomes. It was not clear whether this was a property of the cells or of the infected mouse antiserum which was used to promote phagocytosis. In unpublished studies, Smith and Mansfield have shown that parasite nonspecific macrophage function in *T. rhodesiense*-infected mice is normal in vitro and in vivo, throughout most of the infection.

No other experimental or clinical studies are currently available on macrophage function in disease. Initiation of such studies would be worthwhile, considering the pivotal role that the macrophage cell plays in the initiation and regulation of immune responses, in facilitating the clearance of trypanosomes, and perhaps in the development of infection-associated pathology. With respect to the latter point it seems clear that an altered MPS may not readily clear immune complexes from blood or other tissues.

B. Mechanism of Suppression

The central enigma of African trypanosomiasis is that B- and T-cell responses to a variety of antigens are depressed, yet the infected host is capable of making immune responses to a succession of VSSA. How and why the VSSA-specific immune responses are spared while parasite unrelated immune responses are depressed is not clear. Several theories have evolved from experimental studies which attempt to explain the cellular and molecular bases of parasite-nonspecific immunosuppression.

1. The Trypanosome B-Cell Mitogen

Greenwood [234] and others [220] have proposed that the African trypanosomes have a polyclonal B-cell-activating effect on the host immune system. It has been envisioned that a polyclonal B-cell mitogen is associated with the parasite, or secreted by it, to cause antigen-nonspecific proliferation and maturation of B cells. This would result in some of the immunopathological manifestations of the disease: histological expansion of B-dependent areas of spleen and lymph nodes, elevated serum and cerebrospinal fluid IgM levels, the spontaneous secretion of IgM with heterophile and autoimmune specificities, and "clonal exhaustion" of B cells with resultant immunosuppression.

The first direct evidence in support of this hypothesis was provided by Esuruoso [235]. In this study he demonstrated that normal uninfected mouse spleen cells were stimulated to undergo DNA synthesis in vitro by a trypanosome homogenate prepared from *T. brucei*. In addition it was shown that, whereas spleen cells from immunosuppressed mice (cyclophosphamide treatment) were unresponsive to the trypanosome preparation, spleen cells from nu/nu mice were more responsive than thymus-intact controls. Thus, a mitogenic effect of trypanosomes on B cells was demonstrated. Mansfield et al. [236] reported that extracts of *T. brucei* and *T. congolense* were stimulatory in vitro for normal rabbit spleen cells and peripheral blood lymphocytes. An additive mitogenic effect of trypanosome extracts on cultures stimulated with PHA, but not cultures stimulated with anti-Ig, suggested that the cell being stimulated by the extract was a B cell. However, trypanosome extracts failed to stimulate spleen cells from normal mice, rats, or guinea pigs. In addition the trypanosome extracts failed to induce polyclonal B-cell maturation of mouse spleen cells in an in vitro antibody response system, in contrast to the polyclonal activating effects of LPS. Although others, too, have been unable to confirm the mitogenic affects of trypanosome extracts for mouse B cells [69], the more recent studies of Assoku and Tizard [237] and Assoku et al. [224] demonstrated such activity associated with autolysates of trypanosomes. Assoku and Tizard [237] essentially repeated and confirmed the findings of Esuruoso [235], but with *T. congolense* instead of *T. brucei*. In addition, they suggest that the B-cell mitogen arises from autolysing organisms as the result of free fatty acid accumulation [224,237]. Assoku et al. [224] recently showed that mice acutely infected with *T. congolense* were immunosuppressed, and that autolysates of the organism used for infection were mitogenic for normal spleen cells in vitro. As the result of an examination of free fatty acids present in their preparations, they suggest that saturated fatty acids such as palmitic acid and stearic acid may be the principal mitogenic factors.

Clinical studies have mixed results. Greenwood and Oduloju [239] report that extracts prepared from *T. gambiense* possessed mitogenic activity for normal human peripheral blood and cord blood lymphocytes in vitro. They make several interesting observations. One is that sonication of both an old and freshly isolated strain produced extracts with little or no activity; repeated freeze-thawing of a third, freshly isolated strain produced mitogenically active extracts. Another is that the extracts stimulated IgM secretion by lymphocytes of only two out of five donors. Whether these findings represent technical problems or reflect important genetic differences in hosts and/or parasites should be investigated. Furthermore, when T- and B-cell-enriched cultures were incubated with the trypanosome extracts, only minimal stimulation resulted. Also, preliminary evidence was presented by Greenwood and Oduloju [239] for the mitogen being somewhat heat stable, partially trypsin-sensitive, and, perhaps, membrane bound. No other clinical studies have been reported, but efforts in our laboratory to stimulate human lymphocytes to undergo blastogenesis or polyclonal B-cell activation with extracts of one strain of *T. rhodesiense* have been unproductive.

Although no definitive studies have been reported for cattle, Sollod and Frank [229] imply that dead trypanosomes present in bovine lymphocyte cultures did not contribute significantly to culture incorporation of [^{3}H] thymidine. Thus, while there is some strong experimental evidence for a B-cell mitogen or polyclonal B-cell activator being associated with trypanosomes, the clinical studies have not been generally supportive.

That factors associated with African trypanosomes contribute directly to

B-cell *suppression* (as opposed to polyclonal B-cell *stimulation*) has not been confirmed. With respect to this point, related evidence is of interest. In many studies, control animals or cell cultures exposed to living or dead parasites were not suppressed [68,203,208,223,240]. For example, Moulton and Coleman [68] could not reproduce the suppressive effects of an active infection by injecting irradiated parasites into mice. Wellhausen and Mansfield [240] added the extract-equivalent of 10^7 trypanosomes to primary in vitro antibody response (Mishell-Dutton) cultures and did not observe suppression; enhancement was observed with lower amounts of parasite material. Similarly, when viable trypanosomes were added to in vitro cultures, enhancement of the PFC response with low numbers of parasites was observed; the responses were depressed when $\geqslant 5 \times 10^5$ trypanosomes were added to cultures, but this was attributed to nutrient depletion and death of the responder cells (e.g., artifactual depression). Similar effects were observed by Jayawardena and Waksman [203] for in vitro cultures.

Thus, the trypanosomal B-cell mitogen theory, while perhaps explaining the marked histologic expansion and antigen-nonspecific IgM secretion by B cells, does not adequately provide for B-cell suppression in infected animals. That clonal exhaustion of B cells occurs and, therefore, accounts for immunosuppression, as proposed, does not fit very well with some of the established facts. For example, complete suppression of B-cell function may be observed within several days of infection, yet histologic expansion of the B-cell system and spontaneous secretion of IgM by B cells occurs well beyond this time. Furthermore, the parasite-specific B-cell clones are somehow spared from suppression. Finally, recovery of B-cell function in several of the studies cited above (Section III.A) is quite rapid following trypanocidal chemotherapy, or when antigen and chemotherapy are given simultaneously. These general observations do not fit with a concept of clonal exhaustion resulting from B-cell maturation and proliferation. Also, it is unclear how this effect would lead to T-cell suppression.

Finally, with respect to the demonstrable biological effects in vitro of trypanosomes and/or their products (e.g., mitogenesis, C activation, and hemolysis), the question must be asked whether conditions exist in the host which would be favorable for the formation and activation of these effects. It may be that autolysis of large numbers of trypanosomes in a test tube and destruction of large numbers of trypanosomes in capillaries or tissue spaces are similar in that mitogenic, C-activating, and hemolytic factors are released or formed in sufficient quantity to produce the end effect. However, this remains to be proven experimentally or clinically.

2. Suppressor Cells

While it remains controversial whether or not the African trypanosomes cause immunosuppression by B-cell stimulation leading to clonal exhaustion or unresponsiveness, there is no question that antigen nonspecific suppressor cells are detectable in the spleens of experimentally infected animals.

The first evidence for suppressor cells being associated with the generalized immunosuppression of trypanosomiasis came from the study of Jayawardena and Waksman [203] on *T. brucei*-infected mice. In their study, they demonstrated that spleen cells from acutely infected mice were unresponsive to ConA, PHA, allogeneic cells, and LPS stimulation in vitro. When unresponsive infected mouse spleen cells were mixed with normal spleen cells, the unresponsiveness was passively transferred to the normal cells. Thus, they demonstrated that immunosuppression was *active* in nature rather than *passive* (e.g., it was not due to intrinsic unresponsiveness of responder cells). Contaminating trypanosomes that are present in infected spleen cell suspensions were shown not to be responsible for the suppression observed. Rather, a glass adherent Thy-1 negative cell present in infected mouse spleens was shown to be responsible for transfer of suppression. However, as the suppressor cell was not detectable in the spleens of infected nu/nu mice, Jayawardena and Waksman [203] suggested that the suppressor cell either was an antigen nonspecific suppressor T cell with a low level of membrane Thy-1 or was a suppressor cell dependent upon T cells for its generation.

Using the same strain of *T. brucei*, Corsini et al. [69] studied B-cell proliferation in vitro with spleen cells from infected mice. They found that cell proliferation preceded and accompanied Ig secretion by cells taken soon (up to day 10) after infection; Ig secretion in vitro by B cells taken later in infection (later than day 15) declined markedly. In parallel, spleen cells taken from mice early in infection (day 5) responded rapidly to LPS stimulation, but spleen cells from later in infection (later than day 8) were unresponsive to LPS. When such LPS unresponsive cells were depleted of T cells and macrophages, partial responsiveness and Ig secretion could be restored. However, the depletion techniques were not sufficient to restore responses when the spleen cells were harvested from mice after 12 days of infection. Corsini et al. [69] also passively transferred peritoneal macrophages from infected mice and found that macrophages from mice with infections of increasing duration were increasingly suppressive when mixed with LPS-stimulated normal spleen cells. On the basis of their findings, they suggested that B-cell potential was gradually exhausted by infection, and that suppressor T cells and macrophages may play a participatory role in the suppression observed.

Subsequently, Eardley and Jayawardena [223] demonstrated that spleen cells from *T. brucei*-infected mice were unable to mount primary in vitro PFC responses to SRBC or DNP-Ficoll in a Mishell-Dutton culture system. Following cell transfer experiments, which confirmed that a suppressor cell was present, they demonstrated that suppressor cell activity resided in both the T-cell and macrophage (but not B-cell) fractions of infected mouse spleens. They suggested that the trypanosomes directly stimulated antigen nonspecific suppressor

T cells which then released factors that induced macrophages to become suppressive, as in the manner of ConA-stimulated T cells releasing SIRS which activate suppressor macrophages [241].

In a follow-up study, Jayawardena et al. [242] confirmed the effects of *T. brucei* infection on mouse T-cells. They demonstrated that an early effect (earlier than day 6) of trypanosomes was activation of helper T-cell populations (Thy-1$^+$ and Lyt-1$^+$, 23$^-$) which, upon passive transfer, enhanced the responder culture response to SRBC but not DNP-Ficoll. Later in infection (later than day 6) a suppressor T-cell population (Thy-1$^+$ and Lyt-1$^+$, 23$^+$) was activated which suppressed normal culture responses to both SRBC and DNP-Ficoll. The helper and suppressor functions of trypanosome activated T cells occurred concomitantly in infected mice, but the suppressor effect masked the helper effect after 5 or 6 days of infection. Thus, Jayawardena et al. [242] proposed that direct stimulation of antigen nonspecific helper and suppressor T cells by trypanosomes (or their products) occurs in infected animals. Their results are perhaps similar to the recently defined interactions of T cells expressing the Qal$^+$ phenotype [243]: stimulated helper T cells (Lyt-1$^+$, 23$^-$ with Qal$^+$ and Qal$^-$ phenotypes) activate B cells; subsequently, the stimulated helper T cells with the Qal$^+$ phenotype induce suppressor T cells (Lyt-1$^+$, 23$^+$ Qal$^+$) which then exert feedback inhibition on either the Qal$^-$ helper cells or B cells.

This proposal is attractive in terms of our current understanding of immunoregulatory circuits in animals exposed to high levels of antigen. The recent studies of Askonas et al. [205] and Clayton et al. [206], however, suggest that events other than T-cell stimulation by trypanosomes are central to the polyclonal B-cell stimulation and ultimate immunosuppression occurring in African trypanosomiasis. Askonas et al. [205] examined B- and T-cell function in *T. brucei*-infected mice as a follow-up to the earlier studies of Corsini et al. [69]. It was found that passive transfer of infected mouse memory B cells, in vivo, in the absence of any detectable suppressor cells revealed a gradual loss of intrinsic potential to respond (or a specific depletion of such responsive cells). Similarly, memory helper T cells were transferred and shown to become unresponsive (or depleted) by infection. More importantly, they observed infections of T-deprived mice (see Section II.B.1) in which there was evidence for spontaneously elevated serum Ig levels and also for depression of the response of B cells to LPS, although the response was not depressed as rapidly in the T-deprived mice as in controls. Thus, they suggest that cellular depletion or loss of intrinsic B- and T-cell function occurs during infection, and that these events, and polyclonal B-cell activation, can occur in the absence of T cells. Clayton et al. [206] reported evidence supportive of these conclusions. In *T. brucei*-infected nu/nu mice they found that spontaneous splenic B-cell activation and Ig secretion, and ultimate suppression of B-cell responsiveness, occurred. Also, in a related study, Kobayakawa et al. [49] observed polyclonal B-cell stimulation in nu/nu mice infected with *T. brucei.* Thus, both enhanced Ig production and B-cell suppression develop in the absence of functional T cells.

Confirmation of the existence of splenic suppressor cells in other *Trypanosoma* spp.-infected mice was provided by Wellhausen and Mansfield [240,244, 245] and Mansfield et al. [72]. These investigators demonstrated that spleen cells from *T. rhodesiense*-infected mice were unable to mount primary in vitro PFC responses to SRBC in a Mishell-Dutton culture system within 3 days of infection. Associated with the development of immunosuppression was the appearance of a suppressor cell population in the spleen. The suppressor cells were shown to be macrophages (adherent, Ig⁻, Thy-1⁻, Lyt-23⁻, and nonspecific esterase⁺ cells); no involvement of T cells was detected.

Of importance was the discovery by Wellhausen and Mansfield [240,244] that the suppressor cell population was anatomically restricted to the spleens of infected animals, and that splenic B-cell immunosuppression occurred several weeks before lymph node B-cell suppression developed. Thus, whereas the acquisition of splenic B-cell unresponsiveness could be correlated with suppressor cell activity, the loss of lymph node B-cell function occurred in the absence of any detectable suppressor cell activity. Following trypanocidal chemotherapy, responsiveness returned gradually, first to the lymph nodes and subsequently to the spleen; recovery of splenic B-cell responses paralleled a loss of detectable suppressor cell activity [244].

Lymph-node-associated immunosuppression has not been directly addressed in any other study. However, there are clues that the lymph nodes are not as suppressed as, or are suppressed later than, the spleen in African trypanosomiasis. For example, Murray et al. [64] noted that the proliferative responses in mouse lymph nodes to oxazolone were not significantly depressed until late in infection with *T. brucei.* Similarly, Askonas et al. [205] noted that contact hypersensitivity reactions (probably mediated by regional lymph nodes) were not significantly depressed. Yet, skin allograft rejection was delayed markedly in *T. congolense*-infected mice [231].

Additional evidence for involvement of suppressor cells in the splenic immunosuppression is found in the recent studies of Pearson et al. [231,246] and Roelants et al. [247,248] on *T. congolense*-infected mice. They also describe an association between the loss of splenic B- and T-cell functions and the appearance of suppressor cells. The nature of the suppressor cell population(s) was not resolved but may be a combination of T cells and macrophages. Both immunosuppression and suppressor cell activity gradually were lost in spleens after trypanocidal chemotherapy [248]. Interestingly, they note that the appearance of suppressor cells and immunosuppression paralleled the appearance of parasites in the blood about 5-6 days after infection. This has not been the case in experimental *T. brucei* or *T. rhodesiense* infections [240,242] in which suppressor cell activity could be detected as early as 24-48 hr after infection.

Thus, extensive experimental evidence has accrued to implicate suppressor cells in the immunosuppression of African trypanosomiasis, even though the identity of the suppressor cell(s) is not certain. One question that has not been resolved in the studies of suppressor cells is the nature of the target cell(s). Although it is clear that selected B-cell and/or helper, cytotoxic, and suppressor T-cell functions may be depressed during infection (see Section III.A), it is not clear which of these cell types is/are the targets of the suppressor cell. In general, the studies suggest that both T-dependent and T-independent B-cell subpopulations are the targets of suppressor cells in vitro [205,206,223,242]. Also, the evidence suggests that the helper T-cell is a target in vitro [203,205,246].

There are some interesting variations in the general theme, however. One is that B-cell immunosuppression occurs later in lymph nodes than in spleen, and that loss of B-cell function in the nodes is not correlated with any suppressor cell population [240,244]. Another variation is that even though CTL function is depressed in vitro [231,72], and that CTL function is also lost earlier in spleen than in lymph nodes [72], there are no suppressor cells detectable in either spleen or lymph nodes which depress CTL responses [72]. Thus, an absolute correlation between immunosuppression and suppressor cell activity cannot be made for B-cell responses in lymph nodes and CTL responses in spleen and lymph nodes. With respect to CTL responses (and perhaps also to helper T-cell responses in the MLR culture [205]), an early anatomical dilution of CTL or accessory cells followed later by selective CTL loss (or acquisition of intrinsic unresponsiveness) may be responsible for the observed depression; the evidence is that enrichment for T cells will restore CTL function until the terminal phase of infection [72].

In the suppressor cell-target cell interaction, it is not yet established how the suppressor cell functions. Wellhausen and Mansfield [245] examined the interaction of splenic suppressor macrophages from *T. rhodesiense*-infected mice with responder B cells. They found that a noncytolytic cell-to-cell interaction was necessary to transfer suppression; isolation of suppressor and responder cells by a cell-impermeable membrane failed to cause suppression. Suppressor cell activity was unaffected by irradiation or mitomycin C treatment but was abrogated by exposure to silica particles. Pearson et al. [246] found that suppressor cell effects in *T. congolense*-infected mice were not completely eliminated by irradiation or mitomycin C treatment; they also determined that suppressor cell activity was not H-2 restricted with respect to target cells. No other information is available on mechanism of action of suppressor cells in trypanosomiasis.

All of the foregoing suppressor cell studies are with experimental model systems of African trypanosomiasis. There are no available clinical studies. For this reason, as well as those cited below, it is imperative that undue emphasis not be placed upon such mechanisms of immunosuppression at this time. Furthermore, all of the suppressor cell studies have been performed in vitro; the passive transfer of suppression in vivo with such cells has not yet been demonstrated. In a related study, however, Moulton and Coleman [251] transferred immuno-suppression to normal mice with a soluble substance extracted from *T. brucei*-infected mouse spleen. This is the first report on passive transfer of immuno-suppression in vivo by any agent other than trypanosomes. The source of the suppressor substance (e.g., host cells or parasites) was not determined. The biggest paradox concerning the evidence for suppressor cell activity is the exis-tence of serologic and histologic evidence for nonspecific B-cell activation and the serologic evidence for B-cell responsiveness to VSSA.

It is not clear that the in vitro studies are completely compatible with the in vivo studies. For example, T-independent B-cell responses in vivo may be elevated [66], but such responses in vitro appear to be depressed [223,242]. Also, we have noted that T-dependent B-cell responses in vivo are completely depressed only after about 5-7 days of infection, whereas such responses in vitro are depressed by day 3 [66,240]. Thus, in vitro systems may be more sensitive to suppression and may not be completely representative of changes occurring in vivo.

Alternative proposals to account for immunosuppression have been sug-gested. We [66,92,208,249] and others [94,222] have proposed that exagger-ated B-cell activation and loss of T-dependent types of immune responses may be attributed to selective loss or unresponsiveness of helper and suppressor T cells. For example, it may be that a loss (or dilution, or depression in function) of suppressor T cells allows for unregulated clonal expansion and IgM synthesis by B cells which have been stimulated by the trypanosomal mitogen. (Indeed, the effects of the trypanosome B-cell mitogen may only be optimal in cell popu-lations that are defective in such a regulatory T-cell component; this could ex-plain the difficulty in demonstrating mitogenic effects of trypanosomes on nor-mal lymphoid cell populations.) In addition, a loss of helper T-cell function would prevent the intraclonal switch of stimulated B cells from IgM to IgG syn-thesis; also, an inability of T-dependent B-cell subpopulations to respond appro-priately to antigenic stimulus would occur, and any helper T-cell-dependent responses would be diminished.

However, the facts again do not seem to completely support the hypothesis. Although we have demonstrated a selective loss of helper T-cell-dependent B-cell function in infected animals in concert with a loss of antigen-specific suppressor T-cell function [66], it is a fact that helper T-cell-independent B-cell function is also lost in the terminal phase of disease. Also, as mentioned above, spontaneous helper and suppressor T-cell activation has been noted in other animal model systems of African trypanosomiasis.

Additionally, there are other proposals that have been made but which still do not evade the paradoxes inherent in the observations. For example, Ackerman and Seed [250] have proposed that a trypanosomal metabolite, tryptophol (indole-3-ethanol), may be responsible for immunosuppression, and they have demonstrated that tryptophol is immunosuppressive for experimental animals. Why this suppression would be selective for non–VSSA-specific B cells and why nonspecific B-cell expansion would occur in such an environment are questions that have not been answered.

In reality it may be that immunosuppression is due to multiple, time-dependent, complex interactions of host and parasite factors. Some or all of the proposed mechanisms may be active at selected times during infection. The sequence of stimulatory/suppressive events may be orchestrated according to individual host and variant parasite genotypes. Obviously, much more work is needed in clinical and experimental systems of trypanosome-associated immunosuppression.

C. Immunotherapy

Immunotherapy could be aimed at eliminating the disease-associated generalized immunosuppression and immunopathology, or at strengthening the parasite-specific immune response. As in the field of tumor immunology, an in-depth understanding of the host-parasite immunobiological relationship must precede any meaningful approach to immunotherapy. It should be clear that very little is known about the immunology of clinical trypanosomiasis, and only a little more is known with certainty about the immunology of experimental trypanosomiasis. For this reason, we believe that prospects for immunotherapy of African trypanosomiasis are not promising at this time.

Nevertheless, attempts at immunotherapy have been made. Increased resistance to trypanosomes has been noted following administration of BCG, LPS, and synthetic polyribonucleotides [182,252-254]. However, the protective effects of these types of agents have not been confirmed, or are not readily reproducible [255]. Current studies in our laboratory involving interferon (type II) and thymosin therapy of infected mice have not yet revealed any marked benefits of such treatment.

In all such studies, care should be taken to avoid the possibility of inadvertent exacerbation of the disease process. Inappropriate stimulation of the immune system may result in an increase of immune complex-mediated pathology or elevated suppressor cell activity.

IV. CONCLUSIONS AND SUGGESTIONS

Much information has been accrued on the immunobiology of the host-parasite relationship in African trypanosomiasis. Unfortunately, a disproportionate amount of this information has been derived from experimental studies rather than from clinical cases. In the areas of immunopathology of infection, immune responses to parasites, and immunomodulation, there is a clear need for more clinically relevant material. This is not to suggest, however, that experimental model systems of African trypanosomiasis should not be exploited.

As discussed in Section I, there is much direct and indirect evidence of a clinical and experimental nature which implicates immune complexes in the pathology of disease. Future studies should focus on this type of pathology in infected humans and cattle. For example, the levels of circulating immune complexes should be measured and monitored before, during, and after trypanocidal chemotherapy. Correlations between immune complex levels and observable histopathology (or its resolution) should be made if possible. Detection of immune complexes in biopsy or autopsy material would be informative. Also, an analysis of the composition of immune complexes in terms of Ig class, the nature of trypanosome antigens (VSSA or invariant), and the presence of C components, in both clinical and experimental systems, would shed more light on this pathological process. Perhaps experimental and preliminary clinical studies could be initiated to reduce immune complex levels by artificial means.

Information on the extent and pathological significance of autoantibodies in infected humans and domestic animals is needed. Enumeration of T, B, and macrophage cells in clinical samples of infected blood, spleen, and lymph nodes is also needed to confirm the effects of trypanosomes on the numbers (and percentages) of these cells in various tissues. The experimental studies have suggested that the greatest effect is on B cells and macrophages; clinical correlation would help further our understanding of this aspect of the host-parasite relationship.

In terms of the immune response to trypanosomes, as discussed in Section II, additional experimental information on the VSSA composition of *Trypanosoma* species other than *T. brucei* would be desirable. Exquisitely specific probes of the VSSA molecule are being provided by hybridoma-derived monoclonal antibodies; such antibodies will not only provide domain-specific markers but may also help reveal possible VSSA gene induction by different Ig molecules specific for VSSA components. Further experimental studies on the trypanosome VSSA genes, through cloning into bacteria or by other means, are extremely desirable. Through such studies, the genetics of the VSSA switch will become clear and new avenues of attack in terms of preventing antigenic variation in infected hosts will be provided.

Additional experimental studies on the virulence of different variant types are needed. It may be that a particular few variant types are involved in terminal parasitemias in disease; if this were found to be true, then vaccines prepared with these variants would perhaps abort infections before they could become terminal or would perhaps prevent the extensive pathology and tissue involvement (e.g., CNS) seen with certain trypanosomes. Also, analyses of VSSA density or expression on the different antigenic variant types may reveal that a more T-dependent immune response to effectively eliminate them would be needed.

Although the superficially protective B-cell response is relatively T-independent in most experimental studies, it remains to be seen what the value of a more T-dependent response could be. Perhaps elimination of extravascular trypanosomes is one important function of IgG parasite-specific antibody. Also, the exact mechanism(s) of in vivo destruction or removal of antibody-sensitized parasites must be studied in more detail both clinically and experimentally, especially with reference to the role of the MPS.

One area ripe for continuing experimental as well as initial clinical study is the genetic bases of resistance to trypanosomes. When such bases are elucidated, perhaps biological or genetic manipulations of an appropriate nature will be useful in preventing or controlling disease in man or his domestic animals. Any associations between the MHC (or other genetic loci) and clinical pathology, susceptibility to infection or immunomodulation should be noted in infected humans and domestic animals.

Immunomodulation has been discussed in Section III. It is not yet clear how extensive or significant such trypanosome-induced changes are at the clinical level. While experimental studies should continue to elucidate parasite-induced changes in the immune system in vivo, particularly with respect to parasite-specific suppressor mechanisms, more information is needed on general T-, B-, and macrophage cell function in infected humans and cattle. Any loss of immunocompetence would have grave implications for an infected host in terms of secondary infections. And, for infected cattle, vaccinations needed for protection against the numerous microbes of veterinary interest would not be of value if immunosuppression were a common occurrence. Newer proposals concerning the effects of trypanosomes on immune function should be considered. For example, C activation by immune complexes and/or parasite products may have a preferential stimulatory effect on those cells with membrane receptors for split C components (e.g., B cells and macrophages). The subsequent expansion of these cellular compartments may result in an anatomical dilution of regulatory T cells, resulting in a loss of helper and suppressor functions. Ultimately, B cells and macrophages driven to clonal maturity may become inactive. These and other proposals should be examined for merit.

Currently there are no animal model systems which reproduce in all details the medical or veterinary forms of African trypanosomiasis. However, it is not unreasonable to continue using existing animal model systems of the disease at this time for the following reasons: (1) African trypanosomiasis can be studied in areas of the world more technologically advanced than endemic areas; (2) animal models of chronic trypanosomiasis are available which mimic many of the changes observed in humans or domestic animals; and (3) such model systems can provide valuable clues to the nature of immunopathology, immune responses to trypanosome antigens, and immunomodulation which can be applied to clinical studies. Finally, we as immunologists should not be so overconfident (or shortsighted) as to believe that immunology will provide the only avenues to the control or cure of African trypanosomiasis. A concerted multidisciplinary effort, both basic and clinical science, will be necessary to put this slumbering, smoldering "dragon" [5] to sleep forever.

ACKNOWLEDGMENTS

Studies from the author's laboratory which have been presented in this chapter were supported by funds from the National Institutes of Health (grants AI-15378 and AI-16467).

REFERENCES

1. Ormerod, W. E. (1979). Human and animal trypanosomiases as world public health problems. *Pharmacol. Therapeutics 6:*1.
2. DeRaadt, P. (1976). African sleeping sickness today. *Trans. R. Soc. Trop. Med. Hyg. 70:*114.
3. Baker, J. R. (1974). Epidemiology of African sleeping sickness. In *Trypanosomiasis and Leishmaniasis with Special Reference to Chagas' Disease,* Ciba Foundation Symposium 20. Associated Scientific Publishers, Amsterdam, p. 29.
4. Ormerod, W. E. (1976). Ecological effect of control of African trypanosomiasis. *Science 191:*815.
5. Goodwin, L. G. (1970). The pathology of African trypanosomiasis. *Trans. R. Soc. Trop. Med. Hyg. 64:*797.
6. Hoare, C. A. (1972). *The Trypanosomes of Mammals.* Blackwell Scientific Publications, Oxford.
7. H. W. Mulligan, Ed. (1970). *The African Trypanosomiases.* Allen and Unwin, London.
8. WHO/FAO Committee. (1979). African trypanosomiasis. *WHO Tech. Rep. Service 635:*1.
9. DeRaadt, P., and J. R. Seed (1977). Trypanosomes causing disease in man in Africa. In *Parasitic Protozoa,* Vol. I (J. P. Kreier, Ed.). Academic Press, New York, p. 175.
10. Soltys, M. A., and P. T. K. Woo (1977). Trypanosomes producing disease in livestock in Africa. In *Parasitic Protozoa,* Vol. I (J. P. Kreier, Ed.). Academic Press, New York, p. 239.
11. Fairbairn, H., and D. G. Godfrey (1957). The local reaction in man at the site of infection with *Trypanosoma rhodesiense. Ann. Trop. Med. Parasitol. 51:*464.
12. Apted, F. I. C. (1970). Clinical manifestations and diagnosis of sleeping sickness. In *The African Trypanosomiases* (H. W. Mulligan, Ed.). Allen and Unwin, London, p. 661.
13. Ormerod, W. E. (1970). Pathogenesis and pathology of trypanosomiasis in man. In *The African Trypanosomiases* (H. W. Mulligan, Ed.). Allen and Unwin, London, p. 587.

14. Fiennes, R. N. T.- W.- (1970). Pathogenesis and pathology of animal try-panosomiasis. In *The African Trypanosomiases* (H. W. Mulligan, Ed.). Allen and Unwin, London, p. 729.

15. Doyle, J. J. (1977). Antigenic variation in the salivarian trypanosomes. *Adv. Exp. Med. Biol. 93:*31.

16. Vickerman, K. (1978). Antigenic variation in trypanosomes. *Nature (Lond.) 273:*613.

17. Cross, G. A. M. (1978). Antigenic variation in trypanosomes. *Proc. R. Soc. Lond. [Biol.] 202:*55.

18. Fiennes, R. N. T.-W. (1950). The cattle trypanosomiases: Some consider-ations of pathology and immunity. *Ann. Trop. Med. Parasitol. 44:*42.

19. Losos, G. J., and B. O. Ikede (1972). Review of pathology of diseases in domestic and laboratory animals caused by *Trypanosoma congolense, T. vivax, T. brucei, T. rhodesiense* and *T. gambiense. Vet. Pathol. 9 (Suppl.):* 1.

20. Valli, V. E. O., and C. M. Forsberg (1979). The pathogenesis of *Trypanosoma congolense* infection in calves. V. Quantitative histological changes. *Vet. Pathol. 16:*334.

21. Hornby, H. E. (1921). Trypanosomes and trypanosomiases of cattle. *J. Comp. Pathol. 34:*211.

22. Goodwin, L. G. (1974). The African scene: Mechanisms of pathogenesis in trypanosomiasis. In *Trypanosomiasis and Leishmaniasis with Special Reference to Chagas' Disease,* Ciba Foundation Symposium 20. Associated Scientific Publishers, Amsterdam, p. 107.

23. Mott, F. W. (1906). The changes produced in the nervous system by chronic trypanosome infections. *Lancet ii:*870.

24. Peruzzi, M. R. I. (1928). Pathologico-anatomical and serological observa-tions on trypanosomiases. In *Final Report, League of Nations International Commission on Human Trypanosomiasis, 3.* League of Nations, Geneva, p. 245.

25. McCully, R. M., and N. M. Neitz (1971). Clinico-pathological study on experimental *Trypanosoma brucei* infections in horses. 2. Histopatho-logical finding in the nervous system and other organs of treated and un-treated horses reacting to nagana. *Onderstepoort J. Vet. Res. 38:*141.

26. Boreham, P. F. L. (1968). Immune reactions and kinin formation in chronic trypanosomiasis. *Br. J. Pharmacol. Chemother. 32:*493.

27. Boreham, P. F. L. (1970). Kinin release and the immune reaction in hu-man trypanosomiasis caused by *Trypanosoma rhodesiense. Trans. R. Soc. Trop. Med. Hyg. 64:*394.

28. Boreham, P. F. L., and L. G. Goodwin (1970). The release of kinins as the result of an antigen-antibody reaction in trypanosomiasis. In *Brady-kinin and Related Kinins: Cardiovascular, Biochemical and Neural Actions* (F. Sicuteri, Ed.). Plenum, New York, p. 534.

29. Tizard, I. R., and M. A. Soltys (1971). Cell-mediated hypersensitivity in rabbits infected with *Trypanosoma brucei* and *Trypanosoma rhodesiense. Infect. Immun. 4:*674.

30. Mansfield, J. M., and J. P. Kreier (1972). Tests for antibody- and cell-mediated hypersensitivity to trypanosome antigens in rabbits infected with *Trypanosoma congolense. Infect. Immun. 6:*62.

31. Muschel, L. H., L. A. Simonton, P. A. Wells, and E. H. Fife, Jr. (1961). Occurrence of complement-fixing antibodies reactive with normal tissue constituents in normal and disease states. *J. Clin. Invest. 40:*517.

32. Barrett-Conner, E., R. J. Ugoretz, and A. I. Braude (1973). Disseminated intravascular coagulation in trypanosomiasis. *Arch. Intern. Med. 131:*574.

33. Nagle, R. B., P. A. Ward, H. B. Lindsley, E. H. Sadun, A. J. Johnson, R. E. Berkaw, and P. K. Hildebrandt (1974). Experimental infections with African trypanosomes. VI. Glomerulonephritis involving the alternate pathway of complement activation. *Am. J. Trop. Med. Hyg. 23:*15.

34. Greenwood, B. M., and H. C. Whittle (1976). Complement activation in patients with Gambian sleeping sickness. *Clin. Exp. Immunol. 24:*133.

35. Nielsen, K., J. Sheppard, W. Holmes, and I. Tizard (1978). Experimental bovine trypanosomiasis. Changes in the catabolism of serum immunoglobulins and complement components in infected cattle. *Immunology 35:*811.

36. Nielsen, K., J. Sheppard, W. Holmes, and I. Tizard (1978). Experimental bovine trypanosomiasis. Changes in serum immunoglobulins, complement and complement components in infected animals. *Immunology 35:*817.

37. Lambert, P. H., and V. Houba (1974). Immune complexes in parasitic diseases. In *Progress in Immunology II,* Vol. 5 (L. Brent, and J. Holborow, Eds.). North-Holland Publishing Co., Amsterdam, p. 57.

38. Galvao-Castro, B., A. Hochmann, and P. H. Lambert (1978). The role of the host immune response in the development of tissue lesions associated with African trypanosomiasis in mice. *Clin. Exp. Immunol. 33:*12.

39. Facer, C. E., E. A. Molland, A. B. Gray, and G. C. Jenkins (1978). *Trypanosoma brucei:* Renal pathology in rabbits. *Exp. Parasitol. 44:*249.

40. Mamo, E., and P. H. Holmes (1975). The erythrokinetics of Zebu cattle chronically infected with *Trypanosoma congolense. Res. Vet. Sci. 18:*105.

41. Jennings, F. W., P. K. Murray, M. Murray, and G. M. Urquhart (1974). Anemia in trypanosomiasis: Studies in rats and mice infected with *Trypanosoma brucei. Res. Vet. Sci. 16:*70.

42. Woodruff, A. W., J. L. Ziegler, A. Hathaway, and T. Gwata (1973). Anemia in African trypanosomiasis and "big spleen disease" in Uganda. *Trans. R. Soc. Trop. Med. Hyg. 67:*329.

43. Wellde, B., R. Lotzsch, G. Deindl, E. Sadun, J. Williams, and G. Warui (1974). *Trypanosoma congolense.* Clinical observations of experimentally infected cattle. *Exp. Parasitol. 36:*6.

44. Kobayashi, A., I. R. Tizard, and P. T. K. Woo (1976). Studies on the anemia in experimental African trypanosomiasis. II. The pathogenesis of the anemis in calves infected with *Trypanosoma congolense. Am. J. Trop. Med. Hyg. 25:*401.

45. Ikede, B. O., M. Lule, and R. J. Terry (1977). Anemia in trypanosomiasis:

mechanisms of erythrocyte destruction in mice infected with *Trypanosoma congolense* or *T. brucei. Acta Trop. (Basel) 34:*53.

46. Herbert, W. J., and M. D. Inglis (1973). Immunization of mice against *T. brucei* Infection by the administration of released antigen adsorbed to erythrocytes. *Trans. R. Soc. Trop. Med. Hyg. 67:*268.

47. Dodd, B. E., G. C. Jenkins, P. J. Lincoln, and P. McCrorie (1978). The advantage of a build-up antiglobulin technique for the detection of immuno-globulin on the red cells of rabbits infected with trypanosomes. A prelimi-nary report. *Trans. R. Soc. Trop. Med. Hyg. 72:*501.

48. MacKenzie, A. R., and P. F. L. Boreham (1974). Auto-immunity in try-panosome infections. III. The anti-globulin (Coombs) test. *Acta Trop. (Basel) 31:*360.

49. Kobayakawa, T., J. Louis, S. Izui, and P. H. Lambert (1979). Autoim-mune response to DNA, red blood cells, and thymocyte antigens in asso-ciation with polyclonal antibody synthesis during experimental African trypanosomiasis. *J. Immunol. 122:*296.

50. Greenwood, B. M. (1974). Possible role of a B cell mitogen in hyper-gammaglobulinemia in malaria and trypanosomiasis. *Lancet i:*435.

51. Tizard, I., K. H. Nielsen, J. R. Seed, and J. E. Hall (1978). Biologically active products from African trypanosomes. *Microbiol. Rev. 42:*661.

52. Tizard, I., and W. L. Holmes (1976). The generation of toxic activity from *Trypanosoma congolense. Experientia 32:*1533.

53. Tizard, I., W. L. Holmes, D. A. York, and A. Mellors (1977). The genera-tion and identification of the haemolysin of *Trypanosoma congolense. Experientia 33:*901.

54. Tizard, I. R., J. Sheppard, and K. Nielsen (1978). The characterization of a second class of haemolysins from *Trypanosoma brucei. Trans. R. Soc. Trop. Med. Hyg. 72:*198.

55. Huan, C. N. (1975). Pathogenesis of the anemia in African trypanosomiasis: characterization and purification of a hemolytic factor. *J. Suisse Med. 105:*1582.

56. Musoke, A. J., and A. F. Barbet (1977). Activation of complement by variant-specific surface antigen of *Trypanosoma brucei. Nature (Lond.) 270:*438.

57. Nielsen, K., J. Sheppard, I. Tizard, and W. Holmes (1978). Direct activa-tion of complement by trypanosomes. *J. Parasitol. 64:*544.

58. Thomasson, D. L., J. M. Mansfield, R. J. Doyle, and J. H. Wallace (1973). C-reactive protein levels in experimental African trypanosomiasis. *J. Para-sitol. 59:*738.

59. Poltera, A. A., R. Owor, and J. N. Cox (1977). Pathological aspects of human African trypanosomiasis (HAT) in Uganda. A post-mortem survey of fourteen cases. *Virchows Arch. [Pathol. Anat.] 373:*249.

60. Greenwood, B. M., H. C. Whittle, K. O. Oduloju, and R. R. Dourmashkin (1976). Lymphocytic infiltration of the brain in sleeping sickness. *Br. Med. J. 6047:*1291.

61. Greenwood, B. M., and H. C. Whittle (1965). Production of free light chains in Gambian trypanosomiasis. *Clin. Exp. Immunol. 20:*437.

62. DeRaadt, P., M. P. Cunningham, C. D. Kimber, and E. G. Grainge (1966). Trials of a skin test for sleeping sickness. *East Afr. Trypanosomiasis Res. Org. Rep. 1965:*33.

63. Murray, P. K., F. W. Jennings, M. Murray, and G. M. Urquhart (1974). The nature of immunosuppression in *Trypanosoma brucei* infections in mice. II. The role of the macrophage. *Immunology 27:*815.

64. Murray, P. K., F. W. Jennings, M. Murray, and G. M. Urquhart (1974). The nature of immunosuppression in *Trypanosoma brucei* infections in mice. II. The role of T and B lymphocytes. *Immunology 27:*825.

65. Murray, M. (1974). The pathology of African trypanosomiases. In *Progress in Immunology II*, Vol. 4 (L. Brent, and J. Holborow, Eds.). North-Holland Publishing Co., Amsterdam, p. 181.

66. Mansfield, J. M., and O. Bagasra (1978). Lymphocyte function in experimental African trypanosomiasis. I. B cell responses to helper T cell-dependent and independent antigens. *J. Immunol. 120:*759.

67. Moulton, J. E., and D. R. Stevens (1978). Animal model: Trypanosomiasis in deer mice. *Am. J. Pathol. 91:*693.

68. Moulton, J. E., and J. L. Coleman (1977). Immunosuppression in deer mice with experimentally induced trypanosomiasis. *Am. J. Vet. Res. 38:*573.

69. Corsini, A. C., C. Clayton, B. A. Askonas, and B. M. Ogilvie (1977). Suppressor cells and loss of B-cell potential in mice infected with *Trypanosoma brucei. Clin. Exp. Immunol. 29:*122.

70. Morrison, W. I., G. E. Roelants, K. S. Mayor-Withey, and M. Murray (1978). Susceptibility of inbred strains of mice to *Trypanosoma congolense:* correlation with changes in spleen lymphocyte populations. *Clin. Exp. Immunol. 32:*25.

71. Mayor-Withey, K. S., C. E. Clayton, G. E. Roelants, and B. A. Askonas (1978). Trypanosomiasis leads to extensive proliferation of B, T and null cells in spleen and bone marrow. *Clin. Exp. Immunol. 34:*359.

72. Mansfield, J. M., S. R. Wellhausen, and O. Bagasra (1981). Immunomodulation in African trypanosomiasis. In *The Immunobiology of Parasitic Infections* (H. Friedman and W. Sodeman, Eds.). University Park Press, Baltimore, in press.

73. Luckins. A. G. (1976). The immune response of Zebu cattle to infection with *Trypanosoma congolense* and *T. vivax. Ann. Trop. Med. Parasitol. 70:*133.

74. Mattern, P. (1962). B_2-macroglobulinorachie importante chez des malades atteints de trypanosomiase Africaine. *Ann. Inst. Pasteur (Paris) 102:*64.

75. Mattern, P. (1964). Techniques et intérêt épidémiologique du diagnostic de la trypanosomiase humaine Africaine par la recherche de la B_2-macroglobuline dan le sang et dans le L.C.R. *Ann. Inst. Pasteur (Paris) 107:*415.

76. Cornille, R., and M. Hornung (1968). Determination of serum IgM levels

for the diagnosis of *T. rhodesiense* infections. *Am. J. Trop. Med. Hyg. 17:* 522.

77. Houba, V., K. N. Brown, and A. C. Allison (1969). Heterophile antibodies, M-antiglobulins and immunoglobulins in experimental trypanosomiasis. *Clin. Exp. Immunol. 4:*113.

78. Klein, F., P. Mattern, H. J. Kornman-V.D. Bosch (1970). Experimental induction of rheumatoid factor-like substances in animal trypanosomiasis. *Clin. Exp. Immunol. 7:*851.

79. Frommel, D., D. Y. E. Perey, R. Masseyeff, and R. A. Good (1970). Low molecular weight serum immunoglobulin M in experimental trypanosomiasis. *Nature (Lond.) 228:*1208.

80. Capberg, A., P. Mattern, and R. Pautrizel (1974). Étude comparative du taux des protéines sériques au cours de trypanosomoses à *Trypanosoma gambiense* et à *Trypanosoma cruzi* chez la souris. *Exp. Parasitol. 35:*86.

81. Clarkson, M. J., W. J. Penhale, and R. B. McKenna (1975). Progressive serum protein changes in experimental infections of calves with *Trypanosoma vivax. J. Comp. Pathol. 85:*397.

82. Clarkson, M. J. (1976). Immunoglobulin M in trypanosomiasis. In *Pathophysiology of Parasitic Infection* (E. J. L. Soulsby, Ed.). Academic Press, New York, p. 171.

83. Cunningham, M. P., N. M. Bailey, and C. D. Kimber (1967). The estimation of IgM immunoglobulin in dried blood for use as a screening test in the diagnosis of human trypanosomiasis in Africa. *Trans. R. Soc. Trop. Med. Hyg. 61:*688.

84. Freeman, T., S. R. Smithers, G. A. Targett, and P. J. Walker (1970). Specificity of immunoglobulin G in Rhesus monkeys infected with *Schistosoma mansoni, Plasmodium knowlesi,* and *Trypanosoma brucei. J. Infect. Dis. 121:*401.

85. Massayeff, R. (1969). Les immunoglobulines au cours des trypanosomiases. In *Synthèse Cellulaire et Structure Moléculaire des Immunoglobulines* (B. Halpern, Ed.). Dunod, Paris, p. 339.

86. Henderson-Begg, A. (1946). Heterophile antibodies in trypanosomiasis. *Trans. R. Soc. Trop. Med. Hyg. 40:*331.

87. Houba, V., and A. C. Allison (1966). M-antiglobulins (rheumatoid-factor-like globulins) and other gamma globulins in relation to tropical parasitic infections. *Lancet i:*848.

88. Hudson, K. M., C. Byner, J. Freeman, and R. J. Terry (1976). Immunodepression, high IgM levels and evasion of the immune response in murine trypanosomiasis. *Nature (Lond.) 264:*256.

89. Klein, F., and P. Mattern (1965). Rheumatoid factors in primary and reactive macroglobulinaemia. *Ann. Rheum. Dis. 24:*458.

90. Ross, J. M., and M. H. V. Van Regenmortel (1977). Autoimmunity and absence of rheumatoid factors in experimental *Trypanosoma (Trypanozoon) equiperdum* infections in rabbit. *Ann. Immunol. (Inst. Pasteur) 128C:*817.

91. Seed, J. R., and A. A. Gam (1967). The presence of antibody to a normal rabbit liver antigen in rabbits infected with *Trypanosoma gambiense*. *J. Parasitol. 53:*946.

92. Mansfield, J. M., and J. P. Kreier (1972). Autoimmunity in experimental *Trypanosoma congolense* infections of rabbits. *Infect. Immun. 5:*648.

93. Allt, G., E. M. E. Evans, D. H. L. Evans, and G. A. T. Targett (1971). Effect of infection with trypanosomes on the development of experimental allergic neuritis in rabbits. *Nature (Lond.) 233:*197.

94. MacKenzie, A. R., and P. F. L. Boreham (1974). Autoimmunity in trypanosome infections. I. Tissue autoantibodies in *Trypanosoma (Trypanozoon) brucei* infections of the rabbit. *Immunology 26:*1225.

95. Lindsley, H. B., S. Kysela, and A. D. Steinberg (1974). Nucleic acid antibodies in African trypanosomiasis: Studies in rhesus monkeys and man. *J. Immunol. 113:*1921.

96. Ingram, D. G., and M. A. Soltys (1960). Immunity in trypanosomiasis. IV. Immunoconglutinin in animals infected with *Trypanosoma brucei*. *Parasitology 50:*231.

97. Boreham, P. F. L., and C. A. Facer (1974). Autoimmunity in trypanosome infections. II. Anti-fibrin/fibrinogen (Anti-F) autoantibody in *Trypanosoma (Trypanozoon) brucei* infections of the rabbit. *Int. J. Parasitol. 4:*601.

98. Rickman, W. J., and H. W. Cox (1979). Association of autoantibodies with anemia, splenomegaly, and glomerulonephritis in experimental African trypanosomiasis. *J. Parasitol. 65:*65.

99. Vickerman, K. (1969). On the surface coat and flagellar adhesion in trypanosomes. *J. Cell Sci. 5:*163:

100. Vickerman, K., and A. G. Luckins (1969). Localization of variable antigens in the surface coat of *Trypanosoma brucei* using ferritin conjugated antibody. *Nature (Lond.) 224:*1125.

101. Vickerman, K. (1974). The ultrastructure of pathogenic flagellates. In *Trypanosomiasis and Leishmaniasis with Special Reference to Chagas' Disease*, Ciba Foundation Symposium 20. Associated Scientific Publishers, Amsterdam, p. 171.

102. Fruit, J., D. Afchain, A. Petitrrez, N. VanMiervenne, D. LeRay, D. Bout, and A. Capron (1977). Antigenic analysis of a variant-specific component of *Trypanosoma brucei:* Localization on the surface coat with labeled specific antibodies. *Parasitology 74:*185.

103. Cross, G. A. M. (1979). Immunochemical aspects of antigenic variation in trypanosomes. *J. Gen. Microbiol. 113:*1.

104. Barry, J. D., and K. Vickerman (1979). *Trypanosoma brucei:* Loss of variable antigens during transformation from bloodstream to procyclic forms in vitro. *Exp. Parasitol. 48:*313.

105. Seed, J. R. (1964). Antigenic similarity among culture forms of the *brucei* group of trypanosomes. *Parasitology 54:*593.

106. Honigberg, B. M., I. Cunningham, H. A. Stanley, K. E. Su-Lin, and A. G.

Luckins (1976). *Trypanosoma brucei:* Antigenic analysis of bloodstream, vector and culture stages by the quantitative fluorescent antibody methods. *Exp. Parasitol. 39:*496.

107. Ghiotto, V., R. Brun, L. Jenni, and H. Hecker (1979). *Trypanosoma brucei:* Morphometric changes and loss of infectivity during transformation of bloodstream forms to procyclic culture forms in vitro. *Exp. Parasitol. 48:*447.

108. Cross, G. A. M. (1975). Identification, purification and properties of clone-specific glycoprotein antigens constituting the surface coat of *Trypanosoma brucei. Parasitology 71:*393.

109. Cross, G. A. M., and J. G. Johnson (1976). Structure and organization of variant-specific surface antigens of *Trypanosoma brucei.* In *Biochemistry of Parasites and Host-Parasite Relationships* (H. Van den Bossche, Ed.). Elsevier North-Holland, Amsterdam, p. 413.

110. Johnson, J. G., and G. A. M. Cross (1977). Carbohydrate composition of variant-specific surface antigen glycoproteins from *Trypanosoma brucei. J. Protozool. 24:*587.

111. Jackson, P. R. (1977). Lectin binding by *Trypanosoma equiperdum. J. Parasitol. 63:*8.

112. Wright, K. A., and H. Hales (1970). Cytochemistry of the pellicle of *Trypanosoma (Trypanozoon) brucei. J. Parasitol. 56:*671.

113. Bridgen, P. J., G. A. M. Cross, and J. Bridgen (1976). N-terminal amino acid sequence of variant-specific surface antigens from *Trypanosoma brucei. Nature (Lond.) 263:*613.

114. Johnson, J. G., and G. A. M. Cross (1979). Selective cleavage of variant surface glycoproteins from *Trypanosoma brucei. Biochem. J. 178:*689.

115. Weitz, B. (1960). The properties of some antigens of *Trypanosoma brucei. J. Gen. Microbiol. 23:*589.

116. Weitz, B. (1970). Infection and resistance. In *The African Trypanosomiases* (H. W. Mulligan, Ed.). Allen and Unwin, London, p. 97.

117. Allsopp, B. A., A. R. Njogu, and K. C. Humphryes (1971). Nature and location of *Trypanosoma brucei* subgroup exoantigen and its relationship to 4 S antigen. *Exp. Parasitol. 29:*271.

118. Baltz, T., D. Baltz, R. Pautrizel, C. Richet, G. Lamblin, and P. Degand (1977). Chemical and immunological characterization of specific glycoproteins from *Trypanosoma equiperdum* variants. *FEBS Letters 82:*93.

119. Barbet, A. F., and T. C. McGuire (1978). Crossreacting determinants in variant-specific surface antigens of African trypanosomes. *Proc. Natl. Acad. Sci. U.S.A. 75:*1989.

120. Cross, G. A. M. (1979). Crossreacting determinants in the C-terminal region of trypanosome variant surface antigens. *Nature (Lond.) 277:*310.

121. Rovis, L., A. F. Barbet, and R. O. Williams (1978). Characterization of the surface coat of *Trypanosoma congolense. Nature (Lond.) 271:*654.

122. Reinwald, E., H. J. Risse, and R. Selker (1978). Identification of the surface coat protein of *Trypanosoma congolense* by use of diazotised sulfanilic acid. *Hoppe Seylers Z. Physiol. Chem. 359:*939.

123. Cross, G. A. M. (1977). Isolation, structure and function of variant-specific surface antigens. *Ann. Soc. Belg. Med. Trop. 57:*389.

124. World Health Organization Committee (1977). Antigenic variation in African trypanosomiasis: A memorandum. *Bull. WHO 55:*703.

125. Gray, A. R., and A. G. Luckins (1976). Antigenic variation in salavarian trypanosomes. In *Biology of the Kinetoplastids* (W. H. R. Lumsden and D. A. Evans, Eds.). Academic Press, New York, p. 493.

126. Gray, A. R. (1965). Antigenic variation in a strain of *Trypanosoma brucei* transmitted by *Glossina morsitans* and *G. palpalis. J. Gen. Microbiol. 41:*195.

127. Jenni, L. (1977). Comparisons of antigenic types of *Trypanosoma (T.) brucei* strains transmitted by *Glossina m. morsitans. Acta Trop. (Basel) 34:*35.

128. Jones, T. W., and M. J. Clarkson (1972). The effect of syringe and cyclical passage on antigenic variants of *Trypanosoma vivax. Ann. Trop. Med. Parasitol. 66:*303.

129. Gray, A. R. (1965). Antigenic variation in clones of *Trypanosoma brucei. Ann. Trop. Med. Parasitol. 59:*27.

130. LeRay, D., J. D. Barry, C. Easton, and K. Vickerman (1977). First tsetse fly transmission of the "AnTat" serodeme of *Trypanosoma brucei. Ann. Soc. Belg. Med. Trop. 57:*369.

131. LeRay, D., J. D. Barry, and K. Vickerman (1978). Antigenic heterogeneity of metacyclic forms of *Trypanosoma brucei. Nature (Lond.) 273:* 300.

132. Barry, J. D., S. L. Hajduk, K. Vickerman (1979). Detection of multiple variable antigen types in metacyclic populations of *Trypanosoma brucei. Trans. R. Soc. Trop. Med. Hyg. 73:*205.

133. Gray, A. R. (1962). The influence of antibody on serological variation in *Trypanosoma brucei. Ann. Trop. Med. Parasitol. 56:*4.

134. Gray, A. R. (1975). A pattern in the development of agglutinogenic antigens of cyclically transmitted isolates of *Trypanosoma gambiense. Trans. R. Soc. Trop. Med. Hyg. 69:*131.

135. Wilson, A. J., and M. P. Cunningham (1972). Immunological aspects of bovine trypanosomiasis. I. Immune responses of cattle to infection with *Trypanosoma congolense* and the antigenic variation of the infecting organisms. *Exp. Parasitol. 32:*165.

136. McNeillage, G. J. C., W. J. Herbert, and W. H. R. Lumsden (1969). Antigenic type of first relapse variants arising from a strain of *Trypanosoma (Trypanozoon) brucei. Exp. Parasitol. 25:*1.

137. Campbell, G. H., K. M. Esser, B. T. Wellde, and C. L. Diggs (1979). Isolation and characterization of a new serodeme of *Trypanosoma rhodesiense. Am. J. Trop. Med. Hyg. 28:*974.

138. DeGee, A. L. W., S. D. Shah, and J. J. Doyle (1979). *Trypanosoma vivax:* Sequence of antigenic variants in mice and goats. *Exp. Parasitol. 48:*352.

139. Nantulya, V. M., A. J. Musoke, A. F. Barbet, and G. E. Roelants (1979).

Evidence for reappearance of *Trypanosoma brucei* variable antigen types in relapse populations. *J. Parasitol. 65:*673.

140. VanMeirvenne, N., P. G. Janssens, and E. Magnus (1975). Antigenic variation in syringe passaged populations of *Trypanosoma (Trypanozoon) brucei.* I. Rationalization of the experimental approach. *Ann. Soc. Belg. Med. Trop. 55:*1.

141. Seed, J. R., and H. G. Effron (1973). Simultaneous presence of different antigenic populations of *Trypanosoma brucei gambiense* in *Microtus montanus. Parasitology 66:*269.

142. Takayanagi, T., and G. L. Enriquez (1973). Effects of the IgG and IgM immunoblobulins in *Trypanosoma gambiense* infections in mice. *J. Parasitol. 59:*644.

143. Barry, J. D. (1979). Capping of variable antigen on *Trypanosoma brucei,* and its immunological and biological significance. *J. Cell Sci. 37:*287.

144. Balber, A. E., J. D. Bangs, S. M. Jones, and R. L. Proia (1979). Inactivation or elimination of potentially trypanolytic, complement-activating immune complexes by pathogenic trypanosomes. *Infect. Immun. 24:* 617.

145. Cantrell, W. (1958). Mutation rate and antigenic variation in *Trypanosoma equiperdum. J. Infect. Dis. 103:*263.

146. Watkins, J. F. (1964). Observations on antigenic variation in a strain of *Trypanosoma brucei* growing in mice. *J. Hyg. 62:*69.

147. Seed, J. R., and A. A. Gam (1966). Passive immunity to experimental trypanosomiasis. *J. Parasitol. 52:*1134.

148. Seed, J. R. (1974). Antigens and antigenic variability of the African trypanosomes. *J. Protozool. 21:*639.

149. LeRay, D. (1975). Structures antigéniques de *Trypanosoma brucei* (Protozoa, Kinetoplastida). Analyse immunoélectrophorétique et étude comparative. *Ann. Soc. Belg. Med. Trop. 55:*129.

150. Desowitz, R. S. (1970). African trypanosomes. In *Immunity to Parasitic Animals,* Vol. 2 (G. J. Jackson, R. Herman, and I. Singer, Eds.). Appleton-Century-Crofts, New York, p. 551.

151. DeRaadt, P. (1974). Immunity and antigenic variation: Clinical observations suggestive of immune phenomena in African trypanosomiasis. In *Trypanosomiasis and Leishmaniasis With Special Reference to Chagas' Disease,* Ciba Foundation Symposium 20. Associated Scientific Publishers, Amsterdam, p. 199.

152. Mahmoud, M. M., and J. P. Kreier (1972). *Trupanosoma congolense:* Latex fixation test for diagnosis of rabbit infections. *Exp. Parasitol. 31:* 109.

153. Vickerman, K. (1972). The host-parasite interface of parasitic protozoa. In *Functional Aspects of Parasite Surfaces* (A. E. R. Taylor and R. Muller, Eds.). Blackwell Scientific Publishers, Oxford, p.

154. Diffley, P., and B. M. Honigberg (1977). Fluorescent antibody analysis of host forms of African pathogenic trypanosomes. I. Host specificity and time of accretion on *Trypanosoma congolense. J. Parasitol. 63:*599.

155.   Diffley, P., and B. M. Honigberg (1978). Immunologic analysis of host plasma proteins on bloodstream forms of African pathogenic trypanosomes. II. Identification and quantitation of surface-bound albumin, nonspecific IgG, and complement on *Trypanosoma congolense*. *J. Parasitol. 64:*674.

156.   Bogucki, M. S., and J. R. Seed (1978). Parasite-bound heterospecific antibody in experimental African trypanosomiasis. *J. Res. 23:*89.

157.   Diffley, P. (1978). Comparative immunological analysis of host plasma proteins bound to bloodstream forms of *Trypanosoma brucei* subspecies. *Infect. Immun. 21:*605.

158.   Franke, E. (1905). Ueber trypanosomen therapie. *Munch. Med. Wochenschr. 52:*2059.

159.   Soltys, M. A. (1957). Immunity in trypanosomiasis. II. Agglutination reaction with African trypanosomes. *Parasitology 47:*390.

160.   Seed, J. R., R. L. Cornille, E. L. Risby, A. A. Gam (1969). The presence of agglutinating antibody in the IgM immunoglobulin fraction of rabbit antiserum during experimental African trypanosomiasis. *Parasitology 59:* 283.

161.   Takayanagi, T., H. Kambara, and G. L. Enriquez (1973). *Trypanosoma gambiense* immunity with spleen cell and antiserum transfer in mice. *Exp. Parasitol. 33:*429.

162.   Gray, A. R. (1960). Precipitating antibody in trypanosomiasis of cattle and other animals. *Nature (Lond.) 186:*1058.

163.   Seed, J. R. (1972). *Trypanosoma gambiense* and *T. equiperdum:* Characterization of variant specific antigens. *Exp. Parasitol. 31:*98.

164.   Koch, R. (1901). Ein versuch zur immunisirung von rindern gegen tsetse-krankheit (surra). *Deutsch Kolonialblatt (Suppl.) 12:*4.

165.   Lapierre, J., and J. J. Rousset (1961). Étude de l'immunité dans les infections à *Trypanosoma gambiense* chez la souris blanche. Variations antigéniques au cours des crises trypanolytiques. *Bull. Soc. Pathol. Exot. 54:* 332.

166.   Dodin, A., and H. Fromentin (1962). Mise en evidence d'un antigéne vaccinant dans le plasma de souris expérimentallment infectées par *Trypanosoma gambiense* et par *Trypanosoma congolense*. *Bull. Soc. Pathol. Exot. 55:*123.

167.   Johnson, P., R. A. Neal, and D. Gall (1963). Protective effect of killed trypanosome vaccines with incorporated adjuvants. *Nature (Lond.) 200:* 83.

168.   Seed, J. R., and D. Weinman (1963). Characterization of antigens isolated from *Trypanosoma rhodesiense*. *Nature (Lond.) 198:*197.

169.   Seed, J. R. (1963). The characterization of antigens isolated from *Trypanosoma rhodesiense*. *J. Protozool. 10:*380.

170.   Seed, J. R., and A. A. Gam (1966). The properties of antigens from *Trypanosoma gambiense*. *J. Parasitol. 52:*395.

171.   Soltys, M. A. (1964). Immunity in trypanosomiasis. V. Immunization of animals with dead trypanosomes. Parasitology 54:*585*.

172. Herbert, W. J., and W. H. Lumsden (1968). Single-dose vaccination of mice against experimental infection with *Trypanosoma (Trypanozoon) brucei. J. Med. Microbiol. 1:23.*

173. Duxbury, R. E., and E. H. Sadun (1969). Resistance produced in mice and rats by inoculation with irradiated *Trypanosoma rhodesiense. J. Parasitol. 55:859.*

174. Duxbury, R. E., E. H. Sadun, and J. S. Anderson (1972). Experimental infections with African trypanosomes. II. Immunization of mice and monkeys with a gamma-irradiated, recently isolated human strain of *Trypanosoma rhodesiense. Am. J. Trop. Med. Hyg. 21:885.*

175. Duxbury, R. E., E. H. Sadun, J. S. Anderson, B. T. Wellde, I. E. Muriithe, and G. M. Warui (1973). Immunization of rodents, dogs, cattle, and monkeys against African trypanosomiasis by the use of irradiated trypanosomes. In *Isotopes and Radiation in Parasitology II.* International Atomic Energy Agency, Vienna, Austria, p. 179.

176. Petithory, J., J. J. Rousset, and M. F. Liquolt (1971). Immunisation de la souris contre une souche hétérologue par des trypanosomes virulents vivants en chambre de diffusion. *Bull. Soc. Pathol. Exot. 64:337.*

177. Lanham, S. M., and A. E. R. Taylor (1972). Some properties of the immunogens (protective antigens) of a single variant of *Trypanosoma brucei. J. Gen. Microbiol. 72:101.*

178. Wellde, B. T., R. E. Duxbury, E. H. Sadun, H. R. Langbehn, R. Lotzsch, G. Deindl, and G. Warui (1973). Experimental infections with African trypanosomes. IV. Immunization of cattle with gamma-irradiated *Trypanosoma rhodesiense. Exp. Parasitol. 34:62.*

179. Wellde, B. T., M. J. Schoenbechler, C. L. Diggs, H. R. Langbehn, and E. H. Sadun (1975). *Trypanosoma rhodesiense:* Variant specificity of immunity endured by irradiated parasites. *Exp. Parasitol. 37:125.*

180. Fromentin, H. (1974). *Trypanosoma brucei gambiense.* Étude antigenique. I. Protection experimentale de la souris. Résultats partiels. *Bull. Soc. Pathol. Exot. 67:277.*

181. Diggs, C. L., B. Flemmings, J. Dillon, R. Snodgrass, G. Campbell, and K. Esser (1976). Immune serum-mediated cytotoxicity against *Trypanosoma rhodesiense. J. Immunol. 116:1005.*

182. Murray, M., and G. M. Urquhart (1977). Immunoprophylaxis against African trypanosomes. *Adv. Exp. Med. Biol. 93:209.*

183. James, D. M., A. O. Fregene, and K. Salmon (1973). The effect of irradiation on infectivity and immunogenicity of *Trypanosoma brucei. J. Parasitol. 59:489.*

184. Miller, J. K. (1965). Variation of the soluble antigens of *Trypanosoma brucei. Immunology 9:521.*

185. Fulton, J. D., and E. M. Lourie (1946). Immunity of mice cured of trypanosome infections. *Ann. Trop. Med. Parasitol. 40:1.*

186. Duxbury, R. E., J. S. Anderson, B. T. Wellde, E. H. Sadun, and I. E. Muriithi (1972). *Trypanosoma congolense:* Immunization of mice, dogs, and cattle with gamma-irradiated parasites. *Exp. Parasitol. 32:527.*

187. Seed, J. R. (1977). The role of immunoglobulins in immunity to *Try-panosoma brucei gambiense. Int. J. Parasitol. 7:55.*

188. Takayanagi, T. (1971). Protection of mouse from trypanosome infection. *Jap. J. Parasitol. 20:48.*

189. Zahalsky, A. C., and R. L. Weinberg (1976). Immunity to monomorphic *Trypanosoma brucei:* Humoral response. *J. Parasitol. 62:15.*

190. Campbell, G. H., and S. M. Phillips (1976). Adoptive transfer of variant-specific resistance to *Trypanosoma rhodesiense* with B lymphocytes and serum. *Infect. Immun. 14:*1144.

191. Takayanagi, T., Y. Nakatake, and G. L. Enriquez (1974). *Trypanosoma gambiense:* Phagocytosis in vitro. *Exp. Parasitol. 36:*106.

192. Lourie, E. M., and R. J. O'Connor (1936). Trypanolysis in vitro by mouse immune serum. *Ann. Trop. Med. Parasitol. 30:*365.

193. Flemmings, B., and C. L. Diggs (1978). Antibody-dependent cytotoxicity against *Trypanosoma rhodesiense* mediated through an alternative complement pathway. *Infect. Immun. 19:*928.

194. Stevens, D. R., and J. E. Moulton (1978). Ultrastructural and immunological aspects of the phagocytosis of *Trypanosoma brucei* by mouse peritoneal macrophages. *Infect. Immun. 19:*972.

195. Takayanagi, T. Y. Nakatake, and G. L. Enriquez (1974). Attachment and ingestion of *Trypanosoma gambiense* to the rat macrophage by specivid antiserum. *J. Parasitol. 60:*336.

196. Takayanagi, T., and Y. Nakatake (1977). *Trypanosoma gambiense:* The binding activity of antiserum to macrophages. *Exp. Parasitol. 42:*21.

197. Holmes, P. H., J. A. MacAskill, D. D. Whitelaw, F. W. Jennings, and G. M. Urquhart (1979). Immunological clearance of ^{75}Se-labelled *Trypanosoma brucei* in mice. I. Aspects of the radiolabelling technique. *Immunology 36:*415.

198. Young, A. S., G. K. Janhai, and D. A. Stagg (1975). Phagocytosis of *Trypanosoma (Nannamonas) congolense* by circulating macrophages in the African buffalo *(Syncerus caffer). Res. Vet. Sci. 19:*108.

199. Anderson, R. E., and N. L. Warner (1976). Ionizing radiation and the immune response. *Adv. Immunol. 24:*215.

200. Takayanagi, T., and Y. Nakatake (1975). *Trypanosoma gambiense:* Enhancement of agglutinin and protection in subpopulations by immune spleen cells. *Exp. Parasitol. 38:*233.

201. Takayanagi, T., and Y. Nakatake (1976). *Trypanosoma gambiense:* Immunity with thymic cell transfer in mice. *Exp. Parasitol. 39:*234.

202. Campbell, G. H., K. M. Esser, and F. I. Weinbaum (1977). *Trypanosoma rhodesiense* infection in B-cell deficient mice. *Infect. Immun. 18:*434.

203. Jayawardena, A. N., and B. H. Waksman (1977). Suppressor cells in experimental trypanosomiasis. *Nature (Lond.) 265:*539.

204. Campbell, G. H., K. M. Esser, and S. M. Phillips (1978). *Trypanosoma rhodesiense* infection in congenitally athymic (nude) mice. *Infect. Immun. 20:*714.

205. Askonas, B. A., A. C. Corsini, C. E. Clayton, and B. M. Ogilvie (1979). Functional depletion of T- and B-memory cells and other lymphoid cell subpopulations during trypanosomiasis. *Immunology 36:*313.
206. Clayton, C. E., B. M. Ogilvie, and B. A. Askonas (1979). *Trypanosoma brucei* infection in nude mice: B lymphocyte function is suppressed in the absence of T lymphocytes. *Parasite Immunol. 1:*241.
207. Coutinho, A., and G. Moller (1975). Thymus-independent B-cell induction and paralysis. *Adv. Immunol. 21:*113.
208. Mansfield, J. M., and J. H. Wallace (1974). Suppression of cell-mediated immunity in experimental African trypanosomiasis. *Infect. Immun. 10:* 335.
209. Finerty, J. F., E. P. Krehl, and R. L. McKelvin (1978). Delayed-type hypersensitivity in mice immunized with *Trypanosoma rhodesiense* antigens. *Infect. Immun. 20:*464.
210. Bevan, L. E. W. (1936). Notes on immunity in trypanosomiasis. *Trans. R. Soc. Trop. Med. Hyg. 30:*199.
211. Cunningham, M. P. (1966). Immunity in bovine trypanosomiasis. *East Afr. Med. J. 43:*394.
212. Shreffler, D. C., and C. S. David (1975). The H-2 major histocompatibility complex and the I immune response region: genetic variation, function, and organization. *Adv. Immunol. 20:*125.
213. Dausset, J., and A. Svejgaard, Eds. (1977). *HLA and Disease.* Munksgaard, Copenhagen.
214. Morrison, W. I., and M. Murray (1979). *Trypanosoma congolense:* Inheritance of susceptibility to infection in inbred strains of mice. *Exp. Parasitol. 48:*364.
215. Levine, R. F., and J. M. Mansfield (1981). Genetics of resistance to the African trypanosomes. I. Role of the H-2 locus in determining resistance to infection with *Trypanosoma rhodesiense.* (Submitted for publication.)
216. Clayton, C. E. (1978). *Trypanosoma brucei:* Influence of host strain and parasite antigenic type on infections in mice. *Exp. Parasitol. 44:*202.
217. McNeillage, G. J. C., and W. J. Herbert (1968). Infectivity and virulence of *Trypanosoma (Trypanozoon) brucei* for mice. II. Comparison of closely related antigenic types. *J. Comp. Pathol. 78:*345.
218. Krampitz, H. E. (1970). Beobachtungen an experimentellen infektionen ostafrikanischer zeburinder mit wildstämmen von *Trypanosoma congolense. Zeit. Tropenmed. Parasitology 21:*1.
219. Goodwin, L. G., D. G. Green, M. W. Guy, and A. Voller (1972). Immunosuppression during trypanosomiasis. *Br. J. Exp. Pathol. 53:*40.
220. Urquhart, G. M., M. Murray, P. K. Murray, F. W. Jennings, and E. Bate (1973). Immunosuppression in *Trypanosoma brucei* infections in rats and mice. *Trans. R. Soc. Trop. Med. Hyg. 67:*528.
221. Ackerman, S. B., and J. R. Seed (1976). Immunosuppression during *Trypanosoma brucei gambiense* infections in the field vole, *Microtus montanus. Clin. Exp. Immunol. 25:*152.

222. Terry, R. J. (1976). Immunity to African trypanosomiasis. In *Immunology of Parasitic Infections* (S. Cohen and E. H. Sadun, Eds.). Blackwell Scientific Publications, Oxford, p. 203.

223. Eardley, D. D., and A. N. Jayawardena (1977). Suppressor cells in mice infected with *Trypanosoma brucei. J. Immunol. 119:*1029.

224. Assoku, R. K. G., C. A. Hazlett, and I. Tizard (1979). Immunosuppression in experimental African trypanosomiasis. Polyclonal B-cell activation and mitogenicity of trypanosome-derived saturated fatty acids. *Int. Arch. Allergy Appl. Immunol. 59:*298.

225. Greenwood, B. M., H. C. Whittle, and D. H. Molyneux (1973). Immunosuppression in Gambian trypanosomiasis. *Trans. R. Soc. Trop. Med. Hyg. 67:*846.

226. Holmes, P. H., E. Mammo, A. Thomson, P. A. Knight, R. Lucken, P. K. Murray, M. Murray, F. W. Jennings, and G. M. Urquhart (1974). Immunosuppression in bovine trypanosomiasis. *Vet. Rec. 95:*86.

227. Scott, J. M., R. G. Pegram, P. H. Holmes, T. W. F. Pay, P. A. Knight, F. W. Jennings, and G. M. Urquhart (1977). Immunosuppression in bovine trypanosomiasis: Field studies using foot-and-mouth disease vaccine and clostridial vaccine. *Trop. Animal Health Prod. 9:*159.

228. Whitelaw, D. D., J. M. Scott, H. W. Ried, P. H. Holmes, F. W. Jennings, and G. M. Urquhart (1979). Immunosuppression in bovine trypanosomiasis: Studies with louping-ill vaccine. *Res. Vet. Sci. 26:*102.

229. Sollod, A. E., and G. H. Frank (1979). Bovine trypanosomiasis: Effect on the immune response of the infected host. *Am. J. Vet. Res. 40:*658.

230. Rurangirwa, F. R., H. Tabel, G. J. Losos, and I. Tizard (1979). Suppression of antibody response to *Leptospira biflexa* and *Brucella abortus* and recovery from immunosuppression after Berenil treatment. *Infect. Immun. 26:*822.

231. Pearson, T. W., G. E. Roelants, L. B. Lundin, and K. S. Mayor-Withey (1978). Immune depression in trypanosome-infected mice. I. Depressed T lymphocyte responses. *Eur. J. Immunol. 8:*723.

232. Landolfo, S., M. Giovarelli, M. G. Martinotti, L. Varesio, and P. Cappuccinelli (1979). Enhancement versus tumor resistance induced by different levels of immunodepression in BALB/C mice with protozoan infections. *Eur. J. Cancer. 15:*27.

233. Ackerman, S. B., and J. R. Seed (1976). Effects of *Trypanosoma brucei gambiense* infections in *Microtus montanus* on susceptibility to Ehrlich's tumors. *Infect. Immun. 13:*388.

234. Greenwood, B. M. (1974). Possible role of a B-cell mitogen in hypergammaglobulinaemia in malaria and trypanosomiasis. *Lancet i:*435.

235. Esuruoso, G. O. (1976). The demonstration in vitro of the mitogenic effects of trypanosomal antigen on the spleen cells of normal, athymic and cyclophosphamide-treated mice. *Clin. Exp. Immunol. 23:*314.

236. Mansfield, J. M., S. A. Craig, and G. T. Stelzer (1976). Lymphocyte function in experimental African trypanosomiasis: Mitogenic effects of trypanosome extracts in vitro. *Infect. Immun. 14:*976.

237. Assoku, R. K. G., and I. R. Tizard (1978). Mitogenicity of autolysates of *Trypanosoma congolense. Experientia 34:*127.

238. Assoku, R. K. G., I. R. Tizard, and K. H. Nielsen (1977). Free fatty acids, complement activation, and polyclonal B-cell stimulation as factors in the immunopathogenesis of African trypanosomiasis. *Lancet ii:*956.

239. Greenwood, B. M., and A. J. Oduloju (1978). Mitogenic activity of an extract of *Trypanosoma gambiense. Trans. R. Soc. Trop. Med. Hyg. 72:* 408

240. Wellhausen, S. R., and J. M. Mansfield (1979). Lymphocyte function in experimental African trypanosomiasis. II. Splenic suppressor cell activity. *J. Immunol. 122:*818.

241. Tadakuma, T., and C. W. Pierce (1976). Site of action of a soluble immune response suppressor (SIRS) produced by concanavalin A-activated spleen cells. *J. Immunol. 117:*967.

242. Jayawardena, A. N., B. H. Waksman, and D. D. Eardley (1978). Activation of distinct helper and suppressor T cells in experimental trypanosomiasis. *J. Immunol. 121:*622.

243. Cantor, H., J. Hugenberger, L. McVay-Boudreau, D. D. Eardley, J. Kemp, F. W. Shen, and R. K. Gershon (1978). Immunoregulatory circuits among T-cell sets. Identification of a subpopulation of T-helper cells that induces feedback inhibition. *J. Exp. Med. 148:*871.

244. Wellhausen, S. R., and J. M. Mansfield (1980). Lymphocyte function in experimental African trypanosomiasis. III. Loss of lymph node cell responsiveness. *J. Immunol. 124:*1183.

245. Wellhausen, S. R., and J. M. Mansfield (1980). Characteristics of the splenic suppressor cell-target cell interaction in experimental African trypanosomiasis. *Cell. Immunol. 54:*414.

246. Pearson, T. W., G. E. Roelants, M. Pinder, L. B. Lundin, and K. S. Mayor-Withey (1979). Immune depression in trypanosome-infected mice. III. Suppressor cells. *Eur. J. Immunol. 9:*200.

247. Roelants, G. E., T. W. Pearson, H. W. Tyrer, K. S. Mayor-Withey, and L. B. Lundin (1979). Immune depression in trypanosome-infected mice II. Characterization of the spleen cell types involved. *Eur. J. Immunol. 9:*195.

248. Roelants, G. E., T. W. Pearson, W. I. Morrison, K. S. Mayor-Withey, and L. B. Lundin (1979). Immune depression in trypanosome-infected mice. IV. Kinetics of suppression and alleviation by the trypanocidal drug Berenil. *Clin. Exp. Immunol. 37:*457.

249. Mansfield, J. M. (1978). Immunobiology of African trypanosomiasis. *Cell. Immunol. 39:*204.

250. Ackerman, S. B., and J. R. Seed (1976). The effects of tryptophol on immune responses and its implications toward trypanosome-induced immunosuppression. *Experientia 32:*645.

251. Moulton, J. E., and J. L. Coleman (1979). A soluble immunosuppressor substance in spleen in deer mice infected with *Trypanosoma brucei. Am. J. Vet. Res. 40:*1131.

252. Singer, I., E. T. Kimble III, and R. E. Ritts, Jr. (1964). Alterations of

the host-parasite relationship by administration of endotoxin to mice with infections of trypanosomes. *J. Infect. Dis. 114:*243.

253. Herman, R., and S. Baron (1971). Immunologic-mediated protection of *Trypanosoma congolense*-infected mice by polyribonucleotides. *J. Protozool. 18:*661.

254. Murray, M., and W. I. Morrison (1979). Non-specific induction of increased resistance in mice to *Trypanosoma congolense* and *Trypanosoma brucei* by immunostimulants. *Parasitology 79:*349.

255. Gláz, E. T. (1978). Effect of low molecular weight interferon inducers on *Trypanosoma equiperdum* infection of mice. *Ann. Trop. Med. Parasitol. 73:*83.

256. Boothroyd, J. C., G. A. M. Cross, J. H. J. Hoeijmakers, and P. Borst (1980). A variant surface glycoprotein of *Trypanosoma brucei* synthesized with a C-terminal hydrophobic "tail" absent from purified glycoprotein. *Nature 288:*624.

257. Lyon, J. A., J. M. Pratt, R. W. Travis, B. P. Doctor, and J. G. Olenick (1981). Use of monoclonal antibody to immunochemically characterize variant specific surface coat glycoprotein from *Trypanosoma rhodesiense*. *J. Immunol. 126:*134.

258. Pearson, T. W., S. K. Kar, T. C. McGuire, and L. B. Lundin (1981). Trypanosome variable surface antigens: Studies using two-dimensional gel electrophoresis and monoclonal antibodies. *J. Immunol. 126:*823.

259. Doyle, J. J., H. Hirumi, K. Hirumi, E. N. Lupton, and G. A. M. Cross (1980). Antigenic variation in clones of animal-infective *Trypanosoma brucei* derived and maintained in vitro. *Parasitology 80:*359.

260. Miller, E. N., and M. J. Turner (1981). Analysis of antigenic types appearing in first relapse populations of clones of *Trypanosoma brucei*. *Parasitology 82:*63.

261. Williams, R. O., J. R. Young, and P. A. Majiwa (1979). Genomic rearrangements correlated with antigenic variation in *Trypanosoma brucei*. *Nature 282:*847.

262. Hoeijmakers, J. H. J., A. C. C. Frasch, A. Bernards, P. Borst, and G. A. M. Cross (1980). Novel expression-linked copies of the genes for variant surface antigens in trypanosomes. *Nature 284:*78.

263. De Gee, A. L. W., and L. Rovis (1981). *Trypanosoma vivax:* Absence of host protein on the surface coat. *Exp. Parasitol. 51:*124.

264. Sacks, D. L., M. Selkirk, B. M. Ogilvie, and B. A. Askonas (1980). Intrinsic immunosuppressive activity of different trypanosome strains varies with parasite virulence. *Nature 283:*476.

5

Immunology and Immunopathology
of Infections Caused by Filarial Nematodes

BRIDGET M. OGILVIE*   National Institute for Medical Research, London, England

CHARLES D. MACKENZIE   London School of Hygiene and Tropical Medicine, London, England

I.	Introduction	228
II.	Biology of Filarial Nematodes	230
	A. General Properties	230
	B. Surface Properties	231
III.	Antigens	232
	A. Sources of Antigens	232
	B. Diagnosis	233
	C. Attempts to Induce Immunity by Vaccination	236
IV.	Loiasis, Dipetalonemiasis, and Mansonelliasis	237
V.	Onchocerciasis	237
	A. Biology	237
	B. Clinical Characteristics	239
	C. Geographical Differences in the Disease Complex	241
	D. Reactions to Diethylcarbamazine Therapy	243
	E. General Immune Responses	246
	F. Protective Immunity	247
	G. Immunopathology	249
	H. Summary of Reactions to *Onchocerca volvulus*	251
	I. Other *Onchocerca* spp.	252

Present affiliation: The Wellcome Trust, London, England.

  VI. Lymphatic Filariases of Man   252
      A. The Parasites   252
      B. Clinical Characteristics   253
      C. Responses to Anthelmintic Treatment   255
      D. Immune Responses   255
 VII. Tropical Eosinophilic Lung   257
VIII. *Brugia* spp. in Animals   259
      A. *Brugia* spp. in Cats and Dogs   260
      B. *Brugia* spp. in Rodents   261
  IX. Filarial Infections of Rodents   262
      A. *Dipetalonema viteae*   262
      B. *Litomosoides carinii*   265
   X. *Dirofilaria* spp. Infections in Dogs and Man   267
  XI. General Principles and Suggestions for Future Studies   270
      References   274

I. INTRODUCTION

Filariasis is a complex of diseases caused by tissue-dwelling nematodes which are responsible for some of the major helminth-induced diseases of man. Pioneering studies have shown that these infections may have devastating effects on the health and well-being of the communities afflicted by them, and that they present many problems which will only be fully understood by the application of modern immunological science. For many years these diseases have been almost completely ignored by the scientific community. The rapid development of immunology in the past decade, together with the recent revival of interest in parasitic diseases of tropical and subtropical areas of the world, hopefully will ensure that much more attention will be paid to these neglected infections.

A number of references cover specific aspects of filarial immunology: the response to *Litomosoides carinii* in rodents [1]; pathology of filariasis [2,3]; human filariasis [4,5]; the response to *Onchocerca volvulus* [6-8], especially in the eye [9], and to *Brugia* spp. [10]. The books by Sasa [5,11] are a monumental compilation of studies of human filariasis and are required reading for anyone interested in this subject.

We have not found any preceding review which attempts to examine the immunology of all filarial infections. In this review we have mainly described those immunological studies related to the time course of the infection in experimentally infected animals, or to the clinical status of individual patients. Both approaches are important since the immune response to each stage in the worm's life cycle varies, and because the clinical signs, which are probably the consequence of the immune response to these parasites, are related to particular stages in the life cycle. Time is a key dimension in the analysis of most biologic phenomena. This is true not only in studies of the host-parasite relationships in long-lived infections typical of filariasis, but also in studies of the pathology of the disease especially when exacerbated by treatment with drugs such as diethyl-carbamazine (DEC).

Compared with other immunological stimuli, the striking characteristic of helminth infections is the great diversity of immune responses which they induce in their hosts. Increases in IgE levels and in the numbers of eosinophils and amine-containing cells (basophils and mast cells) are the hallmarks of helminth infections; they also induce responses in the other immunoglobulin classes. The increases in IgE, eosinophils, and amine-containing cells are regulated by thymus-dependent (T) lymphocytes, which are also essential for the immunological control of most helminth infections [12-16]. Although helminths induce antibody responses in many immunoglobulin classes, absolute levels of immunoglobulins other than IgE are not increased in the way they often are in hosts infected with protozoa. An exception seems to be in mice in which a variety of helminths induce the production of vast amounts of IgG1 [17-19]. The increases in IgG1 in mice, and in total IgE levels, are probably the result of an undefined adjuvant action induced by the worms.

The majority of studies on the antibody response to filariae concern IgG antibodies; IgE antibodies have rarely been studied except by immediate-type hypersensitivity skin tests, usually with crude worm extracts as antigen [15]. The great need in all such studies is for better defined antigens. IgE responses as detected by skin tests, often with heterologous antigens, are notoriously non-specific. We have suggested previously that there may be IgE antibodies specific for antigens particular to each worm species, as well as IgE antibody to common antigens which may mask the specific responses, especially in the extremely sensitive skin test assay [4].

The role of eosinophils in the immune response is currently of great topical interest and is clearly of relevance in filariasis [13]. The first report of eosinophil involvement in antibody-dependent cell-mediated reactions to helminths was the study of eosinophil adherence to IgG-coated *Wuchereria bancrofti* infective larvae by Higashi and Chowdhury in Calcutta [20]. This type of immune response is being actively studied in most of the filarial systems at present, since it may be of paramount importance in the control of these parasites. It is probable that monocytes also may be able to destroy nematodes in the presence of antibodies and/or complement directed against their surface antigens [21-24]. Apart from their possible role as killer cells, eosinophils and the amine-containing cells probably have a major role in the IgE-mediated reactions which may be partly responsible for the pathology of filarial infections (see Sections V and VI).

The role of the immune system in the control and pathology of filariasis has scarcely begun to be studied, but it is already clear that immunological methodology has much to contribute to our understanding of filariasis as a disease process.

II. BIOLOGY OF FILARIAL NEMATODES

A. General Properties

Filarial worms are obligate extracellular parasites causing infections of medical and veterinary importance. The adult worms mature in the vessels, body cavities, or tissues of the vertebrate host. The female worm is ovoviviparous, producing large numbers of microfilariae which may or may not be enclosed in a delicate sheath, according to species. The microfilariae circulate in the blood or subcutaneous tissues of the vertebrate host, according to species, but they may also occur in many other tissues of the host. Microfilariae are ingested by hematophagus arthropods. The infective larval stage is reached after two molts and may be transmitted to a new vertebrate host when the intermediate host takes another meal. The adult stage is reached after two more molts in the mammalian host and the cycle is complete. There are no free-living stages, and both the microfilariae and the adults may persist for a long time (many years in the case of the adult worm) [5,6,10,25].

In many species, microfilariae in the blood exhibit a circadian periodicity (i.e., the numbers present fluctuate in a 24 hr rhythm). This was first discovered by Manson in 1879, who observed that microfilariae of *W. bancrofti* were absent from the blood during the day but reappeared each evening to reach a peak at about midnight [5,26]. Periodicity may be nocturnal or diurnal and varies in the completeness with which the microfilariae appear and disappear. Some species are subperiodic in that, although there is a peak in numbers at one time in the 24 hr cycle, microfilariae are detectable at all times. Moreover, differences in the periodicity of microfilariae may occur not only between species of filariae but also between strains of species such as *W. bancrofti* and *Brugia malayi* which exist both as periodic and subperiodic strains in man [5]. It has long been thought that microfilarial periodicity is a reflection of the close association which exists between filarial parasites and the feeding habits of their invertebrate hosts [5,27]. The factors which control periodicity are physiological and ill-defined, but it is clear that only a small proportion of the total microfilarial population is present in the blood even at the peak of the periodic cycle [27]. The level of microfilariae in the blood cannot be directly correlated with the number of adult females in the host. This is illustrated from studies in jirds infected with *Dipetalonema viteae* [28] and in cats infected with *Brugia pahangi* [29]. Microfilaremia reaches a plateau level which remains constant even when additional microfilariae are added by transfusion or removed by repeated bleeding through plasmaphoresis [30,31].

Knowledge of the biochemical and physiological properties of these parasites is exceedingly slight; in many cases even their basic morphologic structure needs reassessing using modern methods of microscopy. An important reason for the dearth of understanding concerning these organisms is their narrow host specificity. *Onchocerca volvulus* is a parasite of man and the chimpanzee and *W. bancrofti* is known only in man. Of the major human filarial parasites, only worms of the *Brugia* spp. can be readily obtained; the tissue stages of *W. bancrofti* can only be obtained at autopsy, and stages between the infective larvae and adult worms of *O. volvulus* have never been seen. It was a signal advance when it was shown that the *Brugia* spp. which affect man will develop to maturity in the jird, *Meriones unguiculatus* [32,33], and that development will occur entirely within the peritoneal cavity of the jird [34]. As a consequence, rapid progress is occurring in the understanding of these parasites, but those who wish to work with *W. bancrofti* or *O. volvulus* must study naturally infected patients.

B. Surface Properties

There is much evidence that the surface of filariae is antigenic. There is some evidence that, at least with *Brugia,* the cuticle of filariae may function very differently from the cuticle of nematodes of the gut. In the geonematodes the gut is well developed and has the appearance of an organ highly adapted to absorption of nutrients, whereas the cuticle of these nematodes is thought to be impermeable to all molecules except gases and salts [35]. In contrast, the gut of *Brugia* is less well developed, and a recent report showed that adult worms of *B. pahangi* can absorb radiolabeled glucose and amino acids through their cuticle [36].

There have been some ultrastructural studies of the filariae which infect man, including the adult stages of *W. bancrofti* and *B. pahangi* [37] and *B. malayi* [38], the infective larvae of *B. pahangi* and *W. bancrofti* [39,40], and the microfilariae of *O. volvulus* [41,42] and *B. malayi* [43]. The structure of the cuticle of these filariae is much the same as that of nematodes parasitic in the gut, except that the outer layer of the cuticle of the adult worms seems more folded than in nematodes in general, hinting at a greater absorptive capacity [37]. The filarial cuticle does not have the highly developed system of microvilli which is expected of an absorptive surface and which was seen in a nematode parasite of insects [44]. The surface of *O. volvulus* microfilariae has been studied using freeze-fracture techniques, which led the author to conclude that only the hypodermis had the structure usually associated with true cell membranes [41].

The surface of microfilariae may differ from the cuticle of other helminth larvae. Microfilariae do not adsorb host immunoglobulin nonspecifically onto their surface [45]; this is known to occur with other helminth larvae [46,47]. The same study [45] showed that sheathed, but not unsheathed, microfilariae take up blood group substances from their host. The surface of microfilariae stimulates antibodies which are remarkably specific for the filarial species that stimulate them and are implicated in the regulation of microfilaremia by the host (Sections VI and X).

Recent studies of the nature of the surface of the nematode *Trichinella spiralis* probably have general relevance to the study of immunity to nematodes, including filariae. Three stages of *T. spiralis* stimulated their host to produce antibodies to their surface, but these antibodies were specific to the stage which induced them [48]. This shows that the cuticle changes when the worms molt; in addition there is evidence that it may change as the worms of a particular stage grow. The cuticle of newborn larvae of *T. spiralis* does not activate the third component of complement when these worms are newly released from the female worm [48]. As the newborn larvae begin to elongate, however, the cuticle in the midregion of their body (which is presumably newly formed) is able to activate complement [253]. This result suggests the possibility, for example, that the cuticle of infective larvae may change rapidly after they enter the mammalian host, even before they undergo the molt to the fourth stage.

III. ANTIGENS

A. Sources of Antigens

A rational approach to the study of parasite antigens requires an understanding of the likely sources of antigens on and within the worms. Most of the nematodes which parasitize the gut have a series of glandular structures at their anterior end (sometimes in association with sensory organs) which synthesize and release highly antigenic secretions to the exterior [49]; these glands undoubtedly contain antigens which will induce a strong immune response in their host [50]. Comparable structures have not been seen in the filariae, although detailed studies of all stages of the most important filarial parasites of man have not been made, often because they are not obtainable. It seems that sensory structures comparable with those found in nematodes of the gut occur in filariae, but the glandular elements associated with them are vestigial [49]. If this is so, where do the antigens come from? It seems possible with living filarial nematodes that the cuticle is a major antigenic site and that secretions are of less importance as a source of antigens. Once the worms die, however, the host is exposed to a wide variety of antigens originating from both internal structures and the cuticle. We believe that "protective" immune responses (i.e., those which attack the parasite) are induced by antigens associated with the cuticle, and that these may be shown to be extraordinarily specific, even to a particular stage in the life cycle. In contrast, it is our opinion that responses to antigens from the general body tissues of the worms may not be involved in protective immunity but are extremely important in the development of the pathology associated with filariasis. These also show a much lesser degree of specificity than cuticular antigens [51-53].

The studies of antibodies to microfilariae outlined below in this section and elsewhere in this review reinforce the idea of the importance of surface antigens. There are, in addition, several other studies of the antigenicity of the surface of filarial nematodes which indicate the potential value of these antigens in differentiating species and stage-specific antibodies. Rabbit antibodies induced by antigens of a filarial parasite of the slow loris *Breinlia sergenti* react with antigens on the surface of the infective larvae of *Dirofilaria immitis* and *B. pahangi,* but not with *B. malayi* [54] . Sera from patients exposed to *W. bancrofti* agglutinate *L. carinii* microfilariae (Ref. 24 and Subrahmanyam, personal communication). It has also been shown that extracts of adult *Setaria digitata* contain at least two types of antigen. One of the antigens was found to be similar to a surface antigen of *W. bancrofti* microfilariae. The second type of antigen had reactivity against antibodies in both microfilaremic and amicrofilaremic *W. bancrofti*-infected subjects in an enzyme-linked immunosorbent assay (ELISA) system [55] . Knowledge of these interspecific cross reactions are important in the interpretation of diagnostic tests. They could also be exploited in the future, both as a source of antigenic material for the diagnosis of human filariasis and in studies of the mosaic of changing antigens which the worms' surfaces present to the host during their development.

B. Diagnosis

Diagnosis of filarial infections still largely depends upon the detection of the worms themselves, principally of the microfilariae in the blood or the skin. There is, however, a great need for reliable, sensitive, and specific nonparasitologic methods for diagnosis. In many individuals infected with the lymphatic filariae, microfilariae are not detectable in the blood, and the removal of skin snips for diagnosis of onchocerciasis seems a rather primitive (although valuable) technique. Moreover, because the clinical manifestations of filariae vary greatly between individuals, an ideal diagnostic method would not only reveal individuals that are infected or have been exposed to infection, but it would also differentiate between the various clinical manifestations that the lymphatic-dwelling worms, in particular, induce in the infected population. This is important because the pathological reactions induced following treatment with DEC vary with the clinical picture induced by the lymphatic filariae. They are certainly a major problem in onchocerciasis. However, for diagnosis of individual patients it seems that, in practice, a combination of the known history of the patient, the clinical symptoms, and tests such as immunofluorescence using worm sections as antigens, or indirect hemagglutination using crude parasite extracts as antigen, are usually satisfactory [53] .

Three major problems have slowed the development of more sensitive and specific immunological methods for diagnosis: the difficulty in obtaining parasite material from those species which infect man, the extensive cross reactivity which occurs between the antigens of filarial nematodes and other helminths, and the paucity of scientists with the requisite biochemical and immunochemical skells interested in the subject.

1. Antibody Responses

The early diagnostic antibody tests were reviewed in detail [56] and will not be considered here. Most methods used in diagnosis have depended on the detection of immunological responses which involve antibodies rather than cells, and for these, extracts of the dog filarial parasite *D. immitis* have been used extensively, especially in immediate hypersensitivity tests [53,56]. A careful trial of the *D. immitis* allergen [57] revealed the limitations of this test; the results showed 22% false positive and 53-85% negative results in confirmed cases of filariasis [58]. *Dirofilaria immitis* antigen also gave unreliable results in complement fixation tests [53,59]. Passive hemagglutination tests using extracts of a variety of nematodes gave equally nonspecific results with cross reactions not only between filarial nematodes but also with nematodes such as *Ascaris* and *Trichinella* [53,60]. In general, it seems that methods which rely on the detection of antibodies using simple extracts of filarial parasites as antigen, even of homologous parasites, are of little use in diagnosis. For example, using standardized extracts of *B. malayi* infective larvae, microfilariae, or adults for skin tests in populations infected with lymphatic filariae, immediate hypersensitivity reactions were detected with extracts from all three parasite stages in almost all subjects exposed to *W. bancrofti* or *B. malayi* [61]. There was no relationship between skin reactivity and the presence or absence of microfilaremia, or with the severity of clinical disease. However, compared with results using *D. immitis* antigen, false positives were low. About half the subjects from an area of *W. bancrofti* infection reacted to *B. malayi* antigens, although they had no signs of *B. malayi* parasites or disease. In comparison with *D. immitis* antigen, *Brugia* antigen was much more sensitive in detecting *W. bancrofti* infection and was no less specific [61]. In this study as in many others, the infected population came from an area where *D. immitis* is also widespread. These individuals would be exposed to *D. immitis* infective larvae and, in at least some individuals, this parasite may have developed even to the adult stage (see Section X). Thus, in areas of *D. immitis* infection, the human population will be sensitized to *D. immitis* antigen, which makes the use of *D. immitis* antigen in diagnosis of the filarial parasites of man extremely suspect.

Methods which depend on the antigenicity of specific identifiable components of the worms appear to be more reliable in diagnostic methods which detect antibodies. Immunoelectrophoretic analysis which reveals precipitin arcs characteristic for each filarial species with sera from infected individuals is said to be the method of choice, since its specificity appears to be remarkable and unsurpassed [53,62]. Of great interest is the fact that the antigens characteristic of each species can be revealed in this assay using not only extracts of the homologous parasite, but also with extracts of the rodent filarial parasite *D. vitae* or even *Ascaris suum.* Its weakness is that large quantities of antigen and serum are needed [53,62].

Indirect fluorescence using sections of adult worms or smears of microfilariae have also shown interesting results. Antibodies to the surface of *W. bancrofti* or *B. malayi* microfilariae are found only in about 25% of the infected population and never in individuals with microfilaremia. These antibodies were most common in patients with chronic lymphatic obstruction due to *W. bancrofti* or *B. malayi,* and their presence is statistically related to the absence of microfilariae from the blood [24,63-66]. Also, it should be noted that, in cats exposed to *B. pahangi,* the appearance of antibodies to the surface of microfilariae was related to the disappearance of these parasites from the host [67]; similar results have been obtained with *D. immitis* in dogs [68]. In contrast with these results with microfilariae, the appearance of antibodies to the surface of infective larvae or adult *W. bancrofti* or *Brugia* spp. is not related to the clinical status of the infection [20,64,65,67]. When sections of adult worms are used in indirect fluorescence studies, there is considerable cross reactivity between different filarial species; but, when a variety of different worms are studied simultaneously, varying intensities of staining are seen, suggesting that the antigens detected with this assay are present in amounts which differ quantitatively or qualitatively [53]. A recurring observation is that indirect fluorescence assays with all stages of worms are often negative or weak when whole parasites are used as antigen, but fragmented or damaged worms give strong reactions. This has suggested to some that the surface is strongly antigenic only in special circumstances [51,52].

2. Cell-Mediated Responses

The few studies which have been made of the response of lymphocytes from infected individuals to filarial antigens in vitro suggest that assays of this type may be more reliable as a guide to the clinical status of the infected individual. Piessens et al. [69] found that the lymphocytes from patients with elephantiasis, but with no other clinical symptoms caused by *B. malayi,* responded to adult worm antigen in vitro, whereas lymphocytes from patients without clinical or parasitologic evidence of filariasis, and about half of the individuals with amicrofilaremic filariasis, responded to microfilarial antigen. Microfilaremic patients did not respond to microfilarial antigens. Ottesen et al. [70] also showed that lymphocytes from microfilaremic individuals in an area of *W. bancrofti* infection did not respond to filarial antigen prepared from *D. immitis* or *B. malayi.* However, preliminary studies with *O. volvulus*-infected patients have also indicated that high skin burdens of microfilaria are associated with failure of the patient's lymphocytes to respond in vitro to *O. volvulus* antigen [71].

In contrast to these interesting results which assay cell-mediated immunity to filarial antigens by lymphoblast transformation, a study of the delayed skin reaction in an area of endemic infection with lymphatic filariae showed that only a small proportion of patients responded. Moreover, unlike the results of Piessens et al. [69], the authors did not record an association of positive responses with a particular clinical or parasitologic manifestation of infection [61]. This may be because delayed skin tests and lymphoblast transformation reactions do not necessarily measure the same immunological response [72].

It is clear from the paucity of studies that the occurrence of cell-mediated immunity to filariae has scarcely been studied, especially with regard to diagnosis.

C. Attempts to Induce Immunity by Vaccination

Irradiated infective larvae have been successfully used to vaccinate animals against some helminths (reviewed by Smith and Clegg [50]), and attempts have been made to use this approach with filariae. The principle underlying these experiments is to stimulate immunity with the early stages of the parasite which are less pathogenic than the more mature worms. Increasing doses of irradiation progressively inhibit development of the worms, so that the longevity of the early life-cycle stages is increased if they are appropriately irradiated. By this means the host may be exposed to higher levels of antigens released by the early stages over a longer period of time than occurs in infection with normal larvae.

A recent review has summarized the available studies with irradiated filarial larval vaccines [73]. Consistent success has been obtained when dogs were vaccinated against *D. immitis* with larvae irradiated with 15-20 krad [74], or 20 krad ^{60}Co [75]. Challenge infections usually failed to reach patency, and the number of adult worms was greatly reduced and those present were stunted. With *Brugia*, immunity was obtained only by giving a heavy immunization schedule to dogs [76], monkeys [77], or cats [78,79]. These studies suggest that the immature stages of *D. immitis* are more immunogenic than the same stages of *Brugia* spp.

We have strong reservations about the usefulness of this approach in human filariasis. The problems of obtaining infective material in the first place, of maintaining viability and sterility of irradiated larvae, and of guaranteeing correct irradiation and ensuing quality control of batches of larvae are so great that we do not believe this approach has any real future in the practical solution of the problems posed by human filariasis. We believe that the application of modern immunochemical and molecular biologic techniques is both intellectually more satisfying and, in the end, will provide more practical solutions to the problems of human filariasis.

IV. LOIASIS, DIPETALONEMIASIS, AND MANSONELLIASIS

The filariae that are better adapted to their host are obviously those that cause less pathology; three of these which occur in man are loiasis, dipetalonemiasis, and mansonellosis. Loaisis is a disease of tropical Africa caused by *Loa loa*, and in many areas a large proportion of the population can be infected, often with few clinical signs. *Dipetalonema perstans* is widely distributed in Africa and South America. For a long time it had been thought that it caused no clinical signs; however, more recently clinical disease has been recognized. The lesions caused by these two parasites have similarities and, basically, they appear to be caused by hypersensitivity reactions of the immediate type; subcutaneous edema, pain, eosinophilia, and pruritis are common to both. The lesions seen in loaisis also include erythema and a severe reaction to DEC; meningitis and albuminuria are also reported to be exacerbated by this drug [80,81]. It would seem likely that immunological components which are characteristic of a hypersensitivity to helminths (i.e., IgE, eosinophils, and immune complexes) are probably involved in these diseases, but immunological investigations are virtually nonexistent save for serologic diagnostic studies [45,83]. Cross reactions between *Loa loa* and other filariae are common, and *D. immitis* seems to be useful in diagnostic tests, particularly in infections with *D. perstans* [84]. *Mansonella ozzardi* is a parasite known only in man in the Americas and, by virtue of this isolation, may be of interest in comparative studies of the response to antigens in the African and Asiatic filariases. There is some argument as to the pathogenicity of this parasite, but it is recorded that mansonellosis includes edema of the skin, erythematous papular and pruritic skin eruptions, an eosinophilia, and, like loaisis, an arthralgia [84-86]. It is probable that immunopathological mechanisms occurring in all three of these diseases, and other filarioses, have many components in common.

V. ONCHOCERCIASIS

A. Biology

Onchocerciasis of man is caused by *O. volvulus* and is endemic in two main regions of the world: in the rainforest and savanna climates of tropical Africa and in Central and South America, mainly in rainforest areas [6-8,89,90]. This primarily dermal and ocular disease was first described in 1875 by a British naval surgeon, O'Neill [91], who recognized the filarial nature of the parasites he found in the lesions of "craw-craw" in Africans in the Gold Coast. The number of people infected with this parasite is around 30 million in Africa and probably more than 750,000 in the Americas [7]. Much greater medical attention is given to the ocular disease associated with this infection since this aspect has major economic implications. Onchocerciasis is listed as one of the major blinding diseases of the tropics; 250,000 people are blind and a similar number are visually handicapped due to this infection, and many more are likely to become blind as their disease progresses [92].

The parasite is transmitted to man by the blood-feeding blackfly (*Simulium* spp.), whose breeding habitat is swift-running waters; hence, the association of this disease with rivers, which has given rise to the name "river blindness." Whereas *O. volvulus* is taxonomically still described as a single species in all the endemic areas of the world, the *Simulium* species carrying the nematodes vary considerably with geographical ares [7]. The biologic characteristics of these different blackfly species differ in the various regions as do the ecological features of the endemic areas. In Africa the main species involved is the *Simulium damnosum* complex. These breed in relatively large rivers throughout the tropical regions of the continent, and it is this species that is the vector in most of Africa. In East and Central Africa, however, species of the *Simulium naevei* complex also transmit the disease [6]. The distribution of onchocerciasis in Africa stretches from Senegal to Tanzania, and from the southern Sahara down as far as Malawi, areas in which the blackfly lives and breeds [7]. A small focus of onchorcerciasis was found in Yemen by Fawdry [93], and it has been suggested that this focus arose as a result of slave trading from Africa.

In Central and South America onchocerciasis appears to occur in more confined areas than in Africa, and foci are found in Mexico, Guatemala, Colombia, Venezuela, and on the Brasilian-Venezuelan border [8]. The vectors in these areas also appear to be blackflies, and a number of different species have been incriminated. In Mexico and Guatemala, where the disease is endemic on the slopes of the Sierra Madre, the main vector appears to be *Simulium ochraceum* [94,95]. In Venezuela, Brasil, and Colombia, the *Simulium* spp. concerned in transmission have not been defined clearly.

Studies of the life cycle and biology of *O. volvulus* and the disease it causes have been reviewed by a number of authors [5,6,87,90,96]; it remains a fact, however, that many aspects of the life cycle and biology of the nematode and its vector are still unknown. For example, the whereabouts and migration route of the infective larvae, the fourth-stage larvae, and the early adult parasite within the body of man are unknown, as is the actual route of invasion of the tissues of the eye by the microfilariae. The length of the interval between each molting event also is not known. All this information would facilitate studies on antigenic aspects of the immunology of the disease. Much of this information is hard to acquire due to the difficulty in obtaining material.

B. Clinical Characteristics

Extensive clinical studies have been carried out over the last 20 years on the African disease, particularly in Cameroon by Duke and co-workers, and in the last 10 years by Anderson and Fuglsang; many other workers have been involved in other parts of Africa, both francophone and anglophone. The study of the disease in Mexico has been a long one, and prominent among the workers in this country are Martinez-Baez, Mazzotti, Reyes, and Nettel-Flores [97]. In Guatemala, Figueroa and De Leon have been responsible for much of the early research into the clinical disease.

Classically, the descriptions of the clinical manifestations of onchocerciasis divide the symptoms into the dermatologic, ocular, lymphatic, and general systematic.

1. Dermatologic Disease

Unlike *Wuchereria* and *Brugia* infections, where the pathology is mainly caused by the adult stages in the lymphatics, the principal lesions in *O. volvulus* infections result from the pathological and immunological responses of the body to the presence of living or dead microfilariae. Often, the first indication that an individual is infected is the presence of microfilariae in the skin, causing discomfort and the development of skin lesions such as a pruritic rash; the initial clinical signs are often confined to one particular area of the body, such as a leg or an arm. Edema of the skin, known as "peu d'orange," is common in the early stages, as is the presence of microabscesses [6,8,90,98]; these reactions may continue as the disease progresses.

As the condition becomes chronic, skin changes such as pigment variation, hyperkeratitis, and focal parakeratitis occur, where the underlying dermis is infiltrated with chronic inflammatory cells and is often hyperemic [99]. In contrast, the skin of longstanding cases often appears thin and shiny, and histologically there is an atrophy of the epidermis and a thickening of the dermis due to fibrosis.

A well-known characteristic of this disease is the appearance of subcutaneous nodules (onchocercomata) on various parts of the body, particularly on bony prominences such as hips, ribs, and skull [6]. It is presumed that nodules arise from a tissue reaction around adult worms, but it is unclear why they occur when nodules do not usually occur around other filarial adult worms, e.g., *Loa loa*. These structures do not cause any significant debility except by their unaesthetic qualities or possibly from pressure and pain when they are situated in adverse locations. They can be located in areas where it is difficult to detect them such as the base of the spine. It is assumed that the adult worm can live for some time in the subcutaneous fascia before a detectable capsule is formed around them; free worms have been found in the fascia [100].

The skin lesions described above are those commonly associated with the progressive disease which generally affects most of the people living permanently in an endemic area. Certain dermal manifestations of onchocerciasis that have a more acute history are of particular interest to the immunopathologist and will be discussed further in later sections. The first of these is the clinical reaction seen when an infected individual is treated with a microfilaricide such as DEC. An intensely pruritic, papular reaction, known as a Mazzotti reaction [101,102], occurs within a short time of taking the drug. The features of this reaction have many characteristics of a form of immediate hypersensitivity reaction [103]. The second type of skin condition that is of interest to the clinical immunologist is that first described in Yemen by Fawdry and known by the arabic name "so-dah" [93,104]. This particular condition is characterized by hyperpigmented skin which is usually edematous and thickened and is usually confined to one particular area of the body. It has been termed localized onchocercal dermatitis to distinguish it from the more common generalized form described above [105]. This localized form of the disease, although not common in areas other than Yemen, has nevertheless been recognized in Cameroon [71,105], Guatemala (R. Collins, personal communication), and in Mexico [71]. An important feature of these patients is that very few microfilariae are detectable in their skin, and subcutaneous adult-containing nodules are relatively rare. Another interesting form of the skin disease is a type of lesion seen in the Central American disease known as "erisipela de la Costa," where reddish-mauve erythematous lesions appear on the face. A condition known as "mal del morado" is a purplish eruption usually affecting the head and neck regions. Both of these conditions may reflect the involvement of the vascular system in the pathology of this disease.

2. Ocular Disease

The route of entry of microfilariae into the eye is unclear. These parasites could gain access to ocular tissues via the conjunctival tissues, via the vascular system, or perhaps via the optic nerve in the case of disease of the posterior segment [107]. Microfilariae are often seen in high numbers floating in the fluid of the anterior chamber, and live parasites have been seen attached to the lens capsule and surviving there for some time [9]. Dead microfilariae are rarely seen in this fluid, but they are seen in the cornea particularly after DEC treatment. Like the changes in the skin, the pathological events occurring in the eye can be considered as two groups, acute and chronic reactions.

Sclerosing keratitis, commonly a cause of blindness in savanna Africa and

Central America, can be regarded as a long-term process. It is a stromal inflammation characterized by a white haziness which begins in the peripheral cornea and extends inward, containing limbal pigment and invading blood vessels. This change eventually impairs vision by covering the pupillary area [9,108]. It is interesting to note that the condition may stop before the cornea is completely opaque, leaving a relatively clear area of cornea which nevertheless can contain many microfilariae that surprisingly are apparently free of any host reaction. A more acute condition is keratitis, which is frequent in certain regions of endemic onchocerciasis. This inflammatory foci, known as "snowflakes" or fluffy opacities, contain degenerating microfilariae, often with inflammatory cells attached to their bodies [90,108]. These latter lesions usually disappear in a few weeks, leaving virtually no scars.

Iridiocyclitis can be present and, with its complications, can cause severe pathology, including a secondary glaucoma. This type of manifestation is more common in heavily infected people and is often seen in the Central American disease. Chorioretinitis is a major component of the disease of the posterior segment. There is considerable variation in the clinical appearance, but it essentially involves retinal pigment atrophy and, in severe cases, atrophy of the choriocapillaris. It is possible that the basic pathological processes behind these retinal changes involve major changes in the vascular system. Optic atrophy is a significant cause of blindness in the posterior segment eye disease, particularly in West Africa [9,108,109]. Microfilariae have been found in the tissue of the optic nerve, and the possibility that an inflammatory reaction in the optic nerve is the basis of the blindness is supported by clinical data [107].

3. Lymphatic and General Systems

Although onchocerciasis principally causes pathology in dermal and ocular tissues, nevertheless, like the other major filarial infections, it can affect the lymphatic system and in extreme cases can cause elephantiasis [82,99,110]. Anderson et al. [111] reported that groin lymphadenopathy is common in rainforest areas of Cameroon, and the consequent condition, "hanging groin" (adenolymphocoele), is also present. Elephantiasis of the genitalia has been reported in Africa, and an elephantoid condition of the face has been described in Mexico and South America [6]. Generalized debility and wasting have been described in long-term onchocerciasis patients. However, the major systemic symptoms occur after treatment with anthelmintics, as is described in Section V.D.

C. Geographical Differences in the Disease Complex

Much has been written about the variations in clinical manifestations of onchocerciasis that occur from area to area, both describing these variations and discussing the reasons behind them [9,87,112-114]. The differences between the disease occurring in the savanna and in the rainforest areas of West Africa have been at the center of most of the research. In an extensive clinical study, Anderson er al. [98,111] demonstrated a number of clinical variations between these two areas. Relatively few palpable nodules and high skin microfilarial counts are common in the savanna populations, as is a high prevalence of anterior uveitis and sclerosing keratitis. In contrast, infected rainforest people may have large numbers of nodules, but moderate levels of skin microfilariae and relatively little blinding eye disease due to anterior segment lesions. Involvement of the lymphatic system is more common in rainforest-dwelling patients than in those who live in savanna areas [111].

The distribution of the adult worm-containing nodules and the microfilariae in the body of man, as in animals, is not even, and the variations appear to be related to the geographic distribution of the disease [6]. The general distribution of the adult parasites over the body is possibly related to the biting habits of the vector, and it is likely that this distribution itself affects the location of the microfilariae. Kershaw et al. [115] showed that in West Africa the nodules are found mainly below the knee, and here microfilariae are also in highest numbers; other authors report similar trends in the distribution of parasites in this geographic area. In East Africa the distribution of microfilariae is different; they are found mostly around the buttocks, thighs, and torso, and nodules are common on the head [116,117].

The reasons behind these geographic differences in disease are probably many, but the suggestion that different strains of parasite exist [118,119] is of particular interest to the immunologist. Experiments on the transmissibility of *O. volvulus* microfilariae by different *Simulium* spp. have indicated that several strains of the parasite exist. The Sudan-savanna parasite strain, for example, will not survive in vectors from the rainforest, and vice versa [120]; neither will African *O. volvulus* survive in the *Simulium* spp. of Central America [121]. Evidence for antigenic differences between savanna and rainforest strains of *O. volvulus* has been provided by Bryceson et al. [122]. Extension of these findings is urgently needed both for a better understanding of the variations in immunopathology between geographic areas and for use in epidemiologic surveys using immunological diagnostic techniques. Preliminary evidence for antigenic differences between *O. volvulus* found in Mexico and the parasite endemic to Cameroon, West Africa, has recently been provided by serum antibody and skin test investigations [123]. In this study, both intradermal tests and in vitro tests of antibodies to *O. volvulus* comparing material originating from African and Mexican patients indicate that there was some antigenic cross reaction between the two types, but there were also antigens specific to each type.

In attempting to analyze regional differences in the pathological consequences of infection, many other factors must be considered, such as nutritional status, environmental differences, and variations in the biting habits of the vector. Two factors which interest the immunologist are genetic differences in the patients and the effect of the presence of parasitic and other infections on the host response to *O. volvulus*. Although there is little evidence to date that these two factors are of any great significance, it should be pointed out that very little work has been done to determine whether they do play a part in the disease spectrum. Anderson and Fuglsang [9] mention that there is an "abnormal" distribution of MN blood groupings among patients with posterior segment lesions in their eyes. A relationship between leprosy and onchocerciasis has been suggested, but the nature of this interaction is unclear [124].

No evidence exists in the literature to suggest that concurrent or previous infection with other filariae has any significant effect on the clinical manifestations of onchocerciasis, but this possibility must be kept in mind since evidence exists for such interactions in experimental nematode infections [125].

D. Reactions to Diethylcarbamazine Therapy

Adverse clinical reactions to DEC therapy are a characteristic feature of both *O. volvulus* infections and also infections with *W. bancrofti* and *Brugia* spp. The nature and severity of the reactions vary both with the susceptibility of each life-cycle stage to the drug and with the location of the parasite in the body. The reactions are particularly severe in onchocerciasis where DEC kills microfilariae without affecting the adult worms. The effect of this drug on the heavy load of microfilariae in the skin and eyes, and possibly in other organs [126], results in the severe clinical condition known as the Mazzotti reaction [101,102]. The Mazzotti reaction consists of a pruritic papular reaction rash accompanied by systemic effects such as hypotension and nausea. Most findings indicate that this reaction has the hallmarks of an anaphylactoid response [103]. Reactions also occur in the eyes. Following DEC therapy, globule-like lesions appear within hours in the periphery of the cornea and in the limbal area. They are often associated with blood vessels which often have perivascular infiltrates, and microhemorrhages are common [127-129]. The globular lesions develop quickly and appear to correlate with the development and intensity of the inflammatory disease that ensues. The globular infiltrates may be reactions around dead parasites, and the perivascular infiltrates possibly reflect the deposition of immune complexes in the local vessels, causing a vasculitis. Angiographic studies of the effect of DEC on the permeability of vessels in the retinal tissue have shown that during treatment there is considerable vascular leakage [114,130]; this is strong evidence for a vascular component in the pathogenesis of the detrimental effect DEC is reported to have on posterior eye disease. During the Mazzotti reaction patients have reported headache, nausea, dizziness, and arthralgia as well as much discomfort from the pruritic skin condition described above [120,128,131]. Clinicians have detected fever, tachycardia, tachypnoea, hypotension, and tenderness in regional lymph nodes of these patients. Suramin, principally a macrofilaricide with some antimicrofilarial properties as well, can also cause nausea and abdominal discomfort [128,131]. However, its major effect occurs some weeks after administration of the drug at a time when *O. volvulus* is dying. At this time in severe cases, stomatitis, iritis, and exfoliative dermatitis, often with fatal consequences, can occur.

Eosinophil leucocytes are prominent in the histologic and hematologic picture of Mazzotti reactions. Following DEC therapy, a drop occurs in the number of eosinophils in the circulation [103,132], and there is a corresponding increase in vacuolation of the eosinophils which also have a higher proportion of Fc receptors [133]; these findings probably reflect the active involvement of these cells in the Mazzotti reaction. Eosinophils are also common in histologic sections of skin biopsies taken from patients under DEC treatment. The function of eosinophils in this situation is likely to be associated either with the destruction of the parasites or in the pharmacologic events associated with parasite removal. The intimate relationship between eosinophils, parasite antigens, and DEC was exemplified in a study by Thevanthasan and Litt [134], who showed that administration of the drug before dosing guinea pigs with an eosinophilia-inducing extract of *T. spiralis* eliminated the eosinophil response. This phenomenon only occurred on the primary dosage with the extract; DEC did not block the response to subsequent doses. The relevance of this experimental observation to the Mazzotti reaction is not yet clear. DEC has been known for some time to kill *O. volvulus* microfilariae in vivo, but its in vitro effect on the parasite is unclear [135, 136]. Recent experiments indicate that the participation of various components of the host's immune system, particularly eosinophils and antiserum, is required to achieve the microfilaricide effect of DEC in vitro [137].

The nature and antigenic specificity of antibodies which might play a role in Mazzotti reactions are not known. Antibodies to the surface antigens of *O. volvulus* microfilariae do not seem to be present in all infected people, although Mazzotti reactions can occur in virtually all patients. The drug may, as has often been suggested, alter the nature of the surface of the parasite and render the microfilariae recognizable by antibodies in the serum. Although obvious clinical signs of general immune complex disease are not common in onchocerciasis, during drug treatment both with DEC and suramin many of the systemic signs produced may be due to immune complex deposition in various organs. They may also be due to the death of the microfilariae located in internal organs, and consequent inflammation [126].

Complement may be involved in the in vivo action of DEC since it has been shown to enhance most in vitro cell-mediated nematode killing mechanisms. However, serum complement levels were not altered during treatment in a study by

Guerra-Caceras [133]; the study of Merino and Brand [138] did, however, show a drop in C3 levels during treatment. The role of complement may also include the recruitment of eosinophils to the sites of reaction, or perhaps it may be involved in the secondary effects of treatment, i.e., in the removal of parasite-derived material by the phagocytic systems and the induction of immune complex mediated lesions.

The definition of the actual nature of the immunological mechanisms behind the Mazzotti reaction may give some indication as to the immunological mechanisms involved in removal of the parasites and is basic to planning a logical approach to the therapeutic suppression of such reactions [139]. The typical Mazzotti reaction seen at the commencement of therapy is quick in onset and has many features of an immediate hypersensitivity reaction (Duke, personal communication; Mackenzie unpublished observations). It is not clear from the literature whether reactions seen later in the course of therapy differ. With succeeding daily drug dosages, the onset of sumptoms becomes more delayed, with pruritis occurring in some cases as much as 24 hr after drug dosage by the end of a 10-day course of DEC. This change in symptoms may indicate that the immunological characteristics of the reaction are changing from a typical immediate-type hypersensitivity reaction to one which appears to be a mixed immediate/delayed response, perhaps similar to the type described by Solley et al. [140]. Such a move through the hypersensitivity spectrum, perhaps caused by the large amounts of antigen being released early in the course of DEC therapy, will have a marked effect on the type of chemotherapeutic agent suitable for suppressing the adverse effects of the Mazzotti reaction. This may be an explanation for the fact that prevention and treatment of Mazzotti reactions with various antiinflammatory drugs has never met with much success. Betamethasone has been used by Anderson et al. [129,131] to control ocular complications following DEC. The most promising of the drugs that are specifically active against the vasoactive amines may be those that act against serotonin; work in Mexico has shown that during Mazzotti reactions blood and tissue serotonin levels rise [141,142]. These researchers also showed that methyl-L-lysergic acid, which acts as an antagonist to serotonin, diminished or prevented the pruritis, erythema, and conjunctival congestion which occur during DEC treatment [143].

As mentioned earlier in this section, other drugs that are active against *O. volvulus,* such as suramin [112,118] and metrifonate [88], also produce various adverse side reactions during therapy. It is probable that many, if not most, of these reactions (as is likely also with DEC) result from the effects of the presence of damaged or dead parasites. Thus, many of the basic immuno-pathological mechanisms involved will probably be similar regardless of the drug initiating the sequence of parasite damage.

E. General Immune Responses

Logistic problems, and the lack of an experimental model for human onchocerciasis, have resulted in most of the immunological investigations being carried out on serum samples collected in the field and sent to laboratories in other areas. This separation of test material from its source has meant that there has been little correlation of results with clinical data, and that results from individual patients have often been pooled together. There are few studies that carefully define the changes occurring in the immune status of an individual during onchocerciasis [105,144]. The difficulty in obtaining material from endemic areas has also resulted in the use of antigens which are simply crude extracts of preserved *O. volvulus* or materials which have been derived from other filariae. The isolation and characterization of *O. volvulus* antigens is an area of prime importance in immunological and diagnostic studies. Characterization of the antigens of *O. volvulus* is of paramount importance in both diagnosis and research into the immunological response that underlies the clinical changes. Three individual antigens have been isolated from whole worm preparations by Mercoullis et al. [145], but these have to be further characterized for functional significance.

The literature concerning studies of serum components from patients with onchocerciasis often contains conflicting data; this might be expected in studies among people who are usually suffering from a variety of infections, viral to helminthologic. It must also be remembered that the nutritional status of these people is often poor, and this will affect their immunological responsiveness [146]. The study of Capuccinelli et al. [147] of patients in Liberia showed an increase in IgD but not in other immunoglobulin classes. This contrasts with the study of Buck et al. [148], who found that severe onchocerciasis was associated with high IgG and IgA levels in the serum but relatively low IgD concentrations. The population in this latter study was nutritionally deprived, and other parameters of the immune system were depressed which may have complicated the situation. Ngu and Blackett [149] also found higher levels of IgG and IgM than normal in the sera of onchocerciasis patients, and also found increased levels of immunoconglutinin. High IgE levels have been described in 86% of Nigerian onchocerciasis patients [150], whereas Buck et al. [148] did not find any increase in IgE levels in their study. In contrast to all these studies on total immunoglobulin levels in the serum of infected individuals, Merino and Brand [138] found little change in immunoglobulin levels except during treatment.

The level of antibodies specific for *O. volvulus* has generally been studied using antigens prepared from onchocercal nodules. Such antigens will principally be derived from adult and immature microfilariae. Most studies report high antibody responses in *O. volvulus*-infected individuals, generally IgG and complement-fixing antibodies [122,151-153]. A large number of studies have been performed using other filarial worm species, such as *Onchocerca gutturosa* and *D. immitis*

[154], as sources of antigen. Fluorescent antibody studies have been used quite extensively, but there is considerable cross reaction with other filarial parasites [83,153,155], a common finding in other assays as well. An interesting finding made in a study of Guatemalan onchocerciasis patients is an apparent inverse relationship between complement-fixing antibody titers and microfilarial count [156]; this observation needs confirmation in light of the search for the mechanisms involved in the survival and death of microfilariae.

Other assays for antibodies have been used by workers interested in this field [96], but all such tests are limited until the antigens of *O. volvulus* are characterized in more detail. The use of defined antigens in sensitive antibody assays, such as the ELISA test [157], will be of great value to diagnosis and research. Tests for detecting stage-specific antibodies will also be of great value to the subject of immunopathology and immune control and are discussed in the next section.

Intradermal skin tests have been employed in a number of studies and, as mentioned earlier, observations of the delayed skin response to crude *O. volvulus* antigens have been most informative, particularly with regard to diagnosis of the localized form of the disease where microfilariae are hard to detect in skin snip assays. Studies involving the immediate response to intradermal injection of *O. volvulus* [144], or the commonly used heterologous antigen *D. immitis* [5], have not been of great value in diagnosis. A most promising study is carried out in Guatemala using antigen derived from *O. volvulus* microfilariae. In this study, 85.2% of patients with onchocerciasis had a positive immediate reaction, indicating a close relationship between positive tests and the presence of infection [158]. It is not known whether this particular antigen will induce delayed-type hypersensitivity skin responses.

In vitro examination of cell-mediated immunity in this disease is still very much in the early stages of development. Studies of lymphocyte transformation have produced variable results. In one trial cells from infected patients responded relatively normally to standard mitogens such as phytohemagglutinin (PHA) and concanavalin A (ConA) [138]. In another study, that of Ngu and Blackett [149], a spectrum of responses to *O. volvulus* antigen was found, ranging from below normal in generalized onchocerciasis to greater than normal in patients with localized disease. This finding of an in vitro spectrum supports that found in delayed skin reactions seen in similar patients [105]. Intradermal testing with carefully defined and clinically safe antigens should provide much information on the clinical immune status of patients and may be of value in diagnosis.

F. Protective Immunity

A most important question is whether or not any real immunity to reinfection occurs in the natural situation. In an area of heavy transmission in Cameroon, children below the age of 10 have few microfilariae in the skin, but the level rises in children of 11-15 years, and reaches adult levels by 16-20 years, at which time the microfilarial levels remained at a plateau [159]. Similar age-related parasite burdens have been recorded in other helminth diseases of man, for example hookworm [4] ; but it should be remembered that a plateau population of microfilariae in the skin does not necessarily indicate the development of resistance to infection (see Section II). Moreover, Duke [160] studied immunity to reinfection in the same population used for the age-related studies [159] by treating adult patients with drugs to remove the adult worm population and then studying the reappearance of infection by counting microfilariae in the skin. The level of infection reached pretreatment levels 4 years after the drug was given, suggesting little immunity to reinfection, at least in the absence of a permanent adult worm burden.

On the face of it, this clinical study suggests that there is little or no protective immunity to *O. volvulus* infection in endemic populations. However, there are a number of observations that suggest that there is in fact a strong immune response elicited by the parasite. Histologic observations of nodules show a wide range of inflammatory cells, including those particularly related to the immune system (i.e., plasma cells, macrophages, and lymphocytes), thus indicating an active immune response to the parasites present in these lesions. Delayed skin reactions to intradermally injected crude antigen extract [105] are seen in patients with localized reactive skin disease, suggesting the active participation of the immune system in these patients; in contrast, heavily infected people do not respond to the antigen in this test [105,106]. It is possible that the populations studied by Duke [159,160] to assess immunity to reinfection were in the latter category immunologically.

The immunological assay which most closely relates to protective immunity is the antibody-dependent adherence of granulocytes to the surface of living nematodes [48]. In the case of *T. spiralis* this adherence reaction leads to the death of the early forms of this parasite. This assay was used to study antibodies to *O. volvulus* [71,100] ; 100% of sera from patients was found to have antibodies to the surface of infective larvae, 95% to the adult surface, and only 20% to the microfilariae. It is not clear yet whether the antibodies detected in this assay are specific to each parasite stage as they are with *T. spiralis*.

It is most important, not only for studies of protective immunity but also from the viewpoint of diagnosis and immunopathology, to know whether there actually is stage specificity. Bryceson et al. [122] have shown that microfilariae lack some of the antigens possessed by the adults. It is also important to know the locations of antigens, i.e., whether they are on the surface of the parasite, in their secretions, or confined to the somatic tissues. Our unpublished data indicates that the surface of first-stage nematodes changes rapidly during maturation and before the parasite first molts.

If there is one particular stage of the parasite which is to be considered the one of importance in the induction of protective immunity, that is, the stage that protective immunity should be directed against, then we believe that this is the infective stage. It appears to be a highly antigenic form and, unlike most of the other stages, it probably induces little or no pathology. The characterization of specific antigens of the infective larvae is crucial if a successful vaccine is to be developed.

G. Immunopathology

Many of the features of the immunopathology of this infection have already been discussed in previous sections (Sections V.B and V.C). The mechanisms involved in the responses following DEC treatment are probably similar to those occurring continually in the natural disease. It is already clear that a wide variety of immunopathological reactions are involved: immediate and delayed hypersensitivity, antibody-dependent cell-mediated reactions, as well as immune complexes. The involvement of the vascular system in the ocular complications of this disease, for example, the uveitis and the vessel leakage following therapy, probably results from the effects of immune complexes. It is possible that the erythematous conditions seen on the head and upper torso in Central American disease, erisipela de la Costa and mal del morado, may also be manifestations of immune complex disease affecting blood vessels. The presence of immune complexes in serum is described, but their presence in the tissues has yet to be clearly defined. Gibson et al. [161] have suggested that the granular deposits they have seen in electronmicrographs of degenerating microfilariae may be immune complexes. This material may also be partially derived from the eosinophils present in the area, since these cells are known to degranulate following intimate contact with parasites [162].

One characteristic feature of the histopathology in certain phases of the disease is the observation that microfilariae can often be seen lying in the dermis or cornea with very little, if any, inflammatory response around them, or floating free in the anterior chamber apparently unimpeded. It has been calculated that a heavily infected person can have as many as 200 million parasites in his body at one time [7]. The mechanisms behind this apparent lack of recognition by the host's defense system is at present unclear but constitutes a major question in this disease and in parasite immunology generally. The production of factors by microfilariae that might suppress inflammation has not been looked at and, considering the lack of obvious secretory organs, such factors are unlikely to originate from this early stage of this species.

Cell-mediated immune reactions against microfilariae have not been defined in onchocerciasis, and only a few studies using the homologous antigen system have been carried out. Bartlett et al. [105] and others [144] have used crude *O. volvulus* adult extracts to show that African patients with the localized form of dermatitis (sodah) were the only individuals that can produce a specific delayed-type hypersensitivity skin reaction; the majority with generalized skin disease appear to have some mechanism of suppressing delayed hypersensitivity responses to the parasite antigens. Since individuals with sodah characteristically have a reactive skin condition and very few detectable microfilariae, it is likely that they have an active system which removes the parasites that invade their skin. The positive delayed skin tests may reflect the involvement of T-cell mechanisms in controlling the number of parasites and in confining the lesions to one area of the body. A recent study carried out in Mexico suggests that delayed hypersensitivity reactions are a feature of low infections rather than heavy infections, and that the skin test becomes negative as the microfilarial load in the skin increases [106]. In this study *O. volvulus* antigen was used as a dermal test antigen in a group of 70 patients, from an endemic village, whose levels of microfilariae varied from 0 to over 200 per milligram. It was found that positive delayed hypersensitivity reactions were significantly more common in patients with less than approximately 15 microfilariae per milligram of skin, suggesting that a state of anergy was present in heavily infected people but not at low infection loads.

It therefore appears that *O. volvulus* can have considerable influence over the host's defense system, and that the parasite can exist for considerable periods of time in relative harmony with the host. However, there are phases of the disease where there is an intense reaction against the microfilariae. Punctate keratitis consists of localized inflammatory reactions around the microfilariae in the cornea, and similarly, the microabscesses in the skin are reactions around skin-dwelling parasites [99].

The events related to the inflammatory reactions to microfilariae may take place in two phases, the first being the death or degeneration of the parasite induced by either drugs or natural aging processes, the second involving mechanisms of removing the now "foreign" antigenically dangerous material. When the microfilariae die over an extended period of time, as probably occurs in the natural disease, the body's defense system can generally cope with removing the parasite-derived foreign material, and only the clinical lesions associated with chronic disease occur. However, when a majority of the microfilariae are killed at one time, as happens in treatment with DEC, the large amount of dead parasite material that must be eliminated overloads the system and the acute clinical reactions associated with drug therapy occur.

The presence of infective larvae and adult worms in the body may have an effect on the immunological status of an infected individual and, consequently, on various aspects of the immunopathology. Induction of antibody-mediated or cell-mediated immunity against these stages may influence the host's response to the microfilariae or perhaps to the other stages of the parasite. The development of the fibrous capsule around the adult parasite is probably under the influence of the immune system, perhaps in a way similar to that suggested for the development of granulomas in schistosomiasis [163]. The existence of a host mechanism that limits or influences the presence of nodules is suggested by the report from Central America that, following removal of all palpable nodules, a heavily infected individual soon acquires the same number of nodules again [164]. No pathological condition has been attributed to the presence of infective larvae; however, it is not unreasonable to suggest that repeated infection with this relatively antigenic form of the parasite may have a profound effect on the immune status of that individual.

An aspect of the biology of the disease of interest to immunologists is the development of cutaneous allergy to the bite of the blackfly [165]. Individuals vary considerably in their particular response to the bites of *Simulium* spp., and a spectrum of reactions from immediate hypersensitivities through to typical delayed-type hypersensitivity reactions are seen. A homocytotropic antibody specific to the saliva of the blackfly is demonstrable in allergic patients [165].

The effect of this allergy on the uptake of microfilariae into the fly, on the viability of the fly, and on the infective *O. volvulus* that are deposited in the skin, is not known. Whether or not an environment containing the many mediators of hypersensitivity is detrimental or beneficial to the new parasite may seem at present a rather academic question. Nevertheless, there are aspects of the interaction between the fly, the host, and the parasite that, when understood more fully, may be valuable to aspects of control of this disease. It is not impossible to conceive that manipulation of any of the mechanisms involved in the interaction between these three at this level might swing the balance of this disease complex toward control.

H. Summary of Reactions to *Onchocerca volvulus*

It is probable that much of the pathology seen in this disease complex, particularly the acute lesions, is attributable to the effects of dead parasites. This is particularly important in regard to therapeutic regimens; the administration of any drug that kills the parasite successfully, even though the drug itself has no intrinsic side effects, will be followed by effects due to the presence of dead parasites. It is important, therefore, to understand the immunological events occurring in the body and tissues following therapy which may lead to pathology. A careful analysis of the Mazzotti reaction and the immunopathological events surrounding the reaction should lead to the successful clinical control of the adverse reactions occurring on the death of parasites. Until the role of the immune system in the development of lesions of onchocerciasis is clearly understood, caution is needed in any attempts to artificially stimulate the immune system to induce protective immunity. It is to be hoped that protective antibodies and cellular mechanisms will differ in their antigenic specificity from those that induce pathology.

I. Other *Onchocerca* spp.

Research into the immunology of infections caused by other *Onchocerca* species is only just beginning. At least 12 species other than *O. volvulus* are regarded as belonging to this genus [166]. *Onchocerca* spp. are primarily host specific; for example, *O. volvulus* is not reported to exist in any species other than man, the gorilla [167], and, experimentally, the chimpanzee [168]. Onchocerciasis is not a disease of any major significance in veterinary medicine, although dermal pathology is induced in the horse and the donkey by *Onchocerca cervicalis* [169, 170]; *Onchocerca gibsoni* and *O. gutturosa* cause skin pathology in bovidae, affecting the value of hides; and *Onchocerca armillata* has been incriminated as the cause of pathology in the aortae of cattle [171].

The main problem in experimental research into human onchocerciasis is the lack of a disease in domestic or laboratory animals that mimics the clinical and pathological signs induced in man by *O. volvulus*. However, it has been suggested that *O. cervicalis* infection in the horse, and perhaps *O. gutturosa* and *O. gibsoni* infections in cattle, may have aspects of their pathology that are similar to those seen in human onchocerciasis [120]. Research is now underway in a number of institutes to study the immunology and pathology of these infections. Nevertheless, the lack of a true laboratory model of the human disease emphasizes the point that careful correlation of clinical conditions with immunological parameters in the human disease is likely to be the most fruitful approach.

VI. LYMPHATIC FILARIASES OF MAN

A. The Parasites

Three nematode species parasitize the lymphatic system of man: *Wuchereria bancrofti, Brugia malayi,* and *Brugia timori*. They are closely related taxonomically, but their geographic distribution differs and they use different species of mosquitoes as their vectors [5]. In Southeast Asia, *W. bancrofti* and one or two other of the *Brugia* species may occur together. *Wuchereria bancrofti* and *B. malayi* also exist as different physiological races in different parts of the world. These races do not differ morphologically, but because of geographic isolation, the diurnal rhythm of the microfilaremia differs and is related to the circadian rhythm of the biting behavior of the local invertebrate vector species; *B. malayi* and *W. bancrofti* both contain two races, but only one race of *B. timori* has been described. Although the chief difference between races is the time at which microfilariae are found in highest number in the blood, the nature of the clinical symptoms (and, therefore, probably the nature of the immune response) induced by the different races also differs somewhat [5,10]. For example, *W. bancrofti* occurs in urban regions, where *Culex pipiens fatigans* is the vector, as well as in rural populations, where other mosquito vectors are involved. Filariasis due to infection with the *Brugia* spp. occurs only in rural areas, again reflecting vector ecology [5].

The transmission of *W. bancrofti* by mosquitoes was historically the first demonstration of the role of insect vectors as intermediate hosts for infection of mammals, a discovery made by Manson when working as a medical officer in China. Manson also discovered the nocturnal periodicity of the microfilaremia of *W. bancrofti*, (Manson, 1877, 1879, quoted by Sasa [5]). The early history fo the elucidation of the biology of the parasite-vector interaction of *W. bancrofti*, one of the classic stories of tropical medicine and parasitology, has been described in detail [26] and is also summarized by Sasa [5] in his book on human filariasis.

B. Clinical Characteristics

It has been suggested that the clinical symptoms associated with this disease, which are common to all three species of filariae, are closely related to the immune response to the parasite. Lymphatic filariasis is characterized by filarial fever with lymphadenitis and lymphangitis in the acute stage, which progresses to the chronic stage with severe lymphatic obstruction manifesting in lymphoedema and elephantiasis, hydrocoele, and chyluria. In general, the occurrence of acute symptoms, such as attacks of fever and lymphangitis, is more frequent in areas of endemic infection with *Brugia* spp. than in individuals infected with *W. bancrofti*. Lymphoedema and elephantiasis of legs and arms are common to infections with both genera, but the involvement of genitourinal organs, shown by funiculitis, hydrocele, and chyluria, is less common in infections with *Brugia* spp. than in *W. bancrofti* filariasis [5,172,173].

In endemically infected populations exposed to these parasites, there is a wide variation in the response between individuals, even within a single household. Some never show any signs of infection, either parasitologic or clinical, although there may be evidence from entomologic or serologic studies that they have been exposed to infective larvae. A proportion of people have microfilariae present in the blood after they have been exposed to infection for some time; these carriers are probably symptomless initially, and some become spontaneously microfilariae negative without developing clinical symptoms. In areas of heavy endemic infection, man begins to show acute symptoms and later may develop chronic signs such as irreversible elephantiasis. Microfilaremia may persist for some years before chronic symptoms develop; this latter event often, but not always, occurs in individuals who have become amicrofilaremic. The prevalence of microfilaremia rises rapidly in the first decade of life but then remains stable in older age groups. Nevertheless, only 25-50% of persons in endemically infected populations are microfilaremic, although the disease rate may be much greater [5].

In individuals exposed to infection for the first time in adult life, the pattern of development of symptoms is different from that in endemically infected populations. Very detailed studies were made of large numbers of United States servicemen heavily exposed to *W. bancrofti* for short periods in the Pacific during World War II. Although symptoms of lymphatic obstruction occurred within a few months of exposure, few servicemen developed microfilaremia when studied up to 2 years after exposure [174]. Similar reactions were seen in Indonesians aged 5 years or older, 2 years after they had been transferred from regions without filariasis into a *B. timori* endemic area. Microfilaremia did not develop until they had been exposed to infection for more than 2 years, although recurrent attacks of adenolymphangitis with lymphoedema and even elephantiasis were common [173,175]. It has been suggested that the long delay in appearance of microfilariae in the blood after initial exposure to *W. bancrofti* is because the adult female worm takes 2-7 years to become mature; since *W. bancrofti* will only infect man, it is not possible to examine this idea critically. However, *Brugia* spp. reach sexual maturity in animals within 2-3 months [10], which makes the long delay between initial exposure to *Brugia* and the appearance of microfilariae in the blood of man difficult to explain. It seems possible that microfilaremia in man occurs only when the immune response if impaired (see later), and that the clinical symptoms of lymphatic involvement in these individuals results from the immunologically mediated destruction of larvae and adult worms in the lymphatics (Partono, personal communication).

It has been postulated that the range of responses to these parasites is a reflection of variation in the immune response of infected individuals. Similarly, it has been suggested that elephantiasis results from cell-mediated responses to dead adult worms, and symptoms of acute filariasis have been attributed to antibody-dependent responses [176,177]. In some people, these parasites do not appear to develop at all or at least only to the stages that induce changes in the lymphatics; in other individuals they develop to the stage of microfilarial production unhindered. However, in patients with marked clinical symptoms, the parasites are probably killed at some stage in their development, presumably by an immunological mechanism, within the lymphatic system. This marked spectrum in the ability of man to recognize the antigens of the different stages of these worms is of particular immunological interest but is apparently only partially reflected in the animal models of filariasis. The reasons for the variation in man are not known, but they could include the genetic constitution of the population, its nutritional status, the incidence of other helminth and microbial infections, the number of filarial parasites to which individuals are exposed especially initially, as well as the individual's age at first exposure.

C. Responses to Anthelmintic Treatment

The wide variation in response to these parasites is illustrated again by the reaction of infected patients to treatment with DEC. Three types of side effects may occur; these may be frequent and severe and correlate well with the type of clinical symptoms (Partono and Dennis, personal communication). Following DEC administration, fever occurs most commonly in patients with microfilaremia counts of less than 1 per microliter (indicating death of microfilariae), whereas general reactions with or without fever (including headache, body pain, chills, dizziness, inappetence, and malaise) are most common in people with both microfilaremia and signs of disease. Finally, local reactions such as painful lymph node swelling occur in individuals with signs of disease whether or not they have had microfilaremia; these symptoms are probably related to the death of worms in the lymphatics. Symptoms following drug therapy are much more severe in patients infected with *Brugia* spp. compared with those infected with *W. bancrofti* (Ref. 5 and Partono, personal communication). Many of the reactions to DEC in the patients with lymphatic filariasis are similar to those seen in patients with onchocerciasis (see Section V). It is widely believed that these reactions reflect the immune response to filarial antigens suddenly released from the dying worms and probably are caused by complexes of antibodies and antigens.

D. Immune Responses

The great variation in the response of individuals within endemically infected populations, together with the severe clinical reactions which may accompany drug therapy, indicate that the immunological reactions underlying the disease require analysis. Historically, the main impetus for immunological studies usually come from a need for diagnostic methods which do not depend on detection of the parasites themselves. Until recently, because of the great difficulty of obtaining parasite material of those species which infect man for use in diagnosis, the antigens used were prepared from filarial parasites of animals, such as *D. immitis* from dogs or *D. viteae* from rodents [53]. Since it was shown that the *Brugia* spp. will complete their life cycle in the peritoneal cavity of jirds, it has become possible to use *Brugia* antigen in both fundamental and diagnostic studies.

1. Antibody Responses and Antibody-Dependent Cellular Reactions

There is a marked antibody response in all individuals exposed to these parasites; the antibodies have been detected by a variety of methods using extracts of heterologous parasites as antigens [53,56]. However, methods such as immediate skin reactions, complement fixation, or indirect hemagglutination do not differentiate between individuals infected with the same parasite but showing different clinical reactions, nor do they reveal the species of worm (i.e., whether *W. bancrofti* or *Brugia*) which is infecting the patient. Even using *B. malayi* antigen, immediate skin reactions were detected in all individuals exposed to *W. bancrofti* or *B. malayi* without differentiation between these parasites or the clinical status of the infected patients. Indirect fluorescence using sections of *B. malayi* give similar results [61,65].

Several studies have shown that many, but not all, amicrofilaremic individuals exposed to *W. bancrofti* have antibodies in their circulation directed against the sheath of microfilariae. These antibodies have been detected by indirect fluorescence or antibody-mediated cell adherence of leukocytes to the microfilariae sheath in amicrofilaremic individuals exposed to *W. bancrofti* or *B. malayi* [29,63,64,66]. Antibodies to the microfilarial sheath detected by fluorescence in a study of *B. malayi* infection were IgM, IgG, or IgA [66], but antibodies to *W. bancrofti* microfilariae detected by adherence of peripheral blood leukocytes were probably IgG [24]. These antibodies were found particularly in patients with elephantiasis. However, Subrahmanyam et al. [24] also found them in healthy persons living in endemic areas for several years; they have not been found in cases with microfilaremia. In contrast to these studies with microfilariae, antibodies to the infective larvae are present in the sera of both microfilaremic and amicrofilaremic individuals. Higashi and Chowdhury [20] found IgG antibodies mediating eosinophil adherence to *W. bancrofti* infective larvae, whereas others [64] have detected by fluorescence antibodies to the surface of *B. malayi*-infective larvae in patients with and without microfilaremia.

In a study of *W. bancrofti* in the Philippines, patients with asymptomatic microfilaremia or chronic obstructive disease were compared with healthy controls in the same area [178]. As a group, patients with filariasis had raised serum IgG levels and their antibody response to tetanus and typhoid vaccines was impaired. The investigators in this study suggest that immunosuppression in filariasis may result from antigenic competition and may contribute to secondary infection. A study of Malaysians infected with *B. malayi* and *W. bancrofti* revealed that bancroftian filariasis produced significantly higher immunoglobulin levels than *B. malayi* infections; the levels in the latter type of infection differed little from those in control populations [179]. In view of the fact that this finding in *B. malayi* infections differs from the observations in other works, caution must be taken in considering these results, particularly as the effect of other infections (such as malaria) on the immunoglobulin levels has not been assessed in this study.

2. Lymphocyte Transformation Studies in Lymphatic Filariasis

In studies of Filipinos infected with *W. bancrofti* [178] it appeared that the delayed hypersensitivity response to heterologous antigens was equally depressed in patients with asymptomatic microfilaremia and in those with chronic obstructive disease compared with healthy controls from the same area. In contrast, in studies of *W. bancrofti* in the Pacific area [70] and *B. malayi* in Indonesia [69], delayed hypersensitivity responses to nonfilarial antigens were unimpaired, whereas the responses of lymphocytes from infected patients to filarial antigens reflected the clinical and parasitologic status of the patient. In addition, Piessens et al. [69] have provided further evidence of the importance of parasite-stage-specific immune responses in these infections. They showed that marked in vitro blastogenesis of lymphocytes from patients with *B. malayi*-induced elephantiasis occurred when extracts of adult *B. malayi* were used as antigen, but lymphocytes from infected individuals without this clinical symptom did not respond to adult worm antigen. Lymphocytes from most individuals without clinical or parasitologic evidence of filariasis, and about half of those with clinical signs of filariasis but without microfilaremia, responded to microfilarial antigen in vitro. Most people with microfilaremia did not respond to microfilarial antigen. This suggests that nonsymptomatic individuals are not sensitized to adult worm antigens but are sensitized to an antigen which is common to microfilariae and infective larvae [69].

This study with *B. malayi* suggests that microfilaremia is associated with a suppression of cell-mediated immunity specific to microfilarial antigens. Ottesen et al. [70] presented similar evidence in their studies of cell-mediated responses in patients infected with the Pacific race of *W. bancrofti,* but in their case heterologous antigen was used. Amicrofilaremic individuals gave marked cell-mediated responses to filarial antigens, whereas microfilaremic patients did not respond, and all responded equally well to nonfilarial antigens [69]. These two studies raise the interesting hypothesis that the unexpectedly long period between the exposure of man to infection with *W. bancrofti* or *B. malayi* and the detection of microfilariae in the blood may depend on the development of anergy to microfilarial antigens. It is also of considerable interest that an apparently similar antigen-specific anergy to microfilarial antigens occurs in patients heavily infected with *O. volvulus* (Ref. 71: see Section V.E).

VII. TROPICAL EOSINOPHILIC LUNG

Tropical eosinophilic lung is a chronic disease occurring in man in the tropics or subtropics where filariasis is endemic. The manifestations of this disease were described by Donohugh [180] from a review of early work and his own experience with patients, and have been reviewed recently [181]. The pulmonary symptoms are found mostly in males and begin with a dry diurnal cough which rapidly becomes nocturnal and often paroxysmal. The symptoms may last for weeks or months, remit spontaneously, and then later recur, characteristically with wheezing and development of pulmonary infiltration. Extreme persistent eosinophilia and very high IgE levels are characteristic and help to distinguish this condition from other forms of chronic lung disease [180-185]. It has been suggested that the increases in these two responses are related [183,184]. Although microfilariae are not found in the blood of these patients [174], even when treated with cortisone [186], there is good reason to think that this disease represents a response to microfilariae, although it is not yet agreed whether the causative filariae are parasites of man or of animals. The condition usually responds to treatment with DEC which produces a reduction in the blood eosinophilia [174,180]. Serum antibodies to filariae were found to be at levels which were much higher in patients with tropical eosinophilic lung than in patients with other forms of filariasis [181,187]. Microfilariae and their degenerating remains have been seen in biopsies from lungs and lymph nodes taken from eosinophilic patients [186,188,189]. Many aspects of this disease were mimicked when Buckley [190] infected himself first with *B. malayi* and then with *B. pahangi*. Wong [191] succeeded in inducing similar symptoms in dogs by injecting them first with *D. immitis* microfilariae and then following with a larval infection. In those dogs the infective larvae developed to adult worms and eosinophilia developed. However, there was no microfilaremia, although microfilariae were seen trapped in the lungs in granulomata consisting of an initial eosinophil-rich infiltrate of polymorphonuclear cells; these cells were later replaced with monocytes. The onset of the disease in dogs coincided with the appearance of high titers of antibodies to microfilarial surface antigens [192].

It appears that tropical eosinophilic lung disease is a form of filariasis in which the worms reach the adult stage inducing very little pathology in the lymphatics, although there is a marked immunopathological response to the microfilariae in the lungs. It has been suggested that the parasites concerned may be the animal parasites *D. immitis* or *B. pahangi* rather than the human pathogens *W. bancrofti* or *B. malayi* [180], although Beaver [174] felt that the condition represents an atypical infection with *W. bancrofti* or *Brugia* spp. This seems most likely, since the response of man to *W. bancrofti* and *B. malayi*/ *B. timori* is known to vary enormously between individuals (see Section V.I). It also seems most likely that tropical eosinophilic lung is part of this same spectrum. The genetic constitution of the population must be a contributing factor in this special response, and it is thought that race is a major factor in the etiology of tropical eosinophilic lung [189]. This idea seems worth reassessing. Two reports enhance the conclusion that this condition represents a strong immune reaction to *W. bancrofti* and *Brugia* spp. microfilariae. Wong [191] noted, without giving details, that in an immunofluorescence assay with serum from 13 patients with tropical eosinophilic lung, none were positive to *D. immitis* microfilariae, 9 reacted only to *W. bancrofti* microfilariae, 3 only to *B. malayi* microfilariae, and 1 to microfilariae of *B. pahangi*. Ottesen et al. [193] showed that IgE antibodies from tropical eosinophilic lung cases showed species and stage specificity for filarial antigens. In a histamine release assay, peripheral blood leucocytes from tropical eosinophilic lung cases were found to be more sensitive to filarial anti-gens (especially those derived from microfilariae) than peripheral blood leuco-cytes from other filariae-infected individuals; histamine release was greater when *W. bancrofti* and *B. malayi* microfilariae were tested than when *D. immitis* micro-filariae were used in this assay.

The difference in the spectrum of responsiveness to filariae may result from a difference in the ability of individuals to recognize parasite stage-specific antigens. It is possible that some people respond rapidly to developing infective larvae, and so have no disease; others may respond only to the later stages residing in the lymphatics, and hence eventually develop elephantiasis; some respond to the microfilariae and develop tropical eosinophilic lung, while others do not re-spond at all and remain microfilaremic. It would be most interesting to trace the fate of microfilariae labeled with a marker in people with these different re-actions to filarial infection. One would expect microfilariae to be cleared rapidly from the circulation of patients with elephantiasis or tropical eosinophilic lung, but the actual immune mechanisms, or the organ of the body concerned, might differ. It has been suggested that the IgE levels and high eosinophilia in tropical eosinophilic lung are linked [183,184]; increasing evidence indicates that eosino-phils can destroy microfilariae, and perhaps the antigens released in this action may potentiate IgE responses [183,184].

VIII. *BRUGIA* SPP. IN ANIMALS

Whereas *W. bancrofti* and *O. volvulus* are very host specific, the *Brugia* spp. will infect a number of mammals. *Brugia malayi* naturally infects several primates and is occasionally found in cats, whereas *B. pahangi* is found in few primates but readily infects domestic carnivores, especially cats. Periodic *B. malayi* appar-ently infects cats less readily than subperiodic *B. malayi*, and a high percentage of domestic cats exposed to *B. pahangi* become infected [10]. *B. malayi* pro-duces a long lasting infection in most rhesus monkeys (*Macaca mulatta*), and even repeated infections do not induce resistance [194], whereas infection of this host with *B. pahangi* produces either a transient or no microfilaremia [10]. When kittens or monkeys (*Macaca fascicularis*) were exposed to *B. timori*, no infection was established in the monkeys, and the cats only developed a very low-grade infection [195]. The development of *B. pahangi* and *B. malayi* in cats also differs in detail: with both species it takes place in the lymphatic sys-tem, initially in the perinodal lymphatic sinus of the lymph node and later the worms migrate against the flow of lymph to the afferent lymphatic and reach maturity 2-3 months after infection [10].

A major advance occurred when Ash and Riley [32,33] showed that *B. pahangi* and subperiodic *B. malayi* develop in the jird, *M. unguiculatus*. Larvae given subcutaneously develop to the adult stage in the heart, pulmonary arteries, lymphatics, and testes, but if inoculated intraperitoneally all but a few of the worms develop to the adult stage free in the peritoneal cavity [34,196]. *Brugia timori* developed to sexual maturity in male jirds, but no peripheral blood microfilaremia occurred [195]. The discovery of the susceptibility of jirds to *Brugia* spp. has given a great impetus to immunological and biochemical studies of *Brugia,* since it provides a readily accessible source of well-defined parasite material. Multimammate rats (*Praomys natalensis*) are also susceptible to this infection, as are 20-35% of golden hamsters (*Mesocricetus auratus*). Some strains of rats will also develop a microfilaremia, however, mice resist development of *Brugia* spp. [10].

A. *Brugia* spp. in Cats and Dogs

Cats infected with *B. pahangi* develop an infection which may last for several years, but a few animals do not become infected and appear innately resistant [10]. Denham et al. [197] infected susceptible cats repeatedly with 50 *B. pahangi* larvae every 10 days. Even after as many as 50 challenge infections, many of the cats remained susceptible to reinfection, although the microfilaremia remained relatively constant (see Section II). However, after many infections over a long period of time, some cats suddenly became amicrofilaremic and were then highly resistant to reinfection [197]. At the time cats become amicrofilaremic, an antibody directed against microfilariae could be detected, and furthermore, it was found that animals which were producing this antibody rapidly cleared experimentally introduced microfilariae from their circulation. Cats passively protected with this antibody were not resistant to transfused microfilariae or to challenge with infective larvae [67]. In contrast, Wong [198] showed that antibodies and resistance to *B. pahangi* microfilariae could be induced in dogs by immunizing with microfilariae, and that antibodies from these dogs would reduce the microfilaremia in patent animals.

In cats, resistance to microfilariae is associated with the appearance of a particular antibody in the circulation, however, antibodies to infective larvae and adults were found in both resistant cats and in cats susceptible to reinfection [67]. Also in this host, resistance to microfilariae appears to be associated with resistance to infective larvae; infective larvae given to amicrofilaremic cats appeared to be killed very rapidly and before they entered the lymphatics. Living adult worms were found in amicrofilaremic cats if examined soon after the blood had become parasite negative; however, several months later no adult worms were recovered. Thus, some cats became immune to all stages in this worm when repeatedly reinfected over a longer period [10].

McGreevy et al. [199] attempted to investigate whether *B. pahangi* is able to disguise itself from the host's immune response by incorporating hostlike molecules into its outer surface in the manner suggested for schistosomes [200]. Experiments were designed to determine whether infective larvae incorporated antigen from the mosquito vector into the cuticle, or whether cat antigens were incorporated into the surface of the stages found in the mammalian host. No mammalian antigen, and only a small amount of mosquite antigen, was found, and there was no evidence that the presence of these antigens was involved in the longevity of this parasite in the host. This study was by no means conclusive concerning the possible role of "host antigens" in this infection.

The large adult stages of *Brugia* spp. induce marked gross and histopathological changes in the lymph system of infected cats and dogs. Lymphoedema may occur, but it is usually transitory and is seen only in cats which become amicrofilaremic following repeated infection [201]. Elephantiasis has not been seen in cats. Gross changes, including ulceration, were seen only in cats infected with both *B. malayi* and streptococcus [202]. Progressive damage to the lymphatics was caused only by repeated infection [203]. When adult worms were killed in the lymphatics by administration of an anthelmintic, the infected lymphatics were enlarged enormously for some weeks after treatment; but 2 months later the previously affected lymphatic vessels looked completely normal [204].

Following an initial infection in cats, the infected lymph node rapidly develops histologic changes suggestive of a cell-mediated response which wanes after about 2 months. In contrast, signs of an antibody response begin later (at about 2 weeks) but persist for at least 2 years [205]. It should be noted that the animals which responded in this way were not immune to the infection. Although Schacher and Sahyoun [177] suggested from their detailed study of the histopathology of cats and dogs infected with *B. pahangi* that many changes were a response to the presence of parasites or their products, Denham and McGreevy [10] feel that the pathologic changes in cats are not specifically correlated with the presence of parasites.

B. *Brugia* spp. in Rodents

Jirds are highly susceptible to infection with *Brugia* and develop little resistance to reinfection. Although Kowalski and Ash [206] found that fewer *B. pahangi* larvae developed to maturity in jurds given four subcutaneous infections than in animals given a single infection, Suswillo and Denham (quoted in Ref. 10) found no resistance in jirds given many more infections by the intraperitoneal route. These studies suggest that infective larvae of *Brugia* are not highly antigenic in the jird, which is also true for the cat system (see Section III.C), and that the *Brugia*/jird model may not be useful for the study of development of immunity to the parasite itself. However, because at least some of the parasites develop in the lymphatics of the jird, this system may prove useful in the analysis of the pathology induced by these parasites [196], and perhaps the mechanisms by which the parasite avoids developing an immune response.

Immunologically, the outstanding characteristic of lymphatic filariasis in humans is the range of responses seen in endemically infected populations. These vary from apparently total resistance to the development of the parasite, through a variety of clinical changes associated with the presence of worms in the lymphatics, to prolonged and persistent microfilaremia without clinical symptoms. The occurrence of occult or latent infections (the presence of filarial parasites without detectable microfilaremia) seems to be associated with the most severe clinical changes that can eventually lead to elephantiasis. This indicates that a model is required in which immune reactions occur to the adult worms and/or the late third-stage and fourth-stage larvae. The ease with which infections can be established in cats and jirds, and the long persistence of worms in these animals, make them unsuitable animals for this type of study; rats, which are not so easily infected with *B. pahangi*, may be the best model for studying immunity to the later stages of this parasite. Weller [207] studied the cell-mediated response to the different life-cycle stages in Lewis rats infected with *B. pahangi*. Reactions to third-stage larvae were detected early in the infection, responses to adult worm antigen varied with the source of lymphocytes tested throughout the 1½ years of the infection, and responses to microfilariae were detected only as microfilaremia disappeared 8-14 months after its onset.

A generalized suppression of immune responsiveness occurs in jirds and rats infected with *B. pahangi*. A 50-60% reduction in the response of spleen cells from infected jirds to PHA and ConA occurred from 2 months after infection. There was an inverse correlation between the response to adult worm antigen and the depression in PHA responsiveness, suggesting that the cells affected were not involved in the response to the parasite. Both the PHA and ConA reactivity was restored by removal of adherent and phagocytic cells and appeared not to be associated with the presence of any suppressor factors in the serum of infected animals [208]. Periods of hyporesponsiveness to B- and T-cell mitogens were also observed by Weller [207] in his study of *B. pahangi* in rats. Two patterns of hyporesponsiveness were observed: a depression of the spleen cell response in the animals with splenic granulomas was accompanied by a second pattern of hyporesponsiveness in mesenteric node cells which lasted many weeks. Microfilaremia was significantly greater in the immunosuppressed animals and, although the mechanism of the immunosuppression was not determined, it was again not associated with a serum factor.

IX. FILARIAL INFECTIONS OF RODENTS

A. *Dipetalonema viteae*

Dipetalonema viteae is a natural parasite of jirds (*Meriones rhombomys*), in which microfilaremia may persist for 1-2 years [28,209], but it is usually studied experimentally in hamsters. The intermediate host of *D. viteae* is a tick, *Ornitho-dorus tartakovskyi*. The worm develops to maturity largely, but not exclusively, in the subcutaneous tissues. The developing larvae molt to the fourth stage about 7 days after infection, to the fifth stage at about 21 days, and microfilariae are detected in the blood from about day 55 after infection and show no periodicity [210,211]. Large numbers of microfilariae also accumulate throughout the tissues of the host [210]. In most strains of hamsters the microfilaremia rises to a peak after about 75-85 days before falling to very low, and even undetectable, levels approximately 120 days after infection. In some strains of hamsters and in jirds, microfilaremia persists for months [209,210,212,213].

There are several characteristics of immunity to filarial nematodes which have been studied with this parasite model. Most attention has been given to the study of the mechanisms underlying the disappearance of microfilariae from the circulation of hamsters. Once hamsters become amicrofilaremic, the adult worms persist for a considerable time, their longevity depending on the strain of hamster; these worms only gradually lose their ability to survive or renew microfilarial production when transferred to a previously uninfected host [209,212-214]. This provides a model for the condition of occult or latent infections. Two other characteristics of this model have relevance to filarial immunology: the variation in response between strains of hamsters [212,214] and the existence in at least one strain of hamsters of an immunological cross reaction between the response to developing larvae and microfilariae [215,216], a phenomenon which may occur in *B. malayi* infections in man [69].

Once microfilariae disappear from the circulation of hamsters about 4 months after infection they do not reappear after second or subsequent infections [217], although microfilariae will reappear in the blood of singly or multiply infected animals subjected to immunosuppressive therapy [218]. Studies largely by Weiss have shown that the disappearance of microfilariae from the circulation is probably brought about by the combined action of antibodies (thought by Weiss and his colleagues to be IgM) directed to surface antigens of microfilariae and cells which are probably eosinophils and macrophages. Although antibodies (largely 7S) directed against antigens in the somatic tissues of adult worms and microfilariae appear in the circulation soon after hamsters are infected, 19S antibodies to the cuticle of microfilariae are found consistently in the circulation of the hamster strains studied by Weiss [212] only when the microfilariae have been or are in the process of being cleared from the circulation. In contrast, Haque et al. [214] found antibodies in the circulation of both hamsters with prepatent and latent infections that suppressed microfilarial production in vitro and in vivo. Peritoneal cells from normal hamsters adhered to microfilariae in vitro and in vivo in the presence of 19S serum fractions taken from hamsters at the time they were about to suppress, or had already suppressed, their microfilaremia. This reaction led to the destruction of microfilariae in vivo.

In vitro, macrophages were the cells chiefly involved in this reaction, but in vivo mononuclear cells were significant only late in the reaction, with neutrophils and especially eosinophils predominating in the early phases [21,22]. Antibodies alone do not appear to damage *D. viteae* microfilariae because microfilariae kept in millipore chambers to prevent contact with cells survived for at least 3 weeks in the peritoneal cavity even of latent hamsters [22]. If the conclusion that these authors make from this work is that it is IgM antibodies that mediate cell adherence to the cuticle of·this worm, then it must be postulated that cells other than eosinophils are involved here. This may in fact be an example of a response where different cell types are involved depending on the class of the antibody present at that particular time.

In most hamster strains, the adult worms of *D. viteae* survive for many weeks after microfilariae are cleared from the blood, and the survival time varies between hamster strains [210,212,213]. The same percentage of larvae develop to the adult stage in hamsters given multiple heavy infections as in naive hamsters, however, in strains which respond strongly to the parasite, the adult worms may become encapsulated [217]. Little is known of the mechanisms responsible for the death of adult worms. Adult worms will survive and produce microfilariae for some weeks in mice, but they die even in nude mice much sooner than in hamsters [216]. It appears that male worms do not induce immunity [220]. In animals given repeated small infections over a period of 238 days, no immunity to a heavy challenge infection developed [219].

Dipetalonema viteae in hamsters is, to date, the only filarial infection in which it has been possible to change the course of infection by prior exposure to nonliving parasite material. Microfilaremia was suppressed in hamsters immunized with extracts of microfilariae or adult worms; and in animals given extract from a single female worm, the adult worm population which was established from a subsequent infection was greatly reduced, as was the microfilaremia [214]. Conversely, microfilaremia was strikingly enhanced, although not prolonged, in hamsters given extracts from small numbers of microfilariae and was enhanced in animals exposed to the secretions of adult male worms; there was no accompanying increase in the adult worm populations [214,215]. The mechanism of this striking change has not yet been studied in this latter group of animals; however, since the duration of microfilaremia was not affected, it may be that this enhancement reflects an increased diversion of microfilariae into the circulation from other tissues in the body, rather than an actual suppression of resistance.

A relationship between the immune response induced by developing *D. viteae* larvae and that which clears microfilariae from the blood has been shown by Haque et al. [215,216] but not by others working with this infection. Whereas Weiss [212] could detect antibodies to the microfilarial surface only in hamsters at or after the time microfilariae were being cleared from the blood, Haque et al. [214] showed that serum taken from hamsters 30 days after infection (i.e., before sexual maturity of the parasties) can reduce microfilariae production in vitro and in vivo. In contrast, serum taken early in or at the height of microfilaremia had little effect in these assays, although serum from latent (i.e., post-patent) animals suppressed microfilarial production particularly effectively. This result was confirmed by these authors in hamsters and mice using a different experimental approach. The microfilaremia induced by transplanting adult worms was quickly suppressed by developing worms from a superimposed larval infection [215,216].

A puzzling feature of the animals' response to developing larvae is the absence of suppression of microfilaremia produced by the adult worms which develop from this infection. It appears that the antibodies that cross react with microfilariae, which are induced by the developing larvae, cease to be produced during a normal infection before microfilariae develop, and that once microfilariae are produced, they do not stimulate these antibodies in an anamnestic fashion. It would be interesting to compare the microfilaremia in hamsters infected with the same number of adult female worms, either by transplant or after a larval infection, to see whether the microfilaremia is lower in animals already exposed to developing larvae.

A degree of immunosuppression is induced in this infection in hamsters [221,222], but this is probably too slight and too nonspecific to be of any significance in the host-parasite balance.

B. *Litomosoides carinii*

Litomosoides carinii is a natural parasite of cotton rats, *Sigmodon hispidus,* in which the microfilariae can persist for many months. This filarial worm will also infect some strains of laboratory rats, *Rattus norvegicus,* but in these hosts the microfilaremia is relatively short-lived. The intermediate host is a mite, *Ornithonyssus bacoti.* The worms go immediately into the pleural cavity where they develop to maturity, however, in heavy infections they may also be found in the abdominal cavity. In the main, this parasite has been used to study two aspects of immunity. In the 1950s Scott and his colleagues studied the effect of resistance stimulated by previous infection of cotton rats on the development of further infections and also attempted to compare the relative potency of the different life-cycle stages in the induction of this response [224,225]. Recently, Subrahmanyam and his associates have studied this parasite in albino rats to investigate the mechanisms of immunity which inhibit microfilaremia at the end of a primary infection but leave the adult worms alive and active in the pleural cavity (i.e., the immune mechanisms that produce a latent infection).

1. Immunity to Reinfection

The principal reason for the use of this model to study immunity to reinfection is the ease with which worms can quantitatively be recovered from the pleural cavity at any phase of their development. Worms attempting to develop in previously infected animals show retarded growth, delayed molting, and the females are permanently stunted. The main effect of immunity appears to be early in development, especially in the first 7 days. This was shown in a study where it was found that the immune response had no effect on worms which had completed the first 7 days of their development in a nonimmune environment; however, worms recovered from previously infected rats while still in the early third stage were unable to develop when transferred to normal animals [223-225]. Albino rats exposed to infective larvae irradiated with 40 krad were resistant to reinfection, but animals given larvae irradiated with 20 krad were not resistant [226]. The higher dose prevented the worms from molting, and they stayed alive for at least 25 days, i.e., they persisted as third-stage larvae, whereas those with lower doses of irradiation developed to the adult stage. This work is consistent with the studies that show the early stages are the major source of the antigens which stimulate protection. There is no information concerning the nature of the immune response which affects the development of *L. carinii.*

2. Induction of Immunity to Microfilaremia, and Latency

The immune response which inhibits microfilaremia in albino rats infected with *L. carinii* acts by preventing the microfilariae from entering the blood. However, this is not necessarily due to prevention of microfilarial release from adult females since microfilariae may be present in the pleural cavity even if they are not found in the blood of latent rats. Microfilaremia reoccurs in latent rats which are immunosuppressed by a variety of means, such as use of anti-lymphocyte serum, cortisone, cyclophosphamide, or whole-body irradiation [227-229]. Although initial attempts to implicate serum factors in the induction of latency were unsuccessful [229], it has now been shown that the onset of latency is associated with the appearance in the serum of rats of a factor which mediates cell adherence to microfilariae, resulting in cytotoxicity to the microfilariae. Recent studies have confirmed earlier work which suggested that the factor concerned is IgE (Refs. 23, 24, and Subrahmanyam, personal communication). Granulocytes, macrophages, and lymphocytes all adhered to the microfilariae [23]. Termination of the microfilaremia in infected animals is also associated with adhesion of these cells to microfilariae in the pleural cavity [227,230].

The immune mechanisms which cause amicrofilaremia can be induced by the microfilariae themselves or by female adult worms actively producing microfilariae, but not by dead worms, living male worms, or living females exhausted of microfilariae production by serial passage through rats [227]. There are a few studies of immune responses in this infection. 19S agglutinating antibodies were detected 6-7 weeks and 7S antibodies were detected from about 10 weeks after infection of cotton rats, but only with adult worm antigen and not with antigen from infective larvae [231]. These antibodies are probably not related to resistance to reinfection which, as discussed above, is induced particularly by the early developing larvae. A variety of antibodies including IgE antibodies are induced by *L. carinii* in albino rats [229]. This is also the only filarial parasite whose secretions have been shown to be antigenic [232].

3. Cross Reaction between *Litomosoides carinii* and *Wuchereria bancrofti*

The original observation [233] of immunological cross reaction between the antigens of *L. carinii* and *W. bancrofti* has been confirmed [24,228]. *L. carinii* microfilariae are agglutinated by serum from patients exposed to *W. bancrofti*, and extracts of adult *L. carinii* cross react in serologic assays with serum from patients infected with *W. bancrofti*. It is not clear yet whether the antigens concerned are common to all stages of *L. carinii* or associated only with microfilariae and adults. Exploitation of the reaction of *L. carinii* microfilariae with serum from all individuals exposed to *W. bancrofti* may be extremely useful in diagnosis (Ref. 24 and Subrahmanyam, personal communication).

4. Adaptation of Adult Worms

Whereas adult worms transplanted from albino rats to the pleural and peritoneal cavities of naive albino rats apparently establish successfully [229], adult *L. carinii* transplanted from infected to naive cotton rats (*Mastomys natalensis*) or jirds (*Meriones unguiculatus*) do not establish [234-237]. However, worms did establish in previously infected hosts [236,237], and splenectomy enabled worms to establish in naive hosts [234,237]. The significance of these studies is unclear, but the means whereby adult worms of all filarial species persist for so long is a subject which merits further research.

X. *DIROFILARIA* SPP. INFECTIONS IN DOGS AND MAN

The natural host of *D. immitis* and *Dirofilaria repens* is the dog, but aberrant infections of these species and *Dirofilaria tenuis* (a natural parasite of the raccoon *Procyon lotos*) may occur in man. The vectors in all cases are mosquitoes. Worms [238] studied the course of infection with *D. immitis* and *D. repens* in 30 dogs. The prepatent period was 204-349 days with *D. immitis* and 176-289 days in the case of *D. repens*. The microfilaremia varied in its density and duration considerably between dogs, with a maximum duration of microfilaremia of 6.3 years for *D. repens* and 8.5 years for *D. immitis*. In some dogs the maximum density and duration of microfilaremia was much less, and microfilaremia ceased within 18 months; microfilariae were never detected in the blood of other dogs. In all groups an "occult" infection occurred since living adult worms were found for some months after microfilaremia had ceased or when microfilaremia had never been detected. These worms were able to induce a microfilaremia when transferred into susceptible hosts. This study suggests that genetic factors in dogs regulate their ability to become immune to microfilariae.

Dirofilaria immitis infections in dogs are widespread throughout the regions of the world which are warm enough for the mosquito vector to survive. Large numbers of adult worms can be recovered largely from the pulmonary artery and right ventricle of naturally infected dogs at autopsy, and these worms have frequently been used as a source of filarial antigen for the diagnosis of filariasis in man. In regions of endemic infections of Dirofilaria species of animals, people are also exposed to the infective larvae since the mosquito vectors of Dirofilaria spp. will bite man; and, there are many reports of the recovery of adult Dirofilaria from man in such regions. Dirofilaria adult worms have been recovered from subcutaneous nodules in people (D. tenuis in the southern United States [239] and D. repens in Europe [240] or from the heart and lungs, in which cases the worms are invariably D. immitis [241]. The worms recovered from humans are sexually mature and, curiously, are found only in adult patients [241]. It has been suggested that these adult worms in man are noticed only when they die [241], which the study of the duration of Dirofilaria infection in dogs [238] suggests would occur within 6-8 years of infection. In Australia, D. immitis adult worms have never been reported in aboriginals who are continually exposed from childhood to mosquitoes infected with this parasite, whereas cases of D. immitis have been reported from caucasian Australians who are exposed much less frequently [242]. On the basis of a study of antibody responses to D. immitis in these human populations and their dogs, it was suggested that adult D. immitis are found in patients who are exposed to infection only during adult life [242]. These authors [243] also suggested that D. immitis infections in children may be the etiological agent of eosinophilic meningitis, presumably a response to the developing larvae of this parasite. Dirofilaria infections in man may induce a marked eosinophilia, and hemagglutinating antibody titers using D. immitis of greater than 1/160 are diagnostic when taken together with the clinical symptoms [244,245], although in some of these aberrant infections neither of these responses are induced [245]. There may be a history of a migrating lesion in cases of subcutaneous dirofilariasis [244].

The first studies of the immune mechanisms which regulate microfilariae were carried out in 1964 by Wong [198] in dogs infected with D. immitis. She immunized dogs with a course of intravenous injections with living D. immitis microfilariae and showed that resistance to microfilariae developed in association with the appearance of antibodies which agglutinated *D. immitis* microfilariae. These antibodies did not cross react with *B. pahangi* microfilariae, and they were not detected in animals with a microfilaremia. When serum from dogs with antibodies to microfilariae was injected into animals with microfilaremia, the level of the microfilaremia was reduced in 11 of 13 animals. In this same study, it was also shown that leukocytes adhered to microfilariae in immune serum [198].

In a later study of dogs immunized by injections of microfilariae, it was shown that subsequent infections with third-stage larvae developed to the adult stage, but microfilaremia did not occur [192]. These dogs had many of the symptoms associated with tropical eosinophilic lung in man [191]. In a recent study, Wong and Suter [68] described the appearance of antibodies to *D. immitis* microfilariae in dogs exposed to *D. immitis* in various ways and showed that the disappearance or nonappearance of microfilariae in these dogs was always closely associated with the appearance in the circulation of antibodies to *D. immitis* microfilariae. These antibodies persisted even in the absence of adult worms. Wong and Suter [68] also referred to their unpublished studies showing that antibodies to *D. immitis* microfilariae do not cross react with microfilariae of *D. repens, D. tenuis,* or *Dipetalonema reconditum.*

IgE antibodies to adult worm antigens are induced by *D. immitis* in dogs [246], and a variety of antibody responses have been detected by several methods [247]. When treated with DEC, *D. immitis*-infected dogs may show side reactions ranging in severity from minimal or undetectable to death apparently from a syndrome resembling shock [248]. Wong and Suter [68] also found that the most severe pathological changes seen in *D. immitis*-infected dogs were found 2 months after treatment to remove adults or microfilariae. Desowitz et al. [249] showed that, in dogs with moderate or severe adverse reactions to DEC, IgG, and IgE, reactions (measured by long latent PCA in rabbits [246]) were markedly depressed. They conclude that two immune processes occur in DEC treated animals: an IgG dependent, Arthus/serum sickness reaction which gives rise to the febrile response and arthralgia, and the release of pharmacologic mediators from mast cells and platelets by an IgE-dependent reaction which leads to clinical symptoms of urticaria, nausea, vomiting, hypotension, and collapse, which may also occur in human patients infected with *B. malayi* or *O. volvulus* following DEC treatment. It is interesting that antibody responses detected with antigen prepared from adult worms decreased 7-8 months after infection, at a time when both living adult worms and probably microfilariae were still present. This suggests that antibody responses detected in this study were stimulated by developing worms and not by persistent adult stages, a principle which, if it applies to filarial infections generally, may explain the negative results to tests for antibodies often obtained with serum from infected patients [247].

XI. GENERAL PRINCIPLES AND SUGGESTIONS FOR FUTURE STUDIES

The study of the immunology of filariasis is at such an early stage that much of this review is, of necessity, concerned with detailing the clinical and experimental situations that involve filarial nematodes and which require analysis by modern immunological means, rather than giving the results of such studies.

A major problem in immunological studies of filariasis is the paucity of laboratory models. The most important filarial nematodes of man either do not infect laboratory animals (*W. bancrofti* and *O. volvulus*) or only produce infections in rodent species which are at present not well-defined immunologically and do not respond to infection with disease patterns comparable with those seen in man (e.g., *Brugia* spp. in jirds). Nevertheless, the discovery that the *Brugia* spp. will develop in the peritoneal cavity of jirds was a great advance in that it made it possible to obtain living filarial parasites of man in the laboratory and will ensure rapid progress in the immunology of the infections caused by these parasites. The marked host specificity of filarial parasites is expressed particularly strongly against the developing third-stage larvae [250]; many hosts which completely resist the development of the infective stage will nevertheless support, for at least a few weeks, adult worms and microfilariae transplanted into them. This "proxy" host system [216,251] may be particularly valuable in the study of *O. volvulus*. The problems of the laboratory models may be largely overcome by comparing the immunological responses induced in several different hosts in which the same parasite develops to different degrees, including proxy hosts.

In man there is a great variation between individuals in their clinical and parasitologic response to an infection, a difference which the available evidence suggests is probably a reflection of the immune response in the infected person. Some individuals never develop clinical or parasitologic signs of infection, even though it is clear that they are exposed to infection, i.e., they respond as if they were innately resistant. In others, a heavy and prolonged microfilarial infection is established, suggesting that these individuals have little or no ability to develop resistance to any stages of the worms. In some, microfilariae are cleared from the circulation, or the skin, by the immune response, and these individuals may have marked clinical symptoms which are believed to result from the immunological destruction of adult worms or developing larvae in the tissues. These variations in the response of man provide a naturally occurring experimental situation for immunological investigations.

A major, pressing problem especially in onchocerciasis is the severe side reactions associated with the treatment with the antifilarial drug DEC. These reactions probably have an immunological basis, and it has been suggested that they result from the sudden release of large amounts of antigens from dying worms. The clinical reactions extend to painful generalized systemic reactions which may be lethal and, in the case of onchocerciasis, severe lesions in the eyes which may accelerate blindness. These side reactions have proved very difficult to prevent in the case of onchocerciasis, although they can be relatively easily suppressed with the lymphatic filariae. The basis for this difference is not known; it may reflect the relative burden of parasite material and the tissue distribution of the worms rather than fundamental differences in the mechanisms underlying these severe responses. It has been suggested that these reactions are the consequences of serum sickness—Arthus reactions induced by IgG antibodies together with the release of pharmacologic mediators following antigen recognition by IgE antibodies. IgE responses together with eosinophilia are characteristic of these infections, especially onchocerciasis and occult infections such as tropical eosinophilic lung and dirofilariasis of man. Identification of the antigens involved is a pressing requirement of a better understanding of the pathology of filariasis, especially antigens present in immune complexes found in the serum both before and after chemotherapy.

We believe that better knowledge of the antigens concerned is of prime importance not only in the understanding of the immunopathology of filariasis but also for future advance in the other areas in which immunology is important; that is, the development of immunodiagnosis and the understanding of immune mechanisms which inhibit the development of the parasite. A concept which is probably especially important in the study of antigens is that of the stage specificity of the immune response to parasites. There is increasing evidence in the study of resistance to nematodes in general and to filariae in particular that stage-specific antigens may be associated with the surface of these worms. The evidence for this is especially striking in the case of microfilariae where studies with *D. immitis, B. pahangi, B. malayi, L. carinii,* and *D. viteae* all show that antibodies to the microfilarial surface appear in the circulation of the host when the microfilariae are cleared from the blood. In her pioneering studies in 1964, Wong [30] showed the presence of antimicrofilarial antibodies in the serum of dogs resistant to *B. pahangi* or *D. immitis* microfilariae, and in that and subsequent papers has shown that these antibodies are remarkably species specific. No cross reactions occurred between antibodies to the microfilariae of *D. immitis, D. repens,* or *D. tenuis* [68], nor apparently between *W. bancrofti, B. malayi,* and *B. pahangi* [75]. It will be interesting to know if this specificity extends to the microfilariae of different races of the same worm species, particularly *O. volvulus.* There seems little doubt that these antibodies promote the cell-mediated destruction of microfilariae as shown by studies in vitro with *L. carinii, D. viteae,* and *B. pahangi.* It is probable that the antimicrofilarial drug DEC may act by enhancing the recognition of the surface by antibodies, a proposition which urgently requires investigation. Identification of the surface antigen recognized by these antibodies is a problem which is ripe for immediate study. Considering the paucity of immunological studies of filariasis, it is salutary to note that the control of microfilaremia by the combined action of antibodies to their surface and cells is probably the most clearly defined anti-parasite immune mechanism in nematode immunology. The antibodies and cells involved in antibody-dependent cell-mediated adherence to filarial nematodes vary greatly from parasite to parasite. IgM, IgG, and IgE antibodies, eosinophils, macrophages, and neutrophils have all been described in this response by different workers. Further work is needed to clarify the way in which immunoglobulins and cells interact to destroy nematodes via their surface antigens.

There is increasing evidence that the outer surface of parasitic nematodes may change its properties dramatically from one life-cycle stage to another, and that its immunological behavior may vary between life-cycle stages of any one species. It will be interesting to compare the immune response to the sheath and cuticle of those microfilariae which possess sheaths and to contrast the dynamic properties of the cuticle of the different stages in the life cycle of filarial and other nematodes. For example, it is possible that the surface of infective larvae which is developed for life inside the insect vector changes dramatically and rapidly once the larvae enter the mammalian host.

In contrast to the apparent association of antibodies to the surface antigens of microfilariae and their disappearance from the blood, the immune responses which control the development of infective larvae or adult worms have not been defined in any filarial system. Antibodies to the surface of infective larvae have been described, but, unlike the antibodies to microfilarial surfaces, they are not clearly associated with resistance to this stage of the worm. It appears that cell-mediated immune responses may be of more importance in immunity to these stages [69].

It is difficult to envisage how cell-mediated immune responses destroy nematodes. Cytotoxic T lymphocytes could attack nematodes directly only if nematodes have on their surface products of the host's major histocompatibility genes associated with the antigens recognized by the cytotoxic T cells. It seems more likely that cell-mediated immune responses are evoked against worm antigens associated with macrophages that contain worm antigens derived either from the secretions of living worms or from disintegrating dead worms. We suggest that T lymphocytes (e.g., helper T lymphocytes) are most likely to attack worms indirectly via their activating effect on macrophages.

Immunodiagnosis methods able to detect recently acquired infections would be especially useful in areas where eradication of these parasites is being attempted, as will methods which differentiate between different clinical responses to the same parasite. In the first case, methods which would detect either stage-specific antigens released by living worms or the antibodies to them would fulfill the purpose, providing the antibodies did not persist for long periods after the demise or further development of these worms. It is suspected that the differences in the clinical picture seen in infected individuals reflects the ability of the immune response to respond to the different life-cycle stages, and, therefore, the identification of stage-specific antigens is probably also important in this context. The principal problem in diagnosis of filariasis is the identification of suitable antigens; methods such as ELISA which are very sensitive require minute amounts of antigen and are readily adaptable to field conditions already in widespread use for diagnosis of many diseases [157].

The occurrence of latent or occult infections is a common feature of many filarial infections. The classical study by Duke of *Loa loa* in monkeys is a particularly interesting illustration of the development of latent infections [252] which also occurs in the commonly studied infections of animals (*D. immitis* in dogs, *D. viteae* in hamsters, and *L. carinii* in rats). The astonishing longevity of the usually large adult stages of filarial nematodes in the tissues of their hosts is one of the most spectacular examples of the ability of parasites to evade the immune response and provides a major challenge to immunologists. This problem can be approached by attempting to change the antigens of the parasite by, for example, chemical modification of the cuticle. The use of proxy hosts may be valuable for the study of the immunogenic and antigenic properties of adult stages in particular. High levels of microfilariae in human infections have been shown to be associated with a depression in the host's ability to recognize this stage in the life cycle. Prolonged infections with microfilariae are associated with specific immunodepression of the cell-mediated response to microfilarial antigens in *O. volvulus, W. bancrofti,* and *B. malayi* infections [69,70,105]. The long delay before microfilariae are detected in the circulation of people exposed to *Brugia* or *W. bancrofti* in adult life may be related to an immune response to microfilariae; this idea is supported by the association between microfilaremia and anergy to microfilarial antigens. The immune response to microfilariae in microfilarial patients following DEC treatment would be an interesting study.

The filarial parasites that attract most medical attention and financial support for research are those that cause disease. There are, however, many more filariae found both in animals and man that cause little or no discomfort to their host. These extremely successful parasites probably provide the greatest challenge to the immunologist simply because they have so adapted themselves to be able to live in harmony with the immunological response of their host. We believe that it is as important to support studies designed to elucidate their complete success as parasites as it is to encourage research into the immunological responses that are elicited by those filariae which are less successful and, therefore, more damaging parasites.

ACKNOWLEDGMENTS

Some of the investigations on onchocerciasis described in this review were supported by the filariasis component of the UNDP/World Bank/Special Programme for Research and Training in the Tropical Disease.

REFERENCES

1. Bertram, D. S. (1966). Dynamics of parasitic equilibrium in cotton rat filariasis. *Adv. Parasitol. 4:*255.
2. Nelson, G. S. (1966). The pathology of filarial infections. *Helminth Abs. 35:*311.
3. Denham, D. A., and G. S. Nelson (1976). Pathology and pathophysiology of nematode infections of the lymphatic system and blood vessels. In *Pathophysiology of Parasitic Infections* (E. J. L. Soulsby, Ed.). Academic Press, New York, p. 115.
4. Ogilvie, B. M., and M. J. Worms (1976). Immunity to nematode parasites of man with special reference to *Ascaris,* hookworms and filariae. In *Immunology of Parasitic Infections* (S. Cohen and E. H. Sadun, Eds.). Blackwell Scientific Publishers, Oxford, p. 380.
5. Sasa, M. (1976). *Human Filariasis.* University Park Press, Baltimore, Md.
6. Nelson, G. S. (1970). Onchocerciasis. *Adv. Parasitol. 8:*173.
7. World Health Organization (1976). Epidemiology of onchocerciasis. Technical Report Series No. 597.
8. Pan American Health Organization (1974). Onchocerciasis in the Western Hemisphere. Scientific Publication No. 298.
9. Anderson, J., and H. Fuglsang (1977). Ocular onchocerciasis. *Trop. Dis. Bull. 74:*257.
10. Denham, D. A., and P. B. McGreevy (1977). Brugian filariasis: epidemiological and experimental studies. *Adv. Parasitol. 15:*243.
11. Sasa, M. (1976). A catalogue of references to the global survey of human filariasis. Japan Association for Tropical Medicine, Chiyodaku, Tokyo.
12. Askenase, P. W. (1977). Role of basophils, mast cells and vasoamines in hypersensitivity reactions with a delayed time course. *Progr. Allergy 23:* 199.
13. Butterworth, A. E. (1977). The eosinophil and its role in immunity to helminth infection. *Curr. Top. Microbiol. Immunol. 77:*128.
14. Ishizaka, K. (1976). Cellular events in the IgE antibody response. *Adv. Immunol. 23:*1.
15. Sadun, E. H. (1972). Homocytotropic antibody response to parasitic infections. In *Immunity to Animal Parasites* (E. J. L. Soulsby, Ed.). Academic Press, New York, p. 97.
16. Mitchell, G. F. (1978). Metazoan and protozoan parasitic infections in nude mice. *Contemp. Top. Immunobiol. 8:*55.
17. Crandall, R. B., C. A. Crandall, and J. A. Franco (1974). *Heligmosoides polygyrus* (= *Nematospiroides dubius*): Humoral and intestinal immunologic responses to infection in mice. *Exp. Parasitol. 35:*275.
18. Mitchell, G. F., J. J. Marchalonis, P. M. Smith, W. L. Nicholas, and N. L. Warner (1977). Studies on immune responses to larval cestodes in mice. Immunoglobulins associated with the larvae of *Mesocestoides corti. Aust. J. Exp. Biol. Med. Sci. 55:*187.
19. Sher, A., S. McIntyre, and F. von Lichtenberg (1977). *Schistosoma man-*

soni: Kinetics and class specificity of hypergammaglobulinaemia induced during murine infection. *Exp. Parasitol. 41:*415.

20. Higashi, G. I., and A. B. Chowdhury (1970). In vitro adhesion of eosinophils to infective larvae of *Wuchereria bancrofti. Immunology 19:*65.

21. Tanner, M., and N. Weiss (1978). Studies on *Dipetalonema viteae* (Filaroidea) II. Antibody dependent adhesion of peritoneal exudate cells to microfilariae in vitro. *Acta Trop. (Basel) 35:*151.

22. Weiss, N., and M. Tanner (1979). Studies on *Dipetalonema viteae* (Filaroidea). 3. Antibody-dependent cell mediated destruction of microfilariae in vivo. *Z. Tropenmed. Parasitol. 30:*73.

23. Subrahmanyam, D., Y. V. G. B. Rao, K. Mehta, and D. S. Nelson (1976). Serum-dependent adhesion and cytotoxicity of cells to *L. carinii* microfilariae. *Nature (Lond.) 260:*529.

24. Subrahmanyam, D., K. Behta, D. S. Nelson, Y. V. G. B. Rao, and C. K. Rao (1978). Immune reactions in human filariasis. *J. Clin. Microbiol. 8:*228.

25. Muller, R. (1975). *Worms and Disease. A Manual of Medical Helminthology.* William Heinemann Medical Books Ltd., London.

26. Manson-Bahr, P. (1959). The story of Filaria bancrofti. *J. Trop. Med. Hyg. 62:*1.

27. Worms, M. J. (1972). Circadian and seasonal rhythms in blood parasties. In *Behavioural Aspects of Parasite Transmission* (E. U. Canning and C. A. Wright, Eds.). *Zool. J. Linn. Soc. 51*(Suppl. 1):53.

28. Beaver, P. C., T. C. Orihel, and M. H. Johnson (1974). *Dipetalonema viteae* in the experimentally infected jird, *Meriones unguiculatus.* II. Microfilaraemia in relation to worm burden. *J. Parasitol. 60:*310.

29. Denham, D. A., T. Ponnudurai, G. S. Nelson, F. Guy, and R. Rogers (1972). Studies with *Brugia pahangi.* 1. Parasitological observations on primary infections of cats (*Felis catus*). *Int. J. Parasitol. 2:*239.

30. Wong, M. M. (1964). Studies on microfilaraemia in dogs. I. A search for the mechanisms that stabilize the level of microfilaraemia. *Am. J. Trop. Med. Hyg. 13:*57.

31. Greenough, W. B., III, and D. Buckner (1969). Removal of microfilariae from unanaesthetised dogs by continuous flow centrifugation. *Trans. R. Soc. Trop. Med. Hyg. 63:*259.

32. Ash, L. R., and J. M. Riley (1970). Development of *Brugia pahangi* in the jird, *Meriones unguiculatus,* with notes on infections in other rodents. *J. Parasitol. 56:*962.

33. Ash, L. R., and J. M. Riley (1970). Development of *Brugia malayi* in the jird, *Meriones unguiculatus,* with notes on infections in other rodents. *J. Parasitol. 56:*969.

34. McCall, J. W., J. B. Malone, H. S. Ah, and P. E. Thompson (1973). Mongolian jirds (*Meriones unguiculatus*) infected with *Brugia pahangi* by the intraperitoneal route. *J. Parasitol. 59:*436.

35. Lee, D. L. (1965). *The Physiology of Nematodes.* Oliver and Boyd, Edinburgh.

36. Chen, S. N., and R. E. Howells (1979). The uptake in vitro of dyes, mono-saccharides and amino acids by the filarial worm *Brugia pahangi*. *Parasitology 78:*343.

37. Rogers, R., D. A. Denham, and G. S. Nelson (1974). Studies with *Brugia pahangi*. 5. Structure of the cuticle. *J. Helminthol. 48:*113.

38. Vincent, A. L., L. R. Ash, and S. P. Frommes (1975). The ultrastructure of adult *Brugia malayi* (Brug 1927) (Nematoda: Filarioidae). *J. Parasitol. 61:*499.

39. Collin, W. K. (1971). Ultrastructural morphology of the esophageal region of the infective larva of *Brugia pahangi* (Nematoda: Filarioidea). *J. Parasitol. 57:*449.

40. Vincent, A. L., S. P. Frommes, J. K. Portaro, and L. R. Ash (1968). Ultra-structure of the anterior alimentary tract of infective stage *Wuchereria bancrofti* (Nematoda: Filarioidea). *J. Parasitol. 64:*775.

41. Martinez-Palomo, A. (1978). Ultrastructural characterization of the cuticle of *Onchocerca volvulus* microfilaria. *J. Parasitol. 64:*127.

42. Martinez-Palomo, A., and M. Martinez-Baez (1977). Ultrastructure of the microfilaria of *Onchocerca volvulus* from Mexico. *J. Parasitol. 63:*1007.

43. Tongu, Y. (1974). Ultrastructural studies on the microfilaria of *Brugia malayi*. *Acta Med. Okayama 28:*219.

44. Riding, I. L. (1970). Microvilli on the outside of a nematode. *Nature (Lond.) 226:*179.

45. Ridley, D. S., and E. C. Hedge (1977). Immunofluorescent reactions with microfilariae. 2. Bearing on host-parasite relations. *Trans. R. Soc. Trop. Med. Hyg. 71:*522.

46. Coombs, R. R. A., D. D. Pout, and E. J. L. Soulsby (1965). Globulin, possibly of antibody nature, combining with cuticle of *Turbatrix aceti*. *Exp. Parasitol. 16:*311.

47. Hogarth-Scott, R. S. (1968). Naturally occurring antibodies to the cuticle of nematodes. *Parasitology 58:*221.

48. Mackenzie, C. D., P. M. Preston, and B. M. Ogilvie (1978). Immunological properties of the surface of parasitic nematodes. *Nature (Lond.) 276:*826.

49. McLaren, D. J. (1976). Sense organs and their secretions. In *The Organization of Nematodes* (N. A. Croll, Ed.). Academic Press, New York, p. 139.

50. Clegg, J. A., and M. A. Smith (1978). Prospects for the development of dead vaccines against helminths. *Adv. Parasitol. 16:*165.

51. Hedge, E. C., and D. S. Ridley (1977). Immunofluorescent reactions with microfilariae. 1. Diagnostic evaluation. *Trans. R. Soc. Trop. Med. Hyg. 71:*304.

52. Gonzaga dos Santos, L., D. C. Santos, and R. Azevedo (1976). Diagnosis of *Wuchereria bancrofti* filariasis by immunofluorescence using microfilariae as antigen. *Ann. Trop. Med. Parasitol. 70:*219.

53. Ambroise-Thomas, P. (1974). Immunological diagnosis of human filariasis: Present possibilities, difficulties and limitations. (A review.) *Acta Tropica 31:*108.

54. Nelson, M., D. S. Nelson, and V. Zaman (1971). Detection of antigens on filarial larvae by means of immune adherence. *Experientia 27:*191.

55. Dissanayake, A., and M. M. Ismail (1980). Antigens of *S. digitata:* Cross reaction with microfilariae and serum antibodies. *Bull. WHO 58:*655.

56. Kagan, I. G. (1963). A review of immunologic methods for the diagnosis of filariasis. *J. Parasitol. 49:*773.

57. Sawada, T., and K. Sato (1969). Studies on skin test antigen FST for immunodiagnosis of filariasis. I and III. *Jap. J. Exp. Med. 39:*427 and 541.

58. Smith, D. H., T. Wilson, J. A. Berezancev, V. Lykov, M. Myo Pang, V. Chari, and A. Davis (1971). Evaluation of the *Dirofilaria immitis* filarial skin test antigen in the diagnosis of filariasis. *Bull. WHO 44:*771.

59. Tanaka, H., K. Fujita, M. Sasa, M. Tagawa, M. Naito, and K. Kurokawa (1970). Cross reactions in complement fixation test among filaria species. *Jap. J. Exp. Med. 40:*47.

60. Fujita, K., H. Tanaka, M. Sasa, K. Schichinoke, Y. Asai, and K. Kurokawa (1970). Cross reactions among filarial species in haemagglutination test. *Jap. J. Exp. Med. 40:*67.

61. Grove, D. I., B. D. Cabrera, F. S. Valeza, R. S. Guinto, L. R. Ash, and K. S. Warren (1977). Sensitivity and specificity of skin reactivity to *B. malayi* and *D. immitis* antigens in Bancroftian and Malayan filariasis in the Philippines. *Am. J. Trop. Med. Hyg. 26:*220.

62. Capron, A., M. Gentilini, and A. Vernes (1968). Le diagnostic immunologique des filarioses. Possibilitiés nouvelles offertés par l'immunoelectrophorese. *Pathol. Biol. (Paris) 16:*1039.

63. Jayawardene, L. G., and Y. Wijayaratnam (1968). The fluorescent antibody test in the serological diagnosis of the causative organisms of tropical eosinophilia and filariasis. *J. Helminthol. 42:*57.

64. Wong, M. M., and M. F. Guest (1969). Filarial antibodies and eosinophilia in human subjects in an endemic area. *Trans. R. Soc. Trop. Med. Hyg. 63:*796.

65. Grove, D. I., and R. S. Davis (1978). Serological diagnosis of Bancroftian and Malayan filariasis. *Am. J. Trop. Med. Hyg. 27:*508.

66. McGreevy, P. B., S. Ratiwayanto, Sukar Tuti, M. M. McGreevy, and D. T. Dennis (1980). *Brugia malayi:* Relationship between anti-sheath antibodies and amicrofilaraemia in natives living in an endemic area of South Kalimantan, Borneo. *Am. J. Trop. Med. Hyg. 29:*553.

67. Ponnudurai, T., D. A. Denham, G. S. Nelson, and R. Rogers (1974). *Brugia pahangi:* Antibodies against adult and microfilarial stages. *J. Helminthol. 48:*107.

68. Wong, M. M., and P. F. Suter (1979). Indirect fluorescent antibody test in occult Dirofilarias. *Am. J. Vet. Res. 40:*414.

69. Piessens, W. F., P. B. McGreevy, P. W. Piessens, M. McGreevy, I. Koiman, J. S. Saroso, and D. T. Dennis (1980). Immune responses in human infections with *Brugia malayi:* Specific cellular immune unresponsiveness to filarial antigens. *J. Clin. Invest. 65:*172.

70. Ottesen, E. A., P. F. Weller, and L. Heck (1977). Specific cellular immune unresponsiveness in human filariasis. *Immunology 33:*413.
71. Mackenzie, C. D., A. Sierra, L. Ortiz-Ortiz, and H. El-Sheik (1981). Variation in cell-mediated responsiveness in human onchocerciasis. *Z. Tropenmed. Parisitol.* In press.
72. Turk, J. L. (1979). Relation between delayed hypersensitivity and cell mediated immunity. *J. Roy. Soc. Med. 72:*243.
73. Denham, D. A. (1980). Vaccination of filarial worms using irradiation-attenuated vaccines. *International J. Nuclear Med. Biology 7:*105.
74. Ah, H. S., J. C. Peckham, F. E. Mitchell, and P. E. Thompson (1972). Studies on *Dirofilaria immitis* infections in dogs relative to immunizations and antigen-antibody interactions. In *Canine Heartworm Disease: The Current Knowledge* (R. E. Bradley and G. Pacheco, Eds.). University of Florida, Gainesville, p. 55.
75. Wong, M. M., Guest, M. F., M. J. Lavoipierre (1974). *Dirofilaria immitis:* Fate and immunogenicity of irradiated infective larvae in beagles. *Exp. Parasitol. 35:*465.
76. Ah. H. S., J. W. McCall, and P. E. Thompson (1974). Vaccination against experimental *Brugia pahangi* infections in dogs. *Proc. Third Int. Congr. Parasitol. 3:*1236.
77. Wong, M. M., H. J. Fredericks, and C. P. Ramachandran (1969). Studies on immunization against *Brugia malayi* in the rhesus monkey. *Bull. WHO 40:*493.
78. Ramachandran, C. P. (1970). Attempts to immunize domestic cats with X-irradiated infective larvae of subperiodic *Brugia malayi.* 1. Parasitological aspects. *S.E. Asian J. Trop. Med. Publ. Health 1:*78.
79. Oothuman, P., D. A. Denham, P. B. McGreevy, G. S. Nelson, and R. Rogers (1979). Successful vaccination of cats against *Brugia pahangi* with larvae attenuated by irradiation with 10 Krads cobalt 60. *Parasite Immunol. 1:* 209.
80. Gentilini, M., J. M. Pinon, G. Niel, and M. Danis. Étude comparée des reactions de précipitation et d'immunofluorescence indirecte dans le diagnostic des filarioses. *Bull. Soc. Path. Exot. 65:*849.
81. Fain. A. (1969). Notes sur la distribution geographique de la filaire *Loa loa* et des tabanides du genre chrysops au Congo et au Rwanda. *Ann. Soc. Belg. Med. Trop. 49:*499.
82. Gibson, D. W., and D. H. Connor (1978). Onchocercal lymphadenitis: Clinicopathologic study of 34 patients. *Trans. R. Soc. Trop. Med. Hyg. 72:*137.
83. Barbosa, W., P. C. Rombert, and R. P. Rocha (1971). On immunology of filariasis. I. Diagnosis by slide indirect immunofluorescence using a new *Onchocerca volvulus* antigen obtained from nodules. *J. Soc. Ciencias Med. Lisboa. 35:*463.
84. Adolph, P. E., I. G. Kagan, and R. M. McQuay (1962). Diagnosis and treatment of *Acanthocheilonema perstans* filariasis. *Am. J. Trop. Med. Hyg. 11:*76.

85. Marinkelle, C. J. P., and E. German (1970). Mansonelliasis in the Comisaria del Vaupes of Colombia. *Trop. Geog. Med. 22:*101.

86. Biagi, F., and O. Castrejou (1957). Observaciones sobre mansonelosis en la Peninsula de Yucatan. *Medicina (Mexico) 37:*125.

87. Buck, A. A. (1976). Onchocerciasis. In *Epidemiology and Community Health in Warm Climate Countries* (Cruickshank, R., K. L. Standard, and H. B. Russell, Eds.). Churchill Livingstone, Edinburgh, p. 263.

88. Burchard, G. D., E. J. Albiez, and M. Bierther (1979). Electron microscopical studies in onchocerciasis. II. Skin and microfilariae after treatment with metrifonate. *Z. Tropenmed. Parasitol. 30:*97.

89. Martinez-Báez, M., (chairman) (1978). La oncocercosis en Mexico. *Symp. Gae. Med. di Mex. 114:*525.

90. Buck, A. A. (1974). Onchocerciasis. Symptomatology, pathology, diagnosis. *Bull. WHO.*

91. O'Neill, J. (1875). On the presence of a filaria in "craw craw." *Lancet 1:*265.

92. Onchocerciasis—out of the obliette (Editorial). *Br. J. Opthalmol. 62:* 427 (1978).

93. Fawdry, A. L. (1957). Onchocerciasis in South Arabia. *Trans. R. Soc. Trop. Med. Hyg. 51:*253.

94. DeLeon, R., and B. O. L. Duke (1966). Experimental studies on the transmission of Guatemalan and West African strains of *Onchocerca volvulus* by *Simulium ochraceum, S. metallicum* and *S. callidum. Trans. R. Soc. Trop. Med. Hyg. 60:*735.

95. Garms, R. (1975). Observations on filarial infections and parous rates of anthropophilic blackflies in Guatemala, with reference to the transmission of *Onchocerca volvulus. Z. Tropenmed. Parasitol. 26:*169.

96. Mackenzie, C. D., and J. L. Ngu (1979). A consideration of the clinical, immunopathological and immunodiagnostic aspects of human onchocerciasis. *Quart. Rev. Cameroon Med. (Cameroon Med. J. Suppl.):*15.

97. Centro de Investigaciones Ecológicas del Sureste (1976). Oncocercosis en America. Bibliografia Description 1945-1975. No. 1 series Bibliografias.

98. Anderson, J., H. Fuglsang, P. J. Hamilton, and T. Marshall (1974). Studies on onchocerciasis in the United Cameroon Republic. 1. Comparison of populations with and without *Onchocerca volvulus. Trans. R. Soc. Trop. Med. Hyg. 68:*190.

99. Connor, D. H., N. E. Morrison, F. Kerdelvegas, H. A. Berkoff, F. Johnson, R. Tunnicliffe, C. F. Failing, L. N. Hale, K. Lindquist, W. Thornbloom, J. B. McCormick, and S. L. Anderson, (1970). Onchocerciasis. Onchocercal dermatitis, lymphadenitis, and elephantiasis in the Ubango territory. *Human Pathol. 1:*553.

100. Nnochiri, E. (1964). Observations on onchocercal lesions seen in autopsy specimens in Western Nigeria. *Ann. Trop. Med. Parasitol. 58:*89.

101. Fuglsang, H., and J. Anderson (1974). Collapse during treatment of onchocerciasis with diethylcarbamazine. *Trans. R. Soc. Trop. Med. Hyg. 63:* 72.

102. Mazzotti, L. (1948). Posibilidad de utilizan como medio diagnostico auxiliar en la oncocercosis, las reaciones alergicas consecuivas a la administracion del "Hetrazan." *Rev. Inst. Salub. Enform. Trop. 9:*235.

103. Bryceson, A. D., D. A. Warrell, and H. M. Pope (1977). Dangerous reactions to treatment of onchocerciasis with diethylcarbamazine. *Br. Med. J. 1:*742.

104. Omar, N. S., U. Franz, and D. W. Büttner (1979). Some observations on onchocerciasis including Sowda in the Yemen Arab Republic. *Z. Tropenmed. Parasitol. 30:*113.

105. Bartlett, A., J. L. Turk, J. L. Ngu, C. D. Mackenzie, H. Fuglsang, and J. Anderson (1978). Variation in delayed hypersensitivity in onchocerciasis. *Trans. R. Soc. Trop. Med. Hyg. 72:*372.

106. Gomez-Priego, A., R. Rivas-Alcala, A. Sierra, C. Larralde, and F. Beltran (1980). Serology of Mexican onchocerciasis: Serodiagnosis, correlation with stage of disease, and most prominent antigens. *J. Helminthol.* In press.

107. Rodger, F. C. (1973). The effect of heavy parasite loads of *O. volvulus* on human optic nerve. *Helminthol. Bratislava 14:*39.

108. Anderson, J., and R. L. Font (1976). *Ocular Onchocerciasis: Pathology of Tropical and Extraordinary Diseases,* Vol. II (C. H. Binford and D. H. Connor, Eds.), Armed Forces Institute of Pathology, Washington, p. 373.

109. Bird, A. C., J. Anderson, and H. Fuglsang (1976). Morphology of posterior segment lesions of the eye in patients with onchocerciasis. *Br. J. Opthal. 60:*2.

110. Cherry, J. K. (1959). Adenolymphocoele and elephantiasis in onchocerciasis. *East Afr. Med. J. 36:*224.

111. Anderson, J., H. Fuglsang, P. J. Hamilton, and T. Marshall (1974). Studies on onchocerciasis in the United Cameroon Republic. II. Comparison of onchocerciasis in rain forest and Sudan-savanna. *Trans. R. Soc. Trop. Med. Hyg. 68:*209.

112. Duke, B. O. L. (1974). International symposium on research and control of onchocerciasis in the western hemisphere. *Pan American Health Organization Publication 298:*25.

113. Anderson, J., and H. Fuglsang (1974). Some aspects of ocular onchocerciasis. *Pan American Health Organization Publication 298:*30.

114. Trojan, H. (1975). Alterations in the fundus in the sense of a "flecked retina" in onchocerciasis. *Klinische Monsblatter fur Augenheitkunde 166:* 220.

115. Kershaw, W. E., B. O. L. Duke, and F. H. Budden (1954). Distribution of the microfilariae of *O. volvulus* in the skin. Its relation to the skin changes and to eye lesions and blindness. *Br. Med. J. 2:*724.

116. Nelson, G. S. (1958). Onchocerciasis in the West Nile district of Uganda. *Trans. R. Soc. Trop. Med. Hyg. 52:*368.

117. Woodruff, A. N., D. P. Choyce, G. Pringle, A. B. G. Laing, M. Hills, and P. Wegesa (1966). Onchocerciasis in the Usambara mountains, Tanzania: The disease, its epidemiology and its relation to ocular complications. *Trans. R. Soc. Trop. Med. Hyg. 60:*695.

118. Duke, B. O. L., and J. Anderson (1972). A comparison of the lesions produced in the cornea of the rabbit eye by microfilariae of the forest and Sudan-savanna strains of *Onchocerca volvulus* from Cameroon. I. Clinical picture. *Z. Tropenmed. Parasitol. 23:*354.

119. Duke, B. O. L., and A. Garner (1975). Reactions to subconjunctival inoculation of *Onchocerca volvulus* microfilariae in pre-immunized rabbits. *Z. Tropenmed. Parasitol. 26:*435.

120. Duke, B. O. L. (1967). *Onchocerca simulium* complexes. IV. Transmission of a variant of the forest strain of *O. volvulus*. *Ann. Trop. Med. Parasitol. 61:*326.

121. Duke, B. O. L., P. J. Moore, and J. R. De Leon (1967). Onchocerca-simulium complexes. V. The intake and subsequent fate of microfilariae of a Guatemalan strain of *O. volvulus* in forest and Sudan-savanna forms of West African *S. damnosum*. *Ann. Trop. Med. Parasitol. 61:*332.

122. Bryceson, A. D., K. S. Van Veen, A. J. Oduloju, and B. O. L. Duke. (1976). Antigenic diversity among *Onchocerca volvulus* in Nigeria, immunological differences between onchocerciasis in savanna anf forest of Cameroon. *Clin. Exp. Immunol. 24:*168.

123. Mackenzie, C. D., A. Sierra, L. Ortiz-Ortiz, and H. El-Sheik (1981). Variation in cell-mediated responsiveness in human onchocerciasis. *Z. Tropenmed. Parisitol.* In press.

124. Meyers, W. M., and D. H. Connor (1975). Onchocerciasis and streptocerciasis in patients with leprosy: Altered Mazzotti reactions. *Trans. R. Soc. Trop. Med. Hyg. 69:*524.

125. Jenkins, S. N., and J. M. Behnke (1977). Impairment of primary expulsion of *Trichuris muris* in mice concurrently infected with *Nematospiroides dubius*. *Parasitology 75:*71.

126. Meyers, W. M., R. C. Neafie, and D. H. Connor (1977). Onchocerciasis: Invasion of deep organs by *Onchocerca volvulus*. *Am. J. Trop. Med. Hyg. 26:*650.

127. Jones, B. R., J. Anderson, and H. Fuglsang (1978). Effects of various concentrations of diethylcarbamazine citrate applied as eye drops in ocular onchocerciasis, and the possibilities of improved therapy from continuous non-pulsed delivery. *Br. J. Opthamol. 62:*428.

128. Anderson, J., H. Fuglsang, and T. F. Marshall (1976). Effects of suramin on ocular onchocerciasis. *Z. Tropenmed. Parasitol. 27:*279.

129. Anderson, J., H. Fuglsang, and T. F. Marshall (1976). Effects of diethylcarbamazine on ocular onchocerciasis. *Z. Tropenmed. Parasitol. 27:*263.

130. Bird, A. C., A. El-Shiek, J. Anderson, and H. Fuglsang (1979). Visual loss during oral diethylcarbamazine treatment for onchocerciasis. *Lancet 2:*46.

131. Anderson, J., and H. Fuglsang (1978). Further studies on the treatment of ocular onchocerciasis with diethylcarbamazine and suramin. *Br. J. Opthamol. 62:*450.

132. Money, G. L. (1960). "Hetrazan" eosinopenia in onchocerciasis. *J. Trop. Med. Hyg. 63:*238.

133. Guerra-Caceres, J. C., A. D. M. Bryceson, I. Quakyi, and C. J. F. Spry (1980). Studies on the mechanism of adverse reactions produced by diethylcarbamazine in patients with onchocerciasis: The Mazzotti reaction. *Parasite Immunol. 2:*21.

134. Thevathasan, O. I., and M. Litt (1971). Inhibition by diethylcarbamazine (hetrazan) of the eosinophil response which *Trichina* extract elicits in guinea pig lymph nodes. *Clin. Exp. Immunol. 9:*657.

135. Hawking, F., P. Sewell, and J. P. Thurston (1950). The mode of action of hetrazan on filarial worms. *Br. J. Pharmacol. 5:*217.

136. Hobayashi, S. (1968). Chemotherapy of developing stage of *Dirofilaria immitis* in intermediate developmental location. 8. Effect of intermittent medication with diethylcarbamazine dihydrogen citrate. *Jap. J. Vet. Sci. S30:*84.

137. Johnson, P., C. D. Mackenzie, R. R. Suswillo, and D. A. Denham (1981). Serum-mediated adherence of feline granulocytes to microcilaria of *Brugia pahangi* in vitro: Variations with parasite maturation. *Parasite Immunol. 3:*69.

138. Merino, F., and A. Brand (1977). Immunoglobulin studies on onchocercosis patients. *Z. Tropenmed. Parasitol. 28:*229.

139. Henson, P. M., C. D. Mackenzie, and W. G. Spector (1979). Inflammatory reactions in onchocerciasis: A report on current knowledge and recommendation for further study. *Bull. WHO 57:*667.

140. Solley, G. O., G. J. Gleich, R. E. Jordon, and A. L. Schroeter (1976). The late phase of the immediate wheal and flare skin reaction: Its dependence upon IgE antibodies. *J. Clin. Invest. 58:*408.

141. Mallen, M. S., and L. O. Ortiz (1964). Ruevas pruebas en favor de la intervencion de la serotonina en la sintomatologia immediate al Choque Terapeutico. *Salud. Publ. Mex. 4:*565.

142. Mallen, M. S., A. Chevez, S. Calderon, L. O. Ortiz, T. Arias, and D. Gonzales (1962). Mechanismo del Choque Terapeutico. *Salud. Publ. Mex. 4:*1055.

143. Mallen, M. S. (1964). El problema del Choque Terapeutico, la profilaxis y el tratameinto del Ultimo. *Salud. Publ. Mex. 4:*591.

144. Ngu, J. L. (1978). Immunological studies on onchocerciasis. *Acta Trop. (Basel) 35:*269.

145. Marcoullis, G., E. M. Salonen, and R. Grasbeck (1978). Sequential affinity chromatography for the purification of antigens extracted from *Onchocerca volvulus* adult worms. *Z. Tropenmed. Parasitol. 29:*39.

146. Frøland, S. S. (1979). Protein-calorie malnutrition and immunity. *Quart. Rev. Cameroon Med. Soc. (Cameroon Med. J. Suppl.):*41.

147. Capuccinelli, P., R. R. Frentzel-Beyme, L. Sena, and G. Cavallo (1971). Immunoglobulins and parasitic infection. I. Levels of IgG, IgA, and IgM and IgD in different protozoal and helminthic infections in man. *G. Batt. Virol. 64:*155.

148. Buck, A. A., R. I. Anderson, and A. A. Macrae (1973). Serum immunoglobulin levels in five villages of the Republic of Chad and in onchocerciasis patients with or without microfilariae. *Z. Tropenmed. Parasitol. 24:*21.

149. Ngu, J. L., and K. Blackett (1976). Immunological studies on onchocerciasis in Cameroon. *Trop. Geog. Med. 28:*111.

150. Somorin, A. O., D. C. Heiner, and R. E. Ajugwo (1977). Immunoglobulin E in Nigerian onchocerciasis. *Am. J. Hyg. Trop. Med. Hyg. 26:*872.

151. Ikeda, T., I. Tada, and Y. Aoki (1978). The indirect haemagglutination test for onchocerciasis performed with blood collected on filter paper. *J. Parasitol. 64:*786.

152. Bozicevick, J., A. Donovan, L. Mazzotti, A. Francisco-Diaz, and E. Padilla (1947). Intradermal and complement fixation reactions elicited by variour antigens in persons infected with *Onchocerca volvulus*. *Am. J. Trop. Med. Hyg. 27:*51.

153. Ten Eyck, D. R. (1973). *Onchocerca volvulus* and *Wuchereria bancrofti*. Fluorescent antibody staining of frozen homologous sections for diagnosis. *Exp. Parasitol. 34:*154.

154. Mwaiko, G. L., and A. Mkufya (1977). Demonstration of antibodies in people infected with *O. volvulus* using adult *O. gutturosa* as antigen. *East Afr. Med. J. 54:*680.

155. Lucasse, C. H. R. (1962). Fluorescent antibody test for onchocerciasis. *Z. Tropenmed. Parasitol. 13:*404.

156. Macrae, A. A., R. I. Anderson, and L. E. Fazen (1977). Some observations on complement fixation in onchocerciasis in Guatemalans. *Am. J. Trop. Med. Hyg. 26:*658.

157. Ambroise, P. (1978). Diagnosis of parasitic disease by enzyme-linked immunoassay (ELISA) with a modified micromethod. *Bull. WHO 56:* 797.

158. Mashimisa, Y., M. Kawabata, G. Zea, M. Recinos, and O. Flores (1979). Personal communication.

159. Duke, B. O. L., and P. J. Moore (1968). The contributions of different age groups to the transmission of onchocerciasis in a Cameroon forest village. *Trans. R. Soc. Trop. Med. Hyg. 62:*22.

160. Duke, B. O. L. (1968). Reinfections with *Onchocerca colvulus* in cured patients exposed to continuing transmission. *Bull. WHO 39:*307.

161. Gibson, D. W., D. H. Connor, H. L. Brown, H. Fuglsang, J. Anderson, B. O. L. Duke, and A. A. Buck (1976). Onchocercal dermatitis: Ultrastructural studies of microfilariae and host tissues, before and after treatment with diethylcarbamazine (hetrazan). *Am. J. Trop. Med. Hyg. 25:* 74.

162. McLaren, D. J., C. D. Mackenzie, and F. J. Ramalho-Pinto (1977). Ultrastructural observations on the in vitro interaction between rat eosinophils and some parasitic helminths (*Schistosoma mansoni, Trichinella spiralis* and *Nippostrongylus brasiliensis*). *Clin. Exp. Immunol. 30:*105.

163. Warren, K. S., D. L. Boros, L. M. Hang, and A. A. Mahmoud (1975). The *Schistosoma japonicum* egg granuloma. *Am. J. Pathol. 80:*279.

164. Figueroa-Marroquin, H. Personal communication.

165. Mackenzie, C. D., P. Enyong, and A. E. Butterworth. Unpublished observations.

166. Muller, R. (1979). Identification of Onchocerca. In *Problems in the Identification of Parasites and Their Vectors* (A. E. Taylor and R. Muller, Eds.). Blackwell Scientific Publications, Oxford, p. 175.

167. Van den Berghe, L., M. Chardome, and E. Peel (1964). The filarial parasites of the eastern gorilla in the Congo. *J. Helminthol. 38:*349.

168. Duke, B. O. L. (1962). Experimental transmission of *Onchocerca volvulus* to a chimpanzee. *Trans. R. Soc. Trop. Med. Hyg. 56:*571.

169. Mellor, P. S. (1973). Studies on *Onchocerca cervicalis* Raillet and Henry 1910. *Onchocerca cervicalus* in British horses. *J. Helminthol. 47:*97.

170. Cello, R. M. (1970). Ocular onchocerciasis in the horse. *Equine Vet. J. 3:*148.

171. Patnaik, B. (1962). Onchocerciasis due to *Onchocerca armillata* in cattle in Orissa. *J. Helminthol. 36:*313.

172. Dennis, D. T., F. Partono, Purnomo, S. Atmosoedjono, and J. Sulianti Saroso (1976). Timor filariasis: Epidemiologic and clinical features in a defined community. *Am. J. Trop. Med. Hyg. 25:*797.

173. Partono, F. and Purnomo (1978). Clinical features of Timorian filariasis among immigrants to an endemic area in West Flores, Indonesia. *S. E. Asian J. Trop. Med. Publ. Health 9:*338.

174. Beaver, P. C. (1970). Filariasis without microfilaraemia. *Am. J. Trop. Med. Hyg. 19:*181.

175. Partono, F., Purnomo, W. Pribaldi, and A. Soewarts (1978). Epidemiology and clinical features of *Brugia timori* in a newly established village. *Am. J. Trop. Med. Hyg. 27:*910.

176. Lichtenberg, F. (1957). The early phase of endemic bancroftian filariasis in the male: Pathologic study. *J. Mt. Sinai Hosp. 6:*983.

177. Schacher, J. F., and P. F. Sahyoun (1967). A chronological study of the histopathology of filarial disease in cats and dogs caused by *Brugia pahangi. Trans. R. Soc. Trop. Med. Hyg. 61:*234.

178. Grove, D. I., and I. J. Forbes (1979). Immunosuppression in bancroftian filariasis. *Trans. R. Soc. Trop. Med. Hyg. 73:*23.

179. Joon-Wah, M., M. Singh, E-H. Yap, B-C. Ho, and K-L. Kang (1979). Studies on human filariasis in Malaysia: Immunoglobulin and complement levels in persons infected with *Brugia malayi* and *Wuchereria bancrofti. Trans. R. Soc. Trop. Med. Hyg. 73:*395.

180. Donohugh, D. L. (1963). Tropical eosinophilia: An etiological enquiry. *New Engl. J. Med. 269:*1357.

181. Neva, F. A., and E. A. Ottesen (1978). Tropical (filarial) eosinophilia. *N. Engl. J. Med. 298:*1129.

182. Ezeoke, A., A. B. V. Perera, and J. R. Hobbs (1973). Serum IgE elevation with tropical eosinophilia. *J. Allergy 3:*33.

183. Kulpati, D. D., K. Saha, and H. K. Dua (1977). Immunoglobulin E levels in sera and bronchial aspirates of patients with various types of pulmonary eosinophilia. *Ind. J. Med. Res. 65:*206.

184. Ray, D., and K. Saha (1978). Serum immunoglobulin and complement levels in tropical pulmonary eosinophilia, and their correlation with primary and relapsing stages of the illness. *Am. J. Trop. Med. Hyg. 27:*503.

185. Neva, F. A., A. P. Kaplan, G. Pacheco, L. Gray, and T. J. Danaraj (1975). A human model of parasite immunopathology, with observation on serum IgE levels before and after treatment. *J. Allergy Clin. Immunol. 55:*422.

186. Danaraj, T. J., G. Pacheco, K. Shanmugaratnam, and P. C. Beaver (1966). The etiology and pathology of eisinophilic lung (tropical eosinophilia). *Am. J. Trop. Med. Hyg. 15:*183.

187. Danaraj, T. J., L. S. de Silva, and J. F. Schacher (1959). Serological diagnosis of eosinophilic lung (tropical eosinophilia) and its etiological implications. *Am. J. Trop. Med. Hyg. 8:*151.

188. Webb, J. K. G., C. K. Job, and E. W. Gault (1960). Tropical eosinophilia: Demonstration of microfilariae in lung, liver and lymph nodes. *Lancet 1:*835.

189. Joshi, V. V., F. E. Udwadia, and R. K. Gadgil (1969). Etiology of tropical eosinophilia. A study of lung biopsies and review of published reports. *Am. J. Trop. Med. Hyg. 18:*231.

190. Buckley, J. J. C. (1958). Occult filarial infections of human origin as a cause of tropical pulmonary eosinophilia. *East Afr. Med. J. 35:*492.

191. Wong, M. M. (1974). Experimental occult Dirofilariasis in dogs with reference to immunological responses and its relationship to tropical eosinophilia in man. *S.E. Asian J. Trop. Med. Publ. Health 5:*480.

192. Wong, M. M., P. E. Suter, E. A. Rhode, and M. F. Guest (1973). Dirofilariasis without circulating microfilaria: A problem in diagnosis. *J. Am. Vet. Med. Assoc. 163:*133.

193. Ottesen, E. A., F. A. Neva, R. S. Paranjape, S. P. Tripathy, K. V. Thiruvengadam, and M. A. Beaven (1979). Specific allergic sensitization to filarial antigens in tropical eosinophilia syndrome. *Lancet 1:*1158.

194. Wong, M. M., M. F. Guest, K. C. Lim, and S. Sivanandan (1977). Experimental *Brugia malayi* infections in the rhesus monkey. *S.E. Asian J. Trop. Med. Hyg. 8:*265.

195. Partono, F., D. T. Dennis, Purnomo, and A. Atmosoedjono (1977). *Brugia timori:* Experimental infection in some laboratory animals. *S.E. Asian J. Trop. Med. Publ. Health 8:*155.

196. Ah, H. S., and P. E. Thompson (1973). *Brugia pahangi* infections and their effect on the lymphatic system of Mongolian jirds (*Meriones unguiculatus*). *Exp. Parasitol. 34:*393.

197. Denham, D. A., T. Ponnudurai, G. S. Nelson, R. Rogers, and F. Guy (1972). Studies with *Brugia pahangi*. 2. The effect of repeated infection on parasite levels in cats. *Int. J. Parasitol. 2:*401.

198. Wong, M. M. (1964). Studies on microfilaraemia in dogs. II. Levels of microfilaraemia in relation to immunologic responses of the host. *Am. J. Trop. Med. Hyg. 13:*66.

199. McGreevy, P. B., M. M. Ismail, T. M. Phillips, and D. A. Denham (1975).

Studies with *Brugia pahangi.* 10. An attempt to demonstrate the sharing of antigenic determinants between the worm and its hosts. *J. Helminthol. 49:*107.

200. Smithers, S. R., R. J. Terry, and D. J. Hockley (1969). Host antigens in schistosomiasis. *Proc. R. Soc. Lond. [Biol.] 171:*483.
201. Rogers, R., and D. A. Denham (1975). Studies with *Brugia pahangi.* 11. Measurement of lymph flow in infected cats. *S.E. Asian J. Trop. Med. Publ. Health 6:*199.
202. Bosworth, W. E., A. Ewert, and J. Bray (1973). The interaction of *Brugia malayi* and streptococcus in an animal model. *Am. J. Trop. Med. Hyg. 22:*714.
203. Rogers, R., and D. A. Denham (1974). Studies with *Brugia pahangi.* 7. Changes in lymphatics of injected cats. *J. Helminthol. 48:*213.
204. Denham, D. A., and R. Rogers (1975). Structural and functional studies on the lymphatics of cats infected with *Brugia pahangi. Trans. R. Soc. Trop. Med. Hyg. 69:*173.
205. Rogers, R., D. A. Denham, G. S. Nelson, F. Guy, and T. Ponnudurai (1975). Studies with *Brugia pahangi.* III. Histological changes in the affected lymph nodes of infected cats. *Ann. Trop. Med. Parasitol. 69:*77.
206. Kowalski, J. C., and L. R. Ash (1975). Repeated infections of *Brugia pahangi* in the jird *Meriones unguiculatus. S.E. Asian J. Trop. Med. Publ. Health 6:*195.
207. Weller, P. F. (1978). Cell mediated immunity in experimental filariasis: Lymphocyte reactivity to filarial stage-specific antigens and to B- and T-cell mitogens during acute and chronic infections. *Cell. Immunol. 37:*369.
208. Portaro, J. K., S. Britton, and L. R. Ash (1976). *Brugia pahangi:* Depressed mitogen reactivity in filarial infections in the jird, *Meriones unguiculatus. Exp. Parasitol. 40:*438.
209. Weiss, N. (1970). Parasitologische und immunbiologische Unter suchungen über die durch *Dipetalonema viteae* eezengte Nagetierfilariose. *Acta Trop. (Basel) 27:*219.
210. Worms, M. J., R. J. Terry, and A. Terry (1961). *Dipetalonema witei,* filarial parasite of the jird, *Meriones libycus.* 1. Maintenance in the laboratory. *J. Parasitol. 47:*963.
211. Chabaud, A. G. (1954). Sur le cycle évolutif des spirurides et de nematodes ayant une biologie comparable. *Ann. Parasit. Hum. Comp. 29:*238.
212. Weiss, N. (1978). Studies on *Dipetalonema viteae* microfilariae in hamsters in relation to worm burden and humoral immune response. *Acta Trop. (Basel) 35:*137.
213. Neilson, J. T. M. (1978). Primary infections of *Dipetalonema viteae* in an outbred and five inbred strains of golden hamsters. *J. Parasitol. 64:*378.
214. Haque, A., M. N. Lefebvre, B. M. Ogilvie, and A. Capron (1978). *Dipetalonema viteae* in hamsters: Effect of antiserum or immunization with parasite extracts on production of microfilariae. *Parasitology 76:*61.
215. Haque, A., D. Chassoux, B. M. Ogilvie, and A. Capron (1978). *Dipetalonema viteae* infection in hamsters: Enhancement and suppression of microfilariaemia. *Parasitology 76:*77.

216. Haque, A., M. J. Worms, B. M. Ogilvie, and A. Capron (1980). *Dipetalonema viteae* in mice: Microfilariae production in various mouse strains and nude mice. *Exp. Parasitol. 49:*398.

217. Neilson, J. T. M., and D. J. Forrester (1975). The dynamics of primary, secondary and tertiary infections of *Dipetalonema viteae* in hamsters. *Exp. Parasitol. 37:*367.

218. Neilson, J. T. M. (1978). Alteration of amicrofilaraemia in *Dipetalonema viteae* infected hamsters with immunosuppressive drugs. *Acta Trop. (Basel) 35:*57.

219. Neilson, J. T. M. (1976). A comparison of the acquired resistance to *Dipetalonema viteae* stimulated in hamsters by trickle versus tertiary infections. *Z. Tropenmed. Parasitol. 27:*233.

220. Neilson, J. T. M. (1979). Kinetics of *Dipetalonema viteae* infections established by surgical implantation of adult worms into hamsters. *Am. J. Trop. Med. Hyg. 28:*216.

221. D'Alesandro, D. D., and T. R. Klei (1976). Evidence for immunosuppression of Syrian hamsters and Mongolian jirds by *Dipetalonema viteae* infections. *Trans. R. Soc. Trop. Med. Hyg. 70:*534.

222. Weiss, N. (1978). *Dipetalonema viteae:* In vitro blastogenesis of hamster spleen and lymph node cells to phytohemagglutinin and filarial antigens. *Exp. Parasitol. 46:*283.

223. Macdonald, E. M., and J. A. Scott (1953). Experiments on immunity in the cotton rat to the filarial worm, *Litomosoides carinii. Exp. Parasitol. 2:*174.

224. Scott, J. A., and E. M. MacDonald (1958). Immunity to challenging infections of *Litomosoides carinii* produced by transfer of developing worms. *J. Parasitol. 44:*187.

225. Scott, J. A., E. M. MacDonald, and L. J. Olson (1958). The early induction in cotton rats of immunity to their filarial worms. *J. Parasitol. 44:*507.

226. Rao, Y. V. B. G., K. Mehta, and D. Subrahmanyam (1977). *Litomosoides carinii:* Effect of irradiation on the development and immunogenicity of the larval forms. *Exp. Parasitol. 43:*39.

227. Bagai, R. C., and D. Subrahmanyam (1970). Nature of acquired resistance to filarial infection in albino rats. *Nature (Lond.) 228:*682.

228. Subrahmanyam, D., S. Choudhuri, and S. Jain (1974). Antigenic sharing between *Wuchereria bancrofti* and *Litomosoides carinii. Ind. J. Pathol. Bact. 17:*135.

229. Subrahmanyam, D., and S. Choudhuri (1975). Studies on humoral and cellular immune responses in filariasis: Use of nuclear techniques. In *Nuclear Techniques in Helminthology Research.* International Atomic Energy Agency, Vienna.

230. Nelson, D. S., D. Subrahmanyam, Y. V. B. G. Rao, and K. Metha (1976). Cellular morphology in pleural exudate of albino rats infected with *Litomosoides carinii. Trans R. Soc. Trop. Med. Hyg. 70:*254.

231. Fujita, K., and J. Kobayashi (1969). The sequential appearance of 19S and 7S antibodies in cotton rats infected with the cotton rat filaria. *Jap. J. Exp. Med. 39:*481.

232. Ishii, A. (1970). Antigenicity of excretory and secretory products of the cotton rat filaria *Litomosoides carinii. Jap. J. Exp. Med. 40:*39.

233. Culbertson, J. T., H. M. Rose, and C. R. Demarest (1944). *Filariasis bancrofti:* Its diagnosis by immunological tests with antigens derived from *Litomosoides carinii. Am. J. Hyg. 39:*156.

234. Wharton, D. (1946). Transplantation of adult filarial worms, *Litomosoides carinii,* in cotton rats. *Science 104:*30.

235. Fujita, K., and J. Kobayashi (1969). The development of antibodies in the cotton rats transplanted with the adult cotton rat filaria *Litomosoides carinii. Jap. J. Exp. Med. 39:*585.

236. Weiner, D. J., and E. J. L. Soulsby (1976). *Litomosoides carinii:* Effect of splenectomy on the ability of naive *Mastomys natalensis* to accept transplanted adults. *J. Parasitol. 62:*887.

237. Weiner, D. J., and E. J. L. Soulsby (1978). Fate of *Litomosoides carinii* adults transplanted into the pleural or peritoneal cavity of infected and naive multilaminate rats (*Mastomys natalensis*). *Exp. Parasitol. 45:*241.

238. Worms, M. J. (1972). The course of microfilaraemia in primary infections of *Dirofilaria immitis* and *D. repens* in dogs. *Comptes Rendu ler Multicolloque Europeen de Rennes,* p. 324.

239. Orihel, T. C., and P. C. Beaver (1965). Morphology and relationship of *Dirofilaria tenuis* and *Dirofilaria conjuntivae. Am. J. Trop. Med. Hyg. 14:* 1030.

240. de Carneri, I., S. Sacchi, and A. Pazzaglia (1973). Subcutaneous dirofilariasis in man—not so rare. *Trans. R. Soc. Trop. Med. Hyg. 67:*887.

241. Beaver, P. C., and T. V. Orihel (1965). Human infection with filariae of animals in the United States. *Am. J. Trop. Med. Hyg. 14:*1010.

242. Welch. J. S., and C. Dobson (1974). The prevalence of antibodies to *Dirofilaria immitis* in aboriginal and caucasian Australians. *Trans. R. Soc. Trop. Med. Hyg. 68:*466.

243. Dobson, C., and J. S. Welch (1974). Dirofilariasis as a cause of eosinophilic meningitis in man diagnosed by immunofluorescence and Arthus hypersensitivity. *Trans. R. Soc. Trop. Med. Hyg. 68:*223.

244. Jung. R. C., and P. H. Espenan (1972). A case of infection in man with Dirofilaria. *Am. J. Trop. Med. Hyg. 16:*172.

245. Pacheco, G., and H. L. Schofield, Jr. (1968). *Dirofilaria tenuis* containing microfilariae in man. *Am. J. Trop. Med. Hyg. 17:*180.

246. Hsu, C-K, E. C. Melby Jr., and A. E. Farwell, Jr. (1974). Demonstration and intraspecies cross-sensitization of reaginic antibodies in dogs infected with *Dirofilaria immitis. Am. J. Trop. Med. Hyg. 23:*619.

247. Pacheco, G. (1966). Progressive changes in certain serological responses to *Dirofilaria immitis* infection in the dog. *J. Parasitol. 52:*311.

248. Kume, S. (1970). Pathogenesis of allergic shock from the use of diethyl-carbamazine. In *Canine Heartworm Disease: A discussion of the current knowledge* (R. E. Bradley and G. Pacheco, Eds.). University of Florida, Gainesville, p. 7.

249. Desowitz, R. S., J. W. Barnwell, N. E. Palumbo, S. R. Una, and S. F. Perri (1978). Rapid decrease of precipitating and reaginic antibodies in *Dirofilaria immitis*-infected dogs which develop severe adverse reactions following treatment with diethylcarbamazine. *Am. J. Trop. Med. Hyg. 27:* 1148.

250. Suswillo, R. R., G. S. Nelson, R. Muller, P. B. McGreevy, B. O. L. Duke, and D. A. Denham (1977). Attempts to infect jirds (*Meriones unguiculatus*) with *Wuchereria bancrofti, Onchocerca volvulus, Loa loa loa* and *Mansonella ozzardi. J. Helminthol. 51:*132.

251. Nelson, G. S., M. A. Amin, E. J. Blackie, and N. Robson (1966). The maintenance of *Onchocerca gutturosa* microfilariae in vitro and in vivo. *Trans. R. Soc. Trop. Med. Hyg. 60:*17.

252. Duke, B. O. L. (1960). Studies on loiasis in monkeys. II. The population dynamics of the microfilariae of *Loa* in experimentally infected drills (*Mandrillus leucophaeus*). *Ann. Trop. Med. Parasitol. 54:*15.

253. Mackenzie, C. D., M. Jungery, P. M. Taylor, and B. M. Ogilvie (1980). Activation of complement, the induction of antibodies to the surface of nematodes and the effect of these factors and cells on worm survival in vitro. *Eur. J. Immunol. 10:*594.

6

Immunology of *Leishmania* Infections

STEVEN G. REED*   National Research Institute of the Amazon (INPA),
Manaus, Amazonas, Brazil

I.   Introduction   291
II. Cutaneous and Mucocutaneous Leishmaniasis   293
     A. Clinical Studies   293
     B. Experimental Studies: *Leishmania enriettii*   295
     C. Experimental Human Leishmaniasis   298
III. Visceral Leishmaniasis   301
     A. Clinical Studies   301
     B. Experimental Studies   302
IV. Immunization and Cross-Reactivity   304
V.   Conclusions   306
     References   308

I. INTRODUCTION

The *Leishmania* are intracellular protozoan parasites of several mammalian and reptilian species. Like the *Trypanosoma,* they are flagellates belonging to the order Kinetoplastida. They are responsible for various syndromes in humans, ranging from subclinical to fatal infections. The group is a very diversified one, generally classified according to the clinical conditions produced or geographic occurrence. The taxonomy of the *Leishmania* has recently been reviewed [1,1a] and has been summarized in Table 1.

Present affiliation: Cornell University Medical College, New York, New York.
This work was partially supported by NIH Grant AI 16282.

Table 1 Agents of Human Leishmaniasis

Organism[a]	Clinical Disease(s)
Leishmania tropica	Ulcer; oriental sore; long incubation and duration; leishmania recidiva
L. major	Ulcer; "acute" cutaneous leishmaniasis; shorter incubation and duration
L. aethiopica	Ulcer; oriental sore; diffuse cutaneous leishmaniasis (DCL)
L. mexicana mexicana	"Chicleros ulcer"—usually single or few lesions—ear often involved, lesion may persist—no nasopharyngeal lesions
L. m. amazonesis	Ulcers; DCL association
L. m. pifanoi	Rare; DCL association
L. braziliensis braziliensis	Ulcer; single or few lesions; persistent and disfiguring, metastases (mucocutaneous leishmaniasis)
L. b. guyanensis	Ulcer (pian bois); metastases
L. b. panamensis	Ulcer; single or multiple; persistent
L. peruviana	Ulcer; single or few lesions; self-resolving
L. donovani	Visceral leishmaniasis (kala azar), post-kala azar dermal leishmaniasis; also self-limiting dermatoid form
L. infantum	Visceral leishmaniasis (kala azar) of children
L. chagasi	Visceral leishmaniasis of new world

[a]Current designation of species or variant.

The immunology of leishmaniasis is rather poorly understood at present. The diversity of clinical patterns complicates the elucidation of immunological phenomena. Immune responses range from anergic to allergic, with varying degrees between these two extremes.

Leishmania infect and divide within macrophages. Studies of the immunology of leishmaniasis hold significance not only for their potential applicability towards the prevention and treatment of the diseases involved, but also because of the fascinating model represented by parasites which inhabit cells of the immune system.

The following discussion represents an attempt to summarize the recent advances in the immunology of leishmaniasis. More detailed discussions of some of the early studies of *Leishmania* immunology have been presented in previous reviews by Zuckerman [2] and Preston and Dumonde [3]. A discussion of immunodiagnosis has not been included and may be found elsewhere [2]. Because of basic differences in clinical patterns and immunological aspects, cutaneous and visceral leishmaniasis have been discussed separately. Considerations of humoral and cellular immune responses have been integrated to avoid representing these as sharply delineated phenomena.

II. CUTANEOUS AND MUCOCUTANEOUS LEISHMANIASIS

A. Clinical Studies

The distribution of cutaneous and mucocutaneous leishmaniasis generally differs from that of visceral leishmaniasis; the endemic areas are more widespread. The characteristic lesion of cutaneous leishmaniasis begins as a nodule marked by hypertrophy of the stratum corneum and of the papillae. In many cases the lesions do not ulcerate and healing occurs. Often, ulceration does occur following an incubation period of varying lengths. As ulceration progresses, a zone of inflammation develops around the nodule, and infiltration of mononuclear cells, including lymphocytes, plasma cells, monocytes, and macrophages, develops. Amastigotes may be detected in the lesion as it develops but may be difficult to find in a fully developed or healing sore. The lesions of oriental sore have been classified into the moist and dry forms. The moist form is characterized by a relatively short incubation period, rapid ulceration, and often healing within six months. The dry form generally has a longer incubation period, with a persistent slow-healing lesion. Mucocutaneous leishmaniasis has a relatively long incubation period. Beginning from a primary lesion, the disease spreads to the mucous membranes of the nose, pharynx, and mouth, causing severe and debilitating damage. Diffuse cutaneous leishmaniasis, an immunologically anergic form, apparently has several etiologies (Table 1). It is characterized by multiple lesions which contain detectable parasites.

There is relatively little information available concerning the immunological aspects of clinical cutaneous or mucocutaneous leishmaniasis. The basic patterns of response were long ago established, and very little has been done to further elucidate mechanisms involved. However, it is generally recognized that clinical cutaneous leishmaniasis follows one of several courses depending on both host and parasite factors. The most common form consists of a single or few self-resolving lesions, typified by oriental sore. Healing is accompanied by the development of delayed hypersensitivity (DH) to leishmanin (leishmanial antigen) and low or undetectable levels of specific antibody. It is well established that immunity develops following recovery. Guirges [4] reported that of 3420 cured oriental sore cases, all but eight were resistant to natural or experimental reinfection.

Leishmaniasis recidiva represents a nonhealing condition marked by strong immune responses [3,5]. Although the patients may demonstrate strong delayed and immediate hypersensitivity responses to *Leishmania,* the lesions persist and the patient often does not develop resistance to reinfection. This condition has been referred to as an allergic form of cutaneous leishmaniasis. It is most often associated with *Leishmania tropica* and is believed to represent infection with variant strains [6]. The possibility that the condition is primarily a host-mediated phenomenon has not been adequately explored. The number of reported cases is relatively small, and a good laboratory model is not available.

Another clinical form characterized by nonhealing lesions is diffuse cutaneous leishmaniasis (DCL), which has both old and new world forms and is attributed to more than one species of parasite. Convit et al. [7] expressed the view that DCL was the result of host unresponsiveness rather than parasite invasiveness. They inoculated parasites from DCL lesions into normal volunteers which led to the production of characteristic cutaneous lesions. Bryceson [8] suggested that DCL patients may be specifically unresponsive to the parasite. Leishmanin skin tests were negative before treatment, and relapses followed treatment. Although most of the DCL patients could not be sensitized to dinitrochlorobenzene (DNCB), normal skin test responses to tuberculin and lepromin were observed, and no evidence for a generalized depression of cell-mediated responses, as marked by increased susceptibility to other infections, was noted. Dumonde [9] observed that blast transformation responses of peripheral blood leukocytes in DCL patients were not as strong as were those in cutaneous leishmaniasis patients. Immunoglobulin levels in DCL patients were reportedly normal, and specific antibody responses were similar to those of oriental sore patients. Thus, conclusive evidence for the causes of DCL is lacking, but absence of DH responses to leishmanin has led to the classification of DCL as an anergic state of responsiveness. Recent experimental evidence supports this view.

When susceptible mice were inoculated with parasites from a cutaneous leishmaniasis patient or from a DCL patient, the animals developed similar immune responses and infection patterns to each of the inocula [10]. However, two strains of mice had different response patterns. In one strain (C57BL/6) lesions resolved and both DH responses and agglutinating antibodies were detected. Another mouse strain (BALB/c) had weaker immune responses and developed nonhealing metastatic lesions. Insofar as results in mice can be correlated with the clinical situation, these results may be interpreted to support the view that DCL is due not to properties intrinsic to the parasite but rather to host factors. It is apparent that DCL may be the result of immunological deficiency, though the nature of this is not clear. It remains to be determined whether human responses to *Leishmania* may be under genetic control, as has been shown to be true for *Leishmania donovani* infections in mice [11,12].

The development of a positive DH response is characteristic of cured or healing cases of cutaneous leishmaniasis, and this generally correlates well with resistance to reinfection. Adler [13] reported that if cutaneous lesions are sur- givally removed before the patient develops positive DH to leishmanin, neither the response nor the resistance to reinfection will develop. The development of specific DH responses is important for recovery with concomitant immunity in all forms of clinical leishmaniasis [13,14].

Tremonti and Walton [15] observed blast transformation of peripheral blood leukocytes from cutaneous leishmaniasis patients. A recent study [16] has demonstrated that peripheral blood lymphocytes from patients with cured or active cases of cutaneous leishmaniasis responded in vitro to low concentra- tions of leishmanial antigen. When lymphocytes were separated into B- and T- cell-enriched populations and tested for responses to antigen, it was found that the purified T cells, but not purified B cells, responded to the concentrations of antigen tested. Lymphocyte responses were detected in patients that had no detectable anti-*Leishmania* antibodies. It was also noted that leishmanial anti- gen in some cases produced lymphocyte stimulation in uninfected control sub- jects. Although it is not unusual for parasite antigens to produce nonspecific lymphocyte proliferative responses, it is possible that the non-patient positive responders may have been tuberculin positive. Several studies have demon- strated the cross-reactivity of *Leishmania* and *Mycobacteria* (see Section IV).

Although in vivo and in vitro correlates of cell-mediated immune responses have been observed to occur, passive transfer of positive reactions to leishmanin has not been achieved. Adler and Nelken [17] noted no immediate or delayed skin reactions in recipients of leukocytes or whole blood from a leishmanin-posi- tive donor who was shown to be resistant to *L. tropica* and *L. mexicana.* Similar- ly, Bray and Lainson [18] were not able to transfer leishmanin positivity to *L. mexicana* between human volunteers.

Specific antibodies may or may not be detectable during or after cutaneous leishmaniasis infections (reviewed by Preston and Dumonde [3]). Antibody titers generally are low or undetectable in patients with cutaneous leishmaniasis [19-21], although immediate hypersensitivity responses have been noted in persons recovered from *L. tropica* infections [22]. However, metastatic mucocutaneous leishmaniasis cuased by *Leishmania braziliensis* is characterized by the production of specific antibodies [2,19]. This disease involves secondary lesions of the mucous mem- branes of the nose, mouth, hard and soft palates, and pharynx. The disease can be extremely disfiguring, and advanced cases may be difficult to treat. This destruc- tive form of leishmaniasis has been compared with leishmaniasis recidiva [3] and is characterized by persisting lesions and absence of resistance to reinfection.

B. Experimental Studies: *Leishmania enriettii*

The most extensively studied laboratory model of cutaneous leishmaniasis has been *L. enriettii* infections in the guinea pig. This model may be manipulated to resemble either local self-healing or diffuse cutaneous leishmaniasis [23]. Variations in the size or route of the challenge inoculum allow for selection of an infection resembling either of these clinical situations [24]. Insufficient information concerning the immunology of human cutaneous leishmaniasis is available to allow for critical evaluation of the model as one for clinical disease. The guinea pig infection was discovered and is propagated as a laboratory phenomenon. However, the untreated infection runs a course similar to that of oriental sore in humans. A single ulcerating lesion is produced at the site of inoculation. The lesion heals in 8-12 weeks, accompanied by a strong DH response and resistance to reinfection. The guinea pig is apparently the natural host, so problems that may be introduced by using a parasite in a substitute host are avoided. In a small percentage of infected guinea pigs, metastases occur. This bears resemblance to DCL and may represent another example in which differences in host response patterns determine the disease outcome.

The characteristic course of the disease involves a self-limiting lesion, recovery from which confers immunity to further infection. A direct correlation exists between resolution of the lesion and the development of DH [23,25], which has been successfully transferred with lymphoid cells [23]. Lemma and Yau [25] suppressed the immune response of guinea pigs with cyclophosphamide, anti-lymphocyte serum (ALS), or X-irradiation. They noted that negative DH responses were directly correlated with metastasizing infections. The DH response has been shown to persist for several months after resolution of the initial lesion. Macrophage migration inhibitory factor (MIF) and lymphocyte transformation factor have been detected in convalescent guinea pigs [26, 27]. Animals treated with ALS developed more severe infections than did animals treated with normal serum [28,29]. The ALS-treated animals also had depressed DH responses to leishmanin. Behin et al. [30] used an interesting approach to the study of immunology of cutaneous leishmaniasis. Guinea pigs previously sensitized to either Bacillus Calmette-Guerin (BCG) of DNCB were infected with *L. enrietti*. The development of ear lesions was inhibited in sensitized animals when DH responses to the sensitizing agent were elicited at the site of the lesion. Inhibition of lesion growth was observed only when a strong reaction was elicited continuously over a 3-4 week period. However, these animals were not immune to reinfection. Thus, a local cellular immune response, albeit to heterologous antigen, inhibited parasite growth, but immunity was not included.

Poulter [24] observed the kinetics of resistance to reinfection by quantitative methods. Resolution of the primary lesion required approximately 13 weeks. However, challenge inocula at other sites were eliminated within 7 days when administered as early as 3 weeks after infection. This illustrates an interesting phenomenon occurring in cutaneous leishmaniasis. Resistance to lesions at secondary sites developed before resolution of the primary lesion began, and resistance to a secondary challenge was as strong in animals with current infection as in those that had fully recovered. Similarly, even though animals may develop chronic metastatic lesions, they may still be able to resolve the primary lesion [23]. Thus, it appears that a strong local DH response is necessary to heal a lesion, and that the production of sensitized T lymphocytes from prior antigenic exposure aids in the rapid initiation of such a response. This may act to limit intracellular invasion and/or growth of the parasite. Farah et al. [31] observed a decrease in intracellular parasitism in macrophages coated with immune serum, although specific antibodies have been thought to be relatively unimportant against *L. enrietti* infections [23].

To further assess the importance of cellular responses to *L. enriettii*, there have been attempts to demonstrate in vitro cytotoxicity. Guinea pig macrophages were infected in vitro, then overlaid with lymph node cells from normal or convalescent animals. Bray and Bryceson [32] and Bryceson et al. [23] reported that lymph node cells from convalescent guinea pigs were more effective than were those from normal guinea pigs in destroying infected macrophages. It was also noted that lymph node cells from animals immunized with *L. enriettii* antigens, with or without adjuvant, could more effectively destroy infected macrophages than could cells from unimmunized animals. Mauel et al. [33] attempted to reproduce these findings. They compared the cytotoxic effects of lymph node cells from normal or convalescent guinea pigs on infected macrophage monolayers and could detect no differences between the two cell types. These authors noted that the macrophages did not survive well in culture beyond 48 hr. Thus, it appears that the system used may be inadequate for accurate determination of cytotoxic cell-mediated phenomena.

Studies of in vitro phagocytosis by guinea pig macrophages have shown that these cells are not consistently capable of destroying *L. enriettii*, although immune animals were shown to have macrophages capable of increased phagocytosis of *L. enriettii* [23,32]. Macrophages activated to more effectively destroy *Listeria monocytogenes* did not show increased activity against *L. enriettii* [33,34]. It is apparent that the parasites themselves are not unusually resistant to destruction; they were rapidly destroyed by activated mouse macrophages [34]. Peritoneal macrophages from mice or guinea pigs were activated by incubation with *Toxoplasma* antigen and homologous spleen lymphocytes from animals with chronic *Toxoplasma* infections. Activated mouse macrophages were capable of increased killing of *L. enriettii*, but guinea pig macrophages activated in the same manner were not. Interestingly, activated mouse macrophages were not more effective than normal macrophages in destroying *L. tropica.*

In vivo, administration of anti-macrophage serum (AMS) appeared to cause a lessening of severity of lesions and more rapid resolution [29]. The reasons for this observation are not clear, but a decreased number of available host cells in the AMS-treated animals may have been a contributing factor.

Antibody responses have generally been considered to be unimportant in the resolution of *L. enriettii* infections. Bryceson et al. [23] reported that DH responses were present during the course of infection, but that indirect hemagglutinating antibodies and immediate hypersensitivity responses could not be detected. Specific antibody production could be stimulated by inoculation of parasite extract with complete or incomplete Freund's adjuvant. Doyle et al. [35] produced relatively high titers against *L. enriettii* by infecting guinea pigs intradermally and collecting sera during the course of the disease or after rechallenge of animals with healed lesions. These authors were able to demonstrate, by the use of such antiserum, capping of membrane-associated antigens of both amastigote and promastigote forms. Attempts to passively transfer protection to *L. enriettii* with serum from convalescent or immunized guinea pigs were generally unsuccessful [23,36]. However, a recent study by Poulter [37] has demonstrated the passive transfer of partial resistance to *L. enriettii* with serum from convalescent animals. T lymphocytes, but not serum from animals with active infections, were effective in transferring partial protection. Belehu et al. [37a] observed that specific antibody levels resulting from pretreatment of guinea pigs with cyclophosphamide were decreased and that this was associated with larger primary lesions and increased metatastases.

C. Experimental Human Leishmaniasis

Studies to more fully explore the mechanisms of immunity to cutaneous leishmaniasis have been performed using human parasite species in mice. Several strains of inbred mice have proven to be susceptible to parasites of the *L. tropica* and *L. mexicana* groups, and most of the studies have been performed with these systems.

Preston et al. [38] infected CBA mice with *L. tropica* which led to the production of a nodule at the site of inoculation. The lesion ulcerated and healed within approximately 12 weeks. Delayed hypersensitivity responses were detectable after week 1 and persisted throughout the course of the infection. A steadily rising level of specific antibody, detected by immunofluorescence and direct parasite agglutination, was also noted. Sera which contained high levels of agglutinating antibody, but not normal sera, were capable of lysing promastigotes of *L. tropica* in vitro. Immediate hypersensitivity responses were also detected over the course of infection. An increase in numbers of plasma cells in lymph nodes draining the site of the lesion was noted beginning 14 days after infection. Alexander and Philips [39] reported plasma cell increases in draining lymph nodes of mice with *L. tropica* and *L. mexicana* lesions by 6 weeks after infection.

Preston et al. [38] also reported the results of infection of irradiated thymectomized mice with *L. tropica*. The lesions in these animals healed more slowly, although metastases were not noted. Delayed hypersensitivity responses were decreased, but not agglutinating antibody levels, indicating the relative importance of these responses in the healing process. Infection of congenitally athymic (nude) mice with *L. tropica* produced a more serious infection than was seen in thymic-intact littermates, with visceralization of the infection occurring in all of the athymic mice [40]. Alexander and Phillips [40a] reported more efficient adoptive transfer of resistance to *L. mexicana* and *L. tropica* in mice with nylon wool nonadherent cells than with nylon wool adherent cells.

Pérez et al. [41] observed differences in the course of *L. mexicana* infections in several strains of inbred mice. The most severe infections, accompanied by metastases, were seen in BALB/c mice. These animals had poor DH responses to leishmanin in contrast to the strains which were more resistant. Spleen cells from *L. mexicana*-infected BALB/c mice reportedly had lowered in vitro responses to leishmanial antigen than did cells from more resistant C57BL/6 mice [10]. Nasseri and Modabber [42] reported that BALB/c mice were more susceptible to *L. tropica* than were six other strains of inbred mice. The BALB/c, in contrast to the other strains, did not display DH to leishmanin.

Weintraub and Weinbaum [43] reported "detectable levels" of specific antibody in BALB/c mice infected with *L. tropica*. In another study [10], direct agglutinating antibody responses were reportedly lower in BALB/c mice than in more resistant strains, although the data were not very strong. The sera from only five mice were pooled for the test, and titers of only 32 were expressed in responder mice.

Although susceptibility of cutaneous leishmaniasis in mice appears to be under genetic control, the factors responsible for the observed differences are not yet known. One factor being explored is macrophage-parasite interaction. Indeed, activated mouse, but not guinea pig, macrophages destroyed *L. enriettii* in vitro [34], macrophages from guinea pigs recovered from *L. enriettii* infection phagocytosed increased numbers of *L. enriettii* but not *L. braziliensis* or *L. donovani* [23], and *L. enriettii* was found to grow better in guinea pig than in rat macrophages [32].

Evidence that macrophage-lymphocyte interactions may be important in the genetic basis of susceptibility to *L. tropica* comes from a recent study by Handman et al. [43a]. Macrophages from susceptible BALB/c mice were infected with promastigotes in vitro and then incubated with crude soluble parasite antigen. It was found that these macrophages were not as effective in transferring sensitivity to parasite antigen to syngeneic recipients as were uninfected BALB/c macrophages. Further, infected and uninfected macrophages from resistant CBA mice treated in a similar manner were able to transfer sensitivity effectively.

Several studies of human cutaneous leishmaniasis have been designed to examine interactions between macrophages and parasites in vitro. It has generally been observed that promastigotes enter macrophages flagellar end first. The process is considered to involve phagocytosis by the macrophage rather than active penetration by the parasite. Alexander [44] found that monolayers of mouse macrophages cultured in the presence of cytochalasin B to inhibit phagocytosis did not become infected following the addition of *L. mexicana* promastigotes. Merino et al. [45] infected macrophages in vitro with *L. braziliensis*. They postulated an active role by the parasite for initiation of contact between the flagellum and the macrophage surface. The actual entry of *L. braziliensis* into mouse peritoneal macrophages was reported to involve endocytosis. Ardehali and Khoubyar [46] infected mouse peritoneal macrophages with *L. tropica, L. donovani,* or *L. enriettii.* They reported that *L. donovani* and *L. enriettii* were taken up by the macrophages in significantly greater numbers than were *L. tropica*. This finding was somewhat surprising since *L. enriettii* is a guinea pig parasite and *L. tropica* was infective for outbred mice used in the study.

Farah et al. [31] infected peritoneal macrophages from mice or guinea pigs with *L. tropica* and observed parasite multiplication in both cell types. When macrophages were preincubated with anti-*Leishmania* sera of human or rabbit origin, intracellular parasitism was reportedly reduced. It was demonstrated that parasitized macrophages had a higher affinity for anti-*Leishmania* antibody than did normal macrophages, and it was postulated that cytophilic antibody was responsible for inhibition of parasite entry into the host cells.

Not much information is available concerning the intracellular fate of the agents of cutaneous leishmaniasis. Alexander and Vickerman [47] infected macrophages with *L. mexicana.* They observed that parasitophorous vacuoles fused with secondary lysosomes, but that intracellular division of the parasite proceeded. In another study peritoneal macrophages from mice which had recovered from *L. tropica* infection permitted significantly less intracellular growth following in vitro infection with *L. tropica* than did macrophages from normal mice [48].

Both specific and nonspecific immunosuppression may occur during cutaneous leishmaniasis infections. Arrendondo and Pérez [49] reported decreased responses to certain T and B lymphocyte mitogens and to sheep erythrocytes in vitro during the latter stages of *L. mexicana* infection in susceptible BALB/c mice. These animals developed chronic metastisizing infections. Sharma et al. [50] reported suppression of lymphocyte blastogenic responses to PHA-M and to heterologous antigens by whole or fractionated *L. tropica.* There have been indications that suppression of antibody production does not occur during cutaneous leishmaniasis [50a].

Evidence has been presented for the generation of suppressor cells during *L. tropica* infections in mice. Howard et al. [64] found that a parasite-specific suppression of DH responses emerged during the course of infection and that this suppression was associated with a population of T lymphocytes. Thymectomy of susceptible BALB/c mice reportedly slowed progression of the disease, as did sublethal x irradiation. Arredondo and Pérez [49] demonstrated that spleen cells from *L. mexicana*-infected BALB/c mice were capable of suppressing mitogenic responses to T and B lymphocyte mitogens of spleen cells from normal mice.

Although specific antibody may be readily detected during cutaneous leishmaniasis infections in mice, there is as of yet no conclusive evidence that the antibody is protective. The importance of cell-mediated responses in these infections is indicated by the correlation of DH responses to leishmanin with protection, increased severity of infection in athymic mice, and increased parasiticidal activity of macrophages from specifically and nonspecifically immunized mice.

III. VISCERAL LEISHMANIASIS

A. Clinical Studies

Visceral leishmaniasis presents a clinical picture much different from the cutaneous infections. It generally begins with a primary nonulcerating skin lesion which may be undetectable. Following an incubation period which may last several months, parasites may be detected in the reticuloendothelial cells of the liver, spleen, bone marrow, and lymph nodes. Parasite multiplication leads to splenomegaly, hepatomegaly, and lymphadenopathy. Early stages of infection may be characterized by fever, chills, and general malaise. Advanced cases may display degenerative changes in every major organ of the viscera. Anemia, leukopenia, and eventual monocytosis may be observed. Following treatment the symptoms may subside, but in some cases post-kala azar dermal lesions may develop.

Unlike cutaneous leishmaniasis, untreated cases of visceral leishmaniasis are often fatal [5]. When cure occurs, cell-mediated immune responses can be detected [3,13]. However, protective responses apparently do not develop during severe infections, and the mortality rate is high among untreated cases. Resistance to reinfection has been reported [6], but it is not always complete [4] as indicated by the development of post-kala azar dermal lesion in some patients. Patients with active kala azar often have no detectable DH responses to leishmanin [22].

Antibody titers, primarily IgG, rise sharply during visceral leishmaniasis, but the antibody is apparently not protective [5,19,20,51,52]. Most of the antibody produced during infection is not parasite-specific [53], but the hypergammaglobulinemia may have diagnostic value [54]. Kala azar patients generally have high antibody titers [55], but they often do not develop significant titers until after the acute phase of infection. Manson-Bahr [56] noted positive immediate skin reactions during active infections, but not DH.

Chemotherapy is often followed by decreasing antibody levels and the development of DH which corresponds to the initiation of resistance to reinfection. Cured cases of kala azar are generally leishmanin positive [57].

Veress et al. [58] reported histologic examinations of the spleen and lymph nodes in cases of fatal visceral leishmaniasis. They noted extensive fibrosis of the thymus-dependent areas, depletion of small lymphocytes, and plasma cell hyperplasia. Rezai et al. [52] noted a decrease in circulating T lymphocytes in kala azar patients. These observations may help to explain the lack of DH or protective cell-mediated immunity during visceral leishmaniasis. Lack of available T lymphocytes coupled with the presence of parasites within phagocytic cells would be likely to have an inhibitory effect on the ability of the host to mount an effective cell-mediated immune response. It has not yet been ascertained whether the lack of DH to leishmanin during infection is the result of a general or specific immunosuppression phenomenon. It has been shown that mice acutely infected with a reticulotropic strain of *Trypanosoma cruzi* have suppressed cell-mediated responses to heterologous agents [59,60].

The factors that lead to disseminated infections with *L. donovani* are not well understood. It is likely that host factors and others, such as parasite strain and inoculum size, are important in determining the course of infection. It has been recognized that a mild dermal form of *L. donovani* infection exists and is apparently quite common in some areas [61,62]. Such infections are thought to be often asymptomatic and may represent successful host responses prior to internal dissemination of the infection [63].

B. Experimental Studies

Visceral leishmaniasis in animal models have been primarily performed using *L. donovani* in mice or hamsters. The susceptibility of mice to *L. donovani* has been found to be under genetic control [11,12,63a-c]. It was found that BALB/c mice were relatively susceptible and that DBA/2, C3H/He, CBA/Ce, and A mice were relatively resistant. The susceptibility trait was found to be inherited in a Mendelian pattern and appeared to be due to the effects of a single gene or tightly linked group of genes. It is of interest that, in *L. tropica* infections, the expression of genetic susceptibility or resistance has been shown to be determined by hematopoietic bone marrow cells [50b]. Chimaeras were produced by lethally irradiating mice of susceptible and resistant strains and transferring bone marrow cells. It was found that susceptibility patterns in recipient mice were determined by that of the cell donors. Therefore the hematopoietic cells and not other physiological factors appear to determine susceptibility to *L. tropica* in mice, and the same may be true of *L. donovani* infections.

Resistance to *L. donovani* in mice has been shown to be thymus-dependent [65-68]. Skov and Twohy [67] reconstituted T-cell-depleted mice with either lymph node or thymus cells and tested these and unreconstituted animals for their ability to develop resistance to *L. donovani*. Pretreatment of the cells with azothioprine or anti-Thy-1 serum countered the restorative effects. Peritoneal macrophages from mice with long-term infections were able to inhibit intracellular multiplication of the parasite. However, these inhibitory effects were not seen in macrophages from mice in which the T-cell populations had been suppressed. Therefore, evidence for T-cell dependence of parasite destruction by macrophages was presented. However, Schmuñis and Herman [69] reported that macrophages from thymectomized BALB/c mice did not differ from those from normal mice in their ability to phagocytize *L. donovani*. It is difficult to draw definite conclusions from these studies concerning the nature of T-cell dependence by macrophages for intracellular killing. Neither study included definitive evidence for the absence of T-cell function, and the methods of T-cell depression were probably differentially effective.

Congenitally athymic mice were shown to be more susceptible to *L. donovani* than were their thymic littermates [68]. The increased susceptibility was directly correlated with decreased immediate and delayed hypersensitivity to parasite antigen, both of which were absent in athymic mice.

The presence of immediate hypersensitivity responses in infected mice indicates the presence of specific antibody. Mice with chronic *L. donovani* infections developed direct agglutinating antibody, the production of which was suppressed by cyclophosphamide (CY) treatment [70]. The presence of protective antibody was suggested by the observation that CY-treated mice developed increased parasite burdens. However "hyperimmune serum" (titer unknown) was unable to reverse the immunosuppressive effects of CY. The authors discussed the possibility that T-lymphocyte depression was responsible for the increased parasite burden observed following CY administration. However, CY may cause a transient increase in DH responses if administered before antigenic stimulation [71,72]. Indeed, Herman and Farrel [70] reported a decrease in parasite burdens in mice challenged 1 day after CY administration. Smrkovski et al. [73] also noted an inhibition of resistance to *L. donovani* following CY treatment. Mice pretreated with two doses of BCG had significantly lower parasite burdens of the liver and spleen than did untreated infected mice. Administration of cortisone or CY to the BCG-immunized mice resulted in abrogation of the protective effects. It was noted that mice challenged with amastigotes of *L. donovani* developed both immediate and delayed hypersensitivity responses to leishmanin during the course of infection. Dwyer [74] observed the effects of specific antibody on amastigotes and promastigotes of *L. donovani* in vitro. He noted differential capping patterns between the two parasite forms. It was found that amastigotes and promastigotes possessed common or cross-reacting membrane antigens as well as unique stage-specific antigens.

With regard to the uncertainty for a definitive role of specific antibody during leishmanial infections, it is interesting to note that normal sera from several species have been found to have lytic and agglutinating activity on *Leishmania* promastigotes [74a,30]. Pearson and Steigbigel [74b] reported that complement activation by the classical pathway appeared to be responsible for the lysis of *L. donovani* promastigotes by normal human sera.

Interactions between macrophages and *L. donovani* have been extensively studied in an effort to determine the role of the macrophage in immunity to visceral leishmaniasis and how parasites can survive intracellularly within phagocytic cells. Peritoneal macrophages from mice previously infected with *L. donovani* inhibited intracellular multiplication of *L. donovani* in vitro [75]. These findings are quite different from those discussed previously concerning survival of *L. enriettii* in guinea pig macrophages.

As has been observed with other *Leishmania* species, entry of *L. donovani* into macrophages is accomplished via phagocytosis, and uptake has been observed to occur anterior end or posterior end first [75-77]. Phagolysosome formation occurs following ingestion. The parasites appear to be capable of surviving and even multiplying within phagolysosomes. Thus, resistance to lysosomal enzymes, or the ability to alter the effects of lysosomal enzymes, appears to be an important survival mechanism of *L. donovani*. This phenomenon has been observed both in hamster [78] and in human [79] macrophages.

It is apparent from clinical and experimental studies that cellular immune responses are essential for the development of resistance to visceral leishmaniasis. As of yet little is known about the mechanisms of acquired resistance, although it appears that macrophages may be activated to limit intracellular growth of *L. donovani*. Macrophage activation is a characteristic feature of BCG immunization and may play a key role in the nonspecific resistance against *L. donovani* produced by BCG. There is evidence for the importance of T lymphocytes in the mediation of resistance to *L. donovani,* but by which of their functions (helper or cytotoxic) their effects are exerted remains to be seen. It is likely that observed genetic differences in susceptibility may be manifested by differential effectiveness of cell-mediated responses. Specific antibody is produced during visceral leishmaniasis but is not well correlated with protection or the development of acquired resistance. There is evidence that cell-bound antibody may be involved in limiting intracellular infection.

IV. IMMUNIZATION AND CROSS-REACTIVITY

From examples of successful immunization attempts it is apparent that individuals may be protected against cutaneous leishmaniasis [80-82]. Because cutaneous leishmaniasis most often proceeds as a self-limiting lesion, it has proven desirable to administer live organisms at a chosen site to avoid future disfigurement [83]. Kojevnikov [84] used *L. tropica major* (*L. major*) promastigotes to immunize against the homologous strain or against *L. tropica minor* (*L. tropica*). However, it was reported that *L. tropica minor* did not confer protection against the more virulent *L. tropica major* [6,55]. There is generally considered to be no cross-immunity between visceral leishmaniasis and the cutaneous forms. Manson-Bahr [56] used a dermatotropic strain of *L. donovani* to immunize volunteers against kala azar, but the method could not be successfully applied on a large scale [85].

Lainson and Bray [86] reported successful immunization of rhesus monkeys against *L. braziliensis* by prior inoculation with *L. mexicana,* although these results have recently been disputed [1]. Lainson and Shaw [87], using only two volunteers, reported that recovery from infection with *L. m. mexicana* by one of the individuals led to immunity against infection with the same parasite but not against infection with *L. b. panamensis.* The other volunteer had reportedly recovered from an infection with *L. b. panamensis* and was shown to be resistant to *L. mexicana.* A recent field study in Brazil [82] involved the use of killed promastigotes of an unidentified species of *Leishmania* from five different Brazilian isolates. Immunization reportedly produced a high percentage of leishmanin positivity, and no new cases of cutaneous or mucocutaneous leishmaniasis arose among the immunized persons during a subsequent 3-year observation period. The authors recognized the possibility of other factors involved in the absence of new cases of leishmaniasis and based the reported efficiency of the immunizing procedure on increases in DH to leishmanin. There are few other reports of immunizing against *Leishmania* with killed preparations, but Preston and Dumonde [88] reported immunizing guinea pigs with a ribsosomal antigen of *L. enriettii.*

In view of the observation that positive DH to leishmanin may occur in persons who have not knowingly experienced leishmaniasis, Edrissian et al. [89] suggested the possibility of sensitization of humans with lizard strains of *Leishmania.* However, cross-immunity between lizard and human strains was not observed experimentally. Southgate [90] suggested that individuals immune to kala azar may have been exposed to *L. alderi,* a parasite of lizards.

Complement-fixing antibodies from kala azar patients have been detected by antigens prepared from *Mycobacterium* [91-94], indicating cross-reactivity between antigens of *Leishmania* and *Mycobacterium.* Smrkovski and Larson [95] detected such cross-reactivity in mice. Mice infected with BCG or *L. donovani* had positive DH reactions to antigens from each of the two organisms and guinea pigs infected with BCG or sensitized with leishmanial antigen prepared from amastigotes displayed DH to antigen from either organism. Similarly, guinea pigs immunized with Freund's complete adjuvant alone had positive DH responses to soluble antigens of *L. enriettii* [23]. BCG was found to have both prophylactic and therapeutic effects against *L. donovani* infections in mice [96]. Intravenous administration of BCG before or after infection with *L. donovani* led to reduced parasite burdens in BALB/c mice. Weintraub and Weinbaum [43] reported that intravenous administration of BCG to BALB/c mice prior to infection with *L. tropica* was protective. Immunized mice had less severe cutaneous lesions, no evidence of visceralization, and decreased mortalities. The authors considered the possibility of the existence of shared antigens between *Mycobacterium* and *Leishmania*. They looked for, but did not detect, *Leishmania* antibodies in the sera of mice immunized with BCG alone. Specific antibodies were present in the sera of mice which received only *L. tropica*. Goble et al. [97] reported that mice previously infected with *L. donovani* had increased resistance to *M. tuberculosis,* and vice versa.

V. CONCLUSIONS

Most of the immunological information available concerning human cutaneous leishmaniasis is based either on studies with infections in guinea pigs, which involve a natural host-parasite relationship, or on studies of mice infected with human parasites. Both models have proven useful and should be pursued to yield more information. It appears that basic response differences exist between the mouse and guinea pig models. Perhaps most noticeable is the specific antibody detected during mouse infections. In this respect, perhaps the guinea pig *L. enriettii* system more closely resembles the clinical situation. It is unfortunate that relatively little use has been made of this model for immunological studies during recent years. It would be of interest to look for host serum components on the surface of *Leishmania* from cutaneous lesions. It may be that *L. enriettii* and some of the agents of human leishmaniasis have means of masking surface antigens to escape detection while in their guinea or human hosts, and that specific antibody is more easily detected in infected mice due to the lack of parasite adaptations in these hosts.

Factors responsible for the induction of resistance to leishmaniasis need clarification. It is evident that DH to leishmanin generally accompanies resistance to reinfection, but the situation is somewhat complicated. A primary lesion may resolve even though secondary lesions may develop elsewhere. Cellular interactions involved in localized parasite destruction have not been clearly defined. Macrophages may apparently become activated to more effectively destroy *Leishmania* in certain host-parasite systems but not in others. Nonspecific activation of macrophages may be an important part of the increased resistance produced by BC6. It is evident that acquired resistance to *Leishmania* is T-cell dependent, although a more thorough elucidation of how T cells mediate their effects is needed.

Perhaps the most exciting possibilities for further investigation are those which involve macrophage-parasite and macrophage-lymphocyte interactions. The predilection of the *Leishmania* for macrophages and their adaptation for intracellular survival provide an excellent model for basic immunological studies.

It has been indicated that *Leishmania* are able to resist intracellular destruction within macrophages of a natural host or, as with *L. donovani* in hamsters, of a host in which natural infection is roughly paralleled. It is not known by what mechanism(s) this resistance occurs. That the phenomenon is somewhat specific is indicated by studies demonstrating differential survival capacities of a single *Leishmania* species within macrophages from different hosts. Inherent differences in the host cell-parasite interactions remain to be explored. Does the parasite possibly have a mechanism whereby it counters destructive effects only in cells of certain hosts? Perhaps intraspecies patterns of susceptibility are reflected at least in part by inherited differences in the ability of macrophages to inhibit intracellular growth of the parasite.

There are differential clinical courses of *Leishmania* infections apparently depending on host immune responses. In some respects the situation is similar to that occurring with human leprosy. The relative ease with which *Leishmania* are grown may facilitate studies of basic phenomena associated with cell-mediated immunity, including the defects thereof. Further characterization of the immune responses of man to *Leishmania* infection are needed. These responses range from negligible to very strong. It has not yet been ascertained whether or not parasite factors, such as antigen type or amount, may contribute to the type of response evoked.

There is very little information regarding the production of specific protective responses with killed parasites or subcellular parasite fractions. Antigenic analysis of the *Leishmania* of humans may reveal common antigens between some of the "species" and "strains." In view of the rapid progress being made in recombinant DNA research, the mass production of specific parasite antigens by bacteria carrying a section of parasite genome may be possible. Studies are needed to characterize antigens and isolate genetic regions which code for them. Such antigens may also be used to increase the specificity of diagnostic tests and further clarify the classification of the *Leishmania*. Hybridoma-derived antibody may also serve as an appropriately specific ligand in these types of studies.

There is evidence that Leishmania infections may be accompanied by suppressed immune responses to heterologous antigens. Suppression of antibody responses to ovalbumin was observed in hamsters infected with *L. donovani*, although total gammaglobulin levels were elevated in these animals [53]. Suppression of immune responses has been observed during the course of other protozoal diseases as well. The mechanisms of immunosuppression associated with visceral leishmaniasis remain to be determined. Perhaps suppressed immune responses will be associated with visceral leishmaniasis; in these patients a condition of anergy appears to exist as indicated by uncontrolled parasite proliferation.

The genetic control of susceptibility to agents of visceral leishmaniasis has been established using a mouse model, and from recent studies it appears that genetic factors are important in cutaneous infections. Studies are needed to evaluate aspects of the genetic status of leishmaniasis patients which may lead to the establishment of a model of genetically influenced susceptibility to an infectious disease in humans.

REFERENCES

1. Zuckerman, A., and R. Lainson (1977). Leishmania. In *Parasitic Protozoa*, Vol. I (J. P. Kreier, Ed.). Academic Press, New York, pp. 98-112.
1a. Williams, P., and M. d. V. Coelho (1978). Taxonomy and transmission of *Leishmania*. In *Advances in Parasitology* (W. H. R. Lumsden, R. Muller, and J. R. Baker, Eds.). Academic Press, New York.
2. Zuckerman, A. (1975). Current status of the immunology of blood and tissue protozoa. I. Leishmania. *Exp. Parasitol. 38:*370-400.
3. Preston, P. M., and D. C. Dumonde (1976). Immunology of clinical and experimental leishmaniasis. In *Immunology of Parasitic Infections* (S. Cohen and E. H. Sadun, Eds.). Blackwell Scientific Publishers, Oxford, pp. 167-202.
4. Guirges, S. Y. (1971). Natural and experimental re-infection of man with Oriental Sore. *Ann. Trop. Med. Parasitol. 65:*197-205.
5. Turk, J. L., and A. D. M. Bryceson (1971). Immunological phenomena in leprosy and related diseases. *Adv. Immunol. 13:*209-266.
6. Manson-Bahr, P. E. C. (1964). Variations in the clinical manifestations of leishmaniasis caused by *Leishmania tropica. J. Trop. Med. Hyg. 67:* 85-87.
7. Convit, J., M. E. Pinardi, and A. J. Rondón (1972). Diffuse cutaneous leishmaniasis: A disease due to an immunological defect of the host. *Trans. R. Soc. Trop. Med. Hyg. 66:*603-610
8. Bryceson, A. D. M. (1970). Diffuse cutaneous leishmaniasis in Ethiopia. Immunological studies. *Trans. R. Soc. Trop. Med. Hyg. 64:*380-387.
9. Dumonde, D. C. (1973). In *Parasitic Protozoa*, Vol. I, (J. P. Kreier, Ed.). Academic Press, New York, p. 100.
10. Pérez, H., B. Arrendondo, and M. González (1978). Comparative study of American cutaneous leishmaniasis and diffuse cutaneous leishmaniasis in two strains of inbred mice. *Infect. Immun. 22:*301-307.
11. Bradley, D. J., and J. Kirkley (1972). Variation in susceptibility of mouse strains to *Leishmania donovani* infection. *Trans. R. Soc. Trop. Med. Hyg. 66:*527-528.
12. Bradley, D. J. (1974). Genetic control of natural resistance to *Leishmania donovani. Nature (Lond.) 250:*353-354.
13. Adler, S. (1964). Leishmania. In *Parasitology*, Vol. 2 (B. Dawes, Ed.). Academic Press, New York, p. 35.
14. Bryceson, A. D. M. (1970). Immunological aspects of clinical leishmaniasis. *Proc. R. Soc. Med. 63:*1056.
15. Tremonti, L., and B. C. Walton (1970). Blast transformation and migration-inhibition in toxoplasomosis and leishmaniasis. *Am. J. Trop. Med. Hyg. 19:*49-56.

16. Wyler, D. J., F. I. Weinbaum, and H. R. Herrod (1979). Characterization of in vitro proliferative responses of human lymphocytes to leishmanial antigens. *J. Infect. Dis. 140:*215-221.

17. Adler, S., and D. Nelken (1965). Attempts to transfer delayed hypersensitivity to *Leishmania tropica* by leucocytes and whole blood. *Trans. R. Soc. Trop. Med. Hyg. 59:*59-63.

18. Bray, R. S., and R. Lainson (1965). Failure to transfer hypersensitivity to *Leishmania* by injection of leukocytes. *Trans. R. Soc. Med. Hyg. 59:* 221-222.

19. Bray, R. S., and R. Lainson (1967). Studies on the immunology and serology of leishmaniasis. V. The use of particles as vehicles in passive agglutination tests. *Trans. R. Soc. Trop. Med. Hyg. 61:*490-505.

20. Bray, R. S. (1972). Leishmaniasis in the old world. *Br. Med. Bull. 28:*39-43.

21. Menzel, S., and U. Bienzle (1978). Antibody responses in patients with cutaneous leishmaniasis of the Old World. *Z. Tropenmed. Parasitol. 29:* 194-197.

22. Maekelt, G. A. (1972). Immune response to intracellular parasites. I. Leishmania. In *Immunity to Animal Parasites,* (E. J. L. Soulsby, Ed.). Academic Press, New York, pp. 352-356.

23. Bryceson, A. D. M., R. S. Bray, R. A. Wolstencroft, and D. C. Dumonde (1970). Immunity of cutaneous leishmaniasis in the guinea-pig. *Clin. Exp. Immunol. 7:*301-341.

24. Poulter, L. W. (1979). The kinetics and quality of acquired resistance in self-healing and metastatic leishmaniasis. *Clin. Exp. Immunol. 36:*30-37.

25. Lemma, A., and P. Yau (1973). Course of development of *Leishmania enriettii* infection in immunodepressed guinea pigs. *Am. J. Trop. Med. Hyg. 22:*477-481.

26. Blewett, T. M., D. M. H. Kadivar, and E. J. L. Soulsby (1971). Cutaneous leishmaniasis in the guinea pig. Delayed-type hypersensitivity, lymphocyte stimulation, and inhibition of macrophage migration. *Am. J. Trop. Med. Hyg. 20:*546-551.

27. Weissberger, H., D. T. Spira, and A. Zuckerman (1973). Delayed hypersensitivity to various leishmania antigens in guinea pigs infected with *Leishmania enriettii. J. Protozool. 20*(Suppl.):534-535.

28. Bryceson, A. D. M., and J. L. Turk (1971). The effect of prolonged treatment with antilymphocyte serum on the course of infections with BCG and *Leishmania enriettii* in the guinea-pig. *J. Pathol. 104:*153-165.

29. Bryceson, A. D. M., P. Preston, R. S. Bray, and D. C. Dumonde (1972). Experimental cutaneous leishmaniasis. II. Effects of immunosuppression and antigenic competition on the course of infection with *Leishmania enriettii* in the guinea-pig. *Clin. Exp. Immunol. 10:*305-335.

30. Behin, R., J. Mauel, and D. S. Rowe (1977). Mechanisms of protective immunity in experimental cutaneous leishmaniasis of the guinea-pig. III. Inhibition of leishmanial lesions in the guinea-pig by delayed hypersensitivity reaction to unrelated antigens. *Clin. Exp. Immunol. 29:*320-325.

31. Farah, F. S., S. A. Samra, and N. Nuwayri-Salti (1975). The role of the macrophage in cutaneous leishmaniasis. *Immunology 29:*755-764.

32. Bray, R. S., and A. D. M. Bryceson (1968). Cutaneous leishmaniasis of the guinea pig. Action of sensitised lymphocytes on infected macrophages. *Lancet ii:*898-899.

33. Mauel, J., R. Behin,   Biroum-Noerjasin, and D. S. Rowe (1975). Mechanisms of protective immunity in experimental cutaneous leishmaniasis of the guinea-pig. I. Lack of effects of immune lymphocytes and of activated macrophages. *Clin. Exp. Immunol. 20:*339-350.

34. Behin, R., J. Mauel,   Biroum-Noerjasin, and D. S. Rowe (1975). Mechanisms of protective immunity in experimental cutaneous leishmaniasis of the guinea-pig. II. Selective destruction of different *Leishmania* species in activated guinea-pig and mouse macrophages. *Clin. Exp. Immunol. 20:* 351-358.

35. Doyle, J. J., R. Behin, J. Mauel, and D. S. Rowe (1974). Antibody-induced movement of membrane components of *Leishmania enriettii*. *J. Exp. Med. 139:*1061-1069.

36. Kretschmar, W. von (1965). Immunitat bei der *Leishmania enriettii* Infektion des Meerschweinschens. *Z. Tropenmed. Parasitol. 16:*277-283.

37. Poulter, L. W. (1980). Mechanisms of immunity to leishmaniasis. I. Evidence for a changing basis of protection in self-limiting disease. *Clin. Exp. Immunol. 39:*14-26.

37a. Belehu, A., L. W. Poulter, and J. L. Turk (1976). Modification of cutaneous leishmaniasis in the guinea pig by cyclophosphamide. *Clin. Exp. Immunol. 24:*125-132.

38. Preston, P. M., R. L. Carter, E. Leuchars, A. J. S. Davies, and D. C. Dumonde (1972). Experimental cutaneous leishmaniasis. III. Effects of thymectomy on the course of infection of CBA mice with *Leishmania tropica*. *Clin. Exp. Immunol. 10:*337-357.

39. Alexander, J., and R. S. Phillips (1978). *Leishmania tropica* and *Leishmania mexicana:* Cross immunity in mice. *Exp. Parasitol. 45:*93-100.

40. Behin, R., J. Mauel, and S. Sordat (1979). *Leishmania tropica:* Pathogenicity and in vitro macrophage function in strains of inbred mice. *Exp. Parasitol. 48:*81-91.

40a. Alexander, J., and R. S. Phillips (1980). *Leishmania mexicana* and *Leishmania tropica major:* Adoptive transfer of immunity in mice. *Exp. Parasitol. 49:*34-40.

41. Pérez, H., F. Labrador, and J. W. Torrealba (1979). Variations in the response of five strains of mice to *Leishmania mexicana*. *Int. J. Parasitol. 9:*27-32.

42. Nasseri, M., and F. Z. Modabber (1979). Generalized infection and lack of delayed hypersensitivity in BALB/C mice infected with *Leishmania tropica major*. *Inf. Immun. 26:*611-614.

43. Weintraub, J., and F. I. Weinbaum (1977). The effect of BCG on experimental cutaneous leishmaniasis in mice. *J. Immunol. 118:*2288-2290.

43a. Handman, E., R. Ceredig, and G. F. Mitchell (1979). Murine cutaneous leishmaniasis: Disease patterns in intact and nude mice of various genotypes and examination of some differences between normal and infected macrophages. *Aust. J. Exp. Biol. Med. Sci. 57:*9-29.

44. Alexander, J. (1975). Effect of the antiphagocytic agent cytochalasin B on macrophage invasion by *Leishmania mexicana* promastigotes and *Trypanosoma cruzi* epimastigotes. *J. Protozool. 22:*237-240.

45. Merino, F., E. Ajjam, A. Hernández, K. Dawidowicz, and E. J. Merino (1977). In vitro infection of murine macrophages by *Leishmania brasiliensis*. Mechanism of penetration. *Int. Arch. Allergy Appl. Immunol. 55:*487-495.

46. Ardehali, S. M., and K. Khoubyar (1978). Uptake of different *Leishmania* by mouse peritoneal exudate cells. *Trans. R. Soc. Trop. Med. Hyg. 72:*645-646.

47. Alexander, J., and K. Vickerman (1975). Fusion of host cell secondary lysosomes with the parasitophorous vacuoles of *Leishmania mexicana*-infected macrophages. *J. Protozool. 22:*502-508.

48. Handman, E., and D. T. Spira (1977). Growth of *Leishmania* amastigotes in macrophages from normal and immune mice. *Z. Parasitenkol. 53:*75-81.

49. Arredondo, B., and H. Pérez (1979). Alterations of the immune response associated with chronic experimental leishmaniasis. *Inf. Immun. 25:*16-22.

50. Sharma, M. K., F. Anaraki, and F. Ala (1978). In vitro suppression of lymphocyte blastogenic response to mitogen and antigen by *Leishmania tropica*. *Clin. Exp. Immunol. 32:*477-483.

50a. Weintraub, J., and F. I. Weinbaum (1976). Absence of suppression of humoral immunity in the pathogenesis of experimental cutaneous leishmaniasis in mice. *Fed. Proc. 35:*738.

50b. Howard, J. G., C. Hale, and F. Y. Liew (1980). Genetically determined susceptibility to *Leishmania tropica* infection is expressed by haematopoietic donor cells in mouse radiation chimeras. *Nature 288:*161-162.

51. Manson-Bahr, P. E. C. (1971). Leishmaniasis. *Int. Rev. Trop. Med. 4:* 123-140.

52. Rezai, H. R., S. M. Ardehali, G. Amirhakimi, and A. Kharazmi (1978). Immunological features of kala azar. *Am. J. Trop. Med. Hyg. 27:*1079-1083.

53. Clinton, B. A., L. A. Stauber, and N. C. Palczuk (1969). *Leishmania donovani:* Antibody response to chicken ovalbumin by infected golden hamsters. *Exp. Parasitol. 25:*171-180.

54. Sen Gupta, P. C. (1969). Immunodiagnosis of kala azar. *Trans. R. Soc. Trop. Med. Hyg. 63:*146-147.

55. Heyneman, D. (1971). Immunology of *Leishmania*. *Bull. WHO 44:*499-514.

56. Manson-Bahr, P. E. C. (1961). Immunity in kala-azar. *Trans. R. Soc. Trop. Med. Hyg. 55:*550-555.

57. Manson-Bahr, P. E. C. (1961b). The leishmanin test and immunity in kala azar. *East Afr. Med. J. 38:*165-167.

58. Veress, B., A. Omer, A. A. Satir, and A. M. El Hassan (1977). Morphology of the spleen and lymph nodes in fatal visceral leishmaniasis. *Immunology 33:*605-610.

59. Reed, S. G., C. L. Larson, and C. A. Speer (1977). Suppression of cell-mediated immunity in experimental Chagas' disease. *Z. Parasitenkd. 52:* 11-17.

60. Reed, S. G., C. L. Larson, and C. A. Speer (1978). Contact sensitivity responses in mice infected with *Trypanosoma cruzi. Inf. Immun. 22:*548-554.

61. Hoogstraal, H., and D. Heyneman (1969a). Leishmaniasis in the Sudan Republic. III. *Leishmania* species in the Paloish-Malakal area. *Am. J. Trop. Med. Hyg. 18:*1133-1153.

62. Hoogstraal, H., and D. Heyneman (1969b). Leishmaniasis in the Sudan Republic. V. Infections in man with Sudanese kala azar. *Am. J. Trop. Med. Hyg. 18:*1170-1182.

63. Garnham, P. C. C., and J. H. Humphrey (1969). Problems in leishmaniasis related to immunology. *Curr. Top. Microbiol. Immunol. 48:*20-42.

63a. Bradley, D. J., B. A. Taylor, J. Blackwell, E. P. Evans, and J. Freeman (1979). Regulation of *Leishmania* populations within the host. III. Mapping of the locus controlling susceptibility to visceral leishmaniasis in the mouse. *Clin. Exp. Immunol. 37:*7-14.

63b. Blackwell, J., J. Freeman, and D. Bradley (1980). Influence of H-2 complex on acquired resistance to *Leishmania donovani* infection in mice. *Nature 283:*72-74.

63c. O'Brien, A. D., D. L. Rosenstreich, and B. A. Taylor (1980). Control of natural resistance to *Salmonella typhimurium* and *Leishmania donovani* in mice by closely linked but distinct genetic loci. *Nature 287:*440-442.

64. Howard, J. G., C. Hale, and F. Y. Liew (1980). Immunological regulation of experimental cutaneous leishmaniasis. III. Nature and significance of specific suppression of cell-mediated immunity in mice highly susceptible to *Leishmania tropica. J. Exp. Med. 152:*594-607.

65. Bradley, D. J. (1971). Inhibition of *Leishmania donovani* reproduction during chronic infections in mice. *Trans. R. Soc. Trop. Med. Hyg. 65:*17-18.

66. Skov, C. B., and D. W. Twohy (1974a). Cellular immunity to *Leishmania donovani.* Effect of T-cell depression on resistance to *L. donovani* in mice. *J. Immunol. 113:*2004-2011.

67. Skov, C. B., and D. W. Twohy (1974b). Cellular immunity to *Leishmania donovani.* II. Evidence for synergy between thymocytes and lymph node cells in reconstitution of acquired resistance to *L. donovani* in mice. *J. Immunol. 113:*2012-2019.

68. Smrkovski, L. L., C. L. Larson, and S. Reed (1979). Effect of visceral leishmaniasis on congenitally athymic mice. *Inf. Immun. 25:*1078-1080.

69. Schmuñis, G. A., and R. Herman (1971). Macrophage activity of thymectomized mice infected with *Leishmania donovani. Experientia 27:*602-604.

70. Herman, R., and J. P. Farrell (1977). Effects of cyclophosphamide on visceral leishmaniasis in the mouse. *J. Protozool. 24:*429-436.

71. Lagrange, P. H., G. B. Mackaness, and T. E. Miller (1974). Potentiation of T-cell mediated immunity by selective suppression of antibody formation with cyclophosphamide. *J. Exp. Med. 139:*1529-1539.

72. Turk, J. L., D. Parker, and L. W. Poulter (1972). Functional aspects of the selective depletion of lymphoid tissue by cyclophosphamide. *Immunology 23:*493-501.

73. Smrkovski, L. L., S. G. Reed, and C. L. Larson (1980). Effect of cortisone and cyclophosphamide on the immunological role of BCG in Balb/c mice challenged with *Leishmania donovani. Am. J. Trop. Med. Hyg. 29:*16-20.

74. Dwyer, D. M. (1976). Antibody-induced modulation of *Leishmania donovani* surface membrane antigens. *J. Immunol. 117:*2081-2091.

74a. Schmuñis, G. A., and R. Herman (1970). Characteristics of so-called natural antibodies in various normal sera against culture forms of *Leishmania. J. Parasitol. 56:*889.

74b. Pearson, R. D., and R. T. Steigbigel (1980). Mechanism of lethal effect of human serum upon *Leishmania donovani. J. Immunol. 125:*2195-2201.

75. Miller, H. C., and D. W. Twohy (1969). Cellular immunity to *Leishmania donovani* in macrophages in culture. *J. Parasitol. 55:*200-207.

76. Akiyama, H. J., and R. D. Haight (1971). Interaction of *Leishmania donovani* and hamster peritoneal macrophages: A phase-contrast microscope study. *Am. J. Trop. Med. Hyg. 20:*539-545.

77. Chang, K. P., and D. M. Dwyer (1978). *Leishmania donovani.* Hamster macrophage interactions in vitro: Cell entry, intracellular survival, and multiplication of amastigotes. *J. Exp. Med. 147:*515-530.

78. Chang, K. P., and D. M. Dwyer (1976). Multiplication of a human parasite (*Leishmania donovani*) in phagolysosomes of hamster macrophages in vitro. *Science 193:*678-680.

79. Berman, J. D., D. M. Dwyer, and D. J. Wyler (1979). Multiplication of *Leishmania* in human macrophages in vitro. *Inf. Immun. 26:*375-379.

80. Gunders, A. E., L. Naggan, and D. Michaeli (1972). Follow-up study of a vaccination programme against cutaneous leishmaniasis. I. Vaccination with a five-year-old human strain of *L. tropica* from the Negev. *Trans. R. Soc. Trop. Med. Hyg. 66:*235-238.

81. Naggan, L., A. E. Gunders, and D. Michaeli (1972). Follow-up of a vaccination programme against cutaneous leishmaniasis. II. Vaccination with a recently isolated strain of *L. tropica* from Jericho. *Trans. R. Soc. Trop. Med. Hyg. 66:*239-243.

82. Mayrink, W., C. A. da Costa, P. A. Magalhães, M. N. Melo, M. Dias, A. Oliveira Lima, M. S. Michalick, and P. Williams (1979). A field trial of a vaccine against American dermal leishmaniasis. *Trans. R. Soc. Trop. Med. Hyg. 73:*385-387.

83. Manson-Bahr, P. E. C. (1963). Active immunization in leishmaniasis. In *Immunity to Protozoa,* (P. C. C. Garnham, A. E. Pierce, and I. Roitt, Eds.). Blackwell Scientific Publishers, Oxford, p. 246.

84. Kojevnikov, P. V. (1961). Some results of the works of Soviet scholars in

314   Reed

the study of cutaneous leishmaniasis. *Dermatologica (Basel) 123:* 341-356.

85. Manson-Bahr, P. E. C., and B. A. Southgate (1964). Recent research on kala azar in East Africa. *J. Trop. Med. Hyg. 67:*79-84.

86. Lainson, R., and R. S. Bray (1966). Studies on the immunology and serology of leishmaniasis. II. Cross-immunity experiments among different forms of American cutaneous leishmaniasis in monkeys. *Trans. R. Soc. Trop. Med. Hyg. 60:*526-531.

87. Lainson, R., and J. J. Shaw (1966). Studies on the immunology and serology of leishmaniasis. III. On the cross-immunity between Panamanian cutaneous leishmaniasis and *Leishmania mexicana* infections in man. *Trans. R. Soc. Trop. Med. Hyg. 60:*533-535.

88. Preston, P. M., and D. C. Dumonde (1971). Immunogenicity of a ribosomal antigen of *Leishmania enriettii. Trans. R. Soc. Trop. Med. Hyg. 65:* 18-19.

89. Edrissian, G. H., A. Nadim, A. Sanati, and A. Afshar (1971). The immunological relationship between *Leishmania tropica* (major) and reptilian leishmania. *Parassitologia 13:*411-413.

90. Southgate, B. A. (1967). Studies in the epidemiology of East African leishmaniasis. V. *Leishmania adleri. J. Trop. Med. Hyg. 70:*33-36.

91. deAlencar, J. E., A. Ilardi, and S. Parpiglioni (1966). The complement-fixation reaction in the diagnosis of visceral leishmaniasis: Antigen from acid alcohol-resistant bacteria. *Parassitologia 8:*147-181.

92. Khalague, K. A. (1965). Complement-fixation test for kala-azar with an antigen prepared from acid fast bacillus. *Pakistan J. Med. Res. 4:*234-420.

93. Nussenzweig, V. (1957). Complement-fixation test for visceral leishmaniasis with *Mycobacterium tuberculosis* antigen. Technique, sensitivity, and specificity. *Hospital (Rio de Janeiro) 51:*217-226.

94. Torrealba, J. W., and J. Chaves-Torrealba (1964). BCG antigen used in the complement-fixation test for the diagnosis of kala-azar. *Rev. Inst. Med. Trop. São Paulo 6:*252-253.

95. Smrkovski, L. L., and C. L. Larson (1977a). Antigenic cross-reactivity between *Mycobacterium bovis* (BCG) and *Leishmania donovani. Inf. Immun. 18:*561-562.

96. Smrkovski, L. L., and C. L. Larson (1977b). Effect of treatment with BCG on the course of visceral leishmaniasis in Balb/c mice. *Inf. Immun. 16:*249-257.

97. Goble, F. C., E. A. Konopka, J. L. Boyd, and L. Lewis (1963). Resistance to experimental leishmaniasis and tuberculosis induced by heterologous inocula. *Proc. 7th Int. Congr. Trop. Med. Malar. 2:*238.

Index

A

Acute schistosomiasis, 28-29
African trypanosomiasis, 139, 167-
226
B cells and, 173-177, 184-189,
193-207
course of infection, 168-169
genetics of resistance, 190-192
immune complexes and, 169-173
immune responses to, 177-192
protective, 184-190
immunology of, 167-210
immunomodulation of, 192-207
immunopathology of, 169-177
immunosuppression of, 192-199
immunotherapy for, 207
macrophages and, 198-199
mechanism of suppression, 199-207
mononuclear phagocytic system
and, 171, 173, 174, 186,
198-199

[African trypanosomiasis]
parasite antigens and, 178-184
T cells and, 172-174, 176, 188-
190, 194, 196-197, 199, 203,
205, 206
variant-specific surface coat antigens
(VSSA) and, 170-173, 177-185,
188, 189, 190, 192, 194, 195,
199, 206, 207, 208
ANKA infections, 91, 92, 107, 115,
120, 121
Anthelmintic treatment, responses to,
255
Antischistosomular effector mechanisms,
schistosomules and, 12-18
eosinophils, 13-16
lethal antibodies, 13
mononuclear phagocytes, 16-18
neutrophils, 16
normal serum, 12-13
Ascaris suum, 235

B

Babesia microti, 98, 99, 102, 103
Babesia pertussis, 109
Babesia rhodhani, 103
Bacillus Calmette-Guerin (BCG), 17
    30-31, 50, 51, 207
    Leishmania infections and, 296,
        303-306
    macrophages and, 141-142
    malaria and, 103-107, 109
Breinlia sergenti, 233
Brucella abortus, 103, 195
Brugia malayi, 230, 231, 233, 234,
    235, 252, 256-259, 261,
    263, 269, 271, 273
Brugia pahangi, 230, 231, 233, 235,
    258-262, 269, 271
Brugia spp., 228, 231, 234, 235, 236,
    243, 253, 254, 255, 258-
    262, 270, 273
Brugia timori, 252, 254, 258, 259,
    260

C

Cercariae, 2-8
    antigens and, 2-3
    host-parasite relationship, 3-5
    regulation of responsiveness, 5-7
Cercarial antigenic preparation (CAP),
    4-8
Cercarial dermatitis, 3-4
Cercarien hüllen Reaktion (CHR), 3,
    4-7
Chagas' disease, 137-166
    antibody-dependent cellular cyto-
        toxicity and, 143, 147-149

[Chagas' disease]
    autoantibodies in, 152-153
    B-cell responses to, 143-144
    cell-mediated immunity in, 149-
        150
    complement role, 144-146
    cytophilic antibodies in, 146-147
    detection and destruction of in-
        fected host hells, 151-152
    host-parasite relationship in, 138-
        140
    immunology of, 137-161
    immunosuppression in, 153-158,
        159
    opsonic antibodies in, 146-147
    perspectives in, 158-161
    protective immunologic responses
        in, 140-153
    role of macrophages in, 141-142
Chronic schistosomiasis, 29-30
Circumovum precipitin test (COPT),
    38, 44
Circumsporozoite (CSP) reaction,
    110, 111
Concanavalin A (ConA), 35, 48, 49,
    154, 196, 202, 203, 247,
    262
Corynebacterium parvum, 17, 31,
    103, 106, 109, 111
Culex pipiens fatigans, 253
Cutaneous *Leishmania* infections,
    293-301
Cyclophosphamide (CY), 46, 121,
    122, 303
Cytophilic antibodies, protective
        immunologic response in
        Chagas' disease, 146-147
Cytotoxic T lymphocytes (CTL),
    18, 49, 196-197, 205

D

Deoxyribonucleic acid (DNA):
    African trypanosomiasis and, 182,
        199
    Chagas' disease and, 148
    effect of adherent cell depletion
        on, 116
    eggs of schistosomes and, 38
    Leishmania infections and, 307
Dermatitis, cercarial, 3-4
Dermatologic disease, 239-240
Diethylcarbamazine (DEC), filarial
        nematodes and, 229, 233,
        237, 240, 249, 250, 258,
        269, 270, 271, 273
    reactions to, 243-245
Diffuse cutaneous leishmaniasis (DCL),
        294, 296
Dinitrochlorobenzene (DNCB), 197,
        294, 296
Dipetalonema perstans, 237
Dipetalonema viteae, 18, 230, 255,
        262-265, 271, 273
Dipetalonemiasis, 237
Dirofilaria immitis, 233-237, 246-
        247, 255, 258, 259, 267-
        269, 271, 273
Dirofilaria repens, 267, 268, 271
Dirofilaria spp., 267, 268, 271

E

Egg antigens, soluble, 38, 44, 45, 47-
        51
    reactions to, 43-44, 45
Eggs of schistosomes, 37-52
    antibodies and, 44-45
    antigens and, 38, 43-44
    cell-mediated responses, 44-45

[Eggs of schistosomes]
    the granulomatous response, 40-42
    host-parasite relationship, 39-45
    induced granulomas, 42-43
    nonspecific immunity, 50-51
    pathogenesis of, 39-40
    regulation of responsiveness, 46-
        50
Elephantiasis, 241
Enzyme-linked immunosorbent
        assay (ELISA), 4, 5, 44
    Chagas' disease and, 148
    filarial nematodes and, 233, 247,
        273
Eosinophil chemotactic factor of
        lymphocytes (ECG-L), 44
Eosinophilic lung, tropical, 257-259
Eosinophils:
    filarial nematodes and, 229, 237
    schistosomules and, 13-16
Eosinophil stimulation promoter
        (ESP), 44, 45, 48
Erythrocytic infections:
    active immunizations against,
        108-110
    protective responses to, 88-108
        the cellular components in,
            103-108
        red blood cells and, 88, 90, 99,
            102, 105, 107, 108
        role of antibodies, 97-102
        role of T cells, 89-97
EVI antibodies, 152-153, 158-159
Exoerythrocytic (EE) development,
        110

F

Fasciola hepatica, 26
Filarial nematodes, 227-289

[Filarial nematodes]
antibodies and, 255-256
    responses, 234-235
antigens and, 232-236
B cells and, 262
biology of, 230-232
Brugia spp. infections in animals,
    259-262
cell-mediated responses to, 235-
    236
DEC and, 229, 233, 237, 240,
    249, 250, 258, 269, 270,
    271, 273
    reactions to, 243-245
dipetalonemiasis and, 237
Dirofilaria spp. infections in dogs
    and man, 267-269
eosinophils and, 229, 237
filarial infections of rodents, 262-
    267
immune responses, 236, 246-247,
    255-257
immunology of, 227-273
immunopathology of, 249-251
loiasis and, 237
lymphatic filariases of man, 252-
    257
mansonelliasis and, 237
onchocerciasis and, 237-252
    biology of, 237-238
    clinical characteristics, 239-
        241
    geographical considerations,
        241-243
    immune responses, 246-247
    immunopathology of, 249-251
    protective responses, 247-249
    reaction to DEC, 243-245
protective response to, 247-249
T cells and, 262, 272
tropical eosinophilic lung, 257-259

[Filarial nematodes]
vaccination for, 236
Filariases of men, lymphatic, 252-
    257
    lymphocyte transformation studies,
        256-257

                        G

Granulomas, induced by eggs of
    schistosomes, 42-43
Granulomatous response, eggs of
    schistosomes, 40-42
Gut-associated proteoglycan (GASP),
    27, 29, 30

                        I

IgA:
    adult worms and, 28, 29
    African trypanosomiasis and, 175
    Chagas' disease and, 143
    eggs of schistosomes and, 48
    filarial nematodes and, 246, 256
    protective responses to erythro-
        cytic infections, 97-98
    schistosomules and, 18
IgD:
    filarial nematodes and, 246
    protective responses to erythro-
        cytic infections, 98
IgE:
    adult worms and, 28, 29
    African trypanosomiasis and, 175,
        193
    eggs of schistosomes and, 48
    filarial nematodes and, 229, 237,
        246, 257-258, 259, 266,
        271, 272

[IgE]
    protective responses to erythro-
        cytic infections, 98
    schistosomules and, 17-18
IgG:
    active immunization against eryth-
        rocytic infections, 109
    adult worms and, 28, 29, 20, 34,
        36
    African trypanosomiasis and, 170,
        171, 175, 177, 183, 185, 186,
        188, 189, 193, 206, 209
    Chagas' disease and, 143, 155
    filarial nematodes and, 229, 246,
        256, 269, 271, 272
    protective responses to erythro-
        cytic infections, 96-102
    schistosomules and, 14, 15, 17,
        18, 19
IgM:
    active immunization against
        erythrocytic infections,
        109
    adult worms and, 28, 29, 30, 34
    African trypanosomiasis and,
        170, 174-177, 181, 183,
        185, 186, 189, 193, 195,
        199, 200, 201, 206
    Chagas' disease and, 143, 155
    filarial nematodes and, 246, 256,
        263, 272
    malaria and, 119
    protective responses to erythro-
        cytic infections, 96-102
    schistosomules and, 18
Immune complexes:
    circulating, 28
    role in African trypanosomiasis,
        169-173

Immunosorbent assay, enzyme-linked,
    4, 5, 44
    Chagas' disease and, 148
    filarial nematodes and, 233, 247,
        273
Immunosuppression:
    in African trypanosomiasis, 192-
        199
    antibodies and, 112-114
    in Chagas' disease, 153-158,
        159
    in malaria, 112-117
    mitogens and, 112
Intercellular substance (ICS) antigens,
    33-34
Iridiocyclitis, 241

J

Jarisch-Herxheimer reaction, 29

L

Leishmania aethiopica, 292
Leishmania alderi, 305
Leishmania braziliensis braziliensis,
    292, 295, 299, 300, 205
Leishmania braziliensis guyanesis,
    292, 299, 300, 305
Leishmania braziliensis panamensis,
    292, 299, 300, 305
Leishmania chagasi, 292
Leishmania donovani, 292, 294,
    299, 302-307
Leishmania enrietti, 295-300, 304,
    305, 306
Leishmania infantum, 292

Leishmania infections, 291-314
  agents of, 292
  antibodies and, 295, 300, 301,
    303-305
  B cells and, 295
  BCG and, 296, 303-306
  B lymphocytes and, 301
  cross-reactivity in, 304-306
  cutaneous, 293-301
  immunization for, 304-306
  immunology of, 291-308
  mucocutaneous, 293-301
  T lymphocytes and, 295, 297,
    298, 300-301, 302, 304
  visceral, 301-304
Leishmania mexicana amazonesis,
    292, 295, 298-301, 305
Leishmania mexicana mexicana,
    292, 295, 298-301, 305
Leishmania mexicana pifanoi,
    292, 295, 298-301, 305
Leishmania peruviana, 292
Leishmania tropica, 292, 294, 295,
    298-300, 306
Leishmania tropica major, 292, 305,
    306
Leishmania tropica minor, 305, 306
Leishmanin, 293
Listeria monocytogenes, 297
Litomosoides carinii, 228, 233, 265-
    267, 271, 273
Loa loa, 237, 239, 273
Loiasis, 237
Lung, tropical eosinophilic, 257-259
Lymphatic filariases of man, 252-
    257
  lymphocyte transformation
    studies, 256-257
Lymphoid organ structure, African
    trypanosomiasis and, 173-
    174

M

Macrophages:
  African trypanosomiasis and, 198-
    199
  BCG and, 141-142
  malaria and, 107-108
  protective immunologic responses
    in Chagas' disease, 141-142
  responses to T-cell dependent
    manifestations of immunity,
    94-95
Major basic protein (MBP), 13
Malaria, immune responses in, 85-
    136
  active immunization against
    erythrocytic infections,
    108-110
  BCG and, 103-107, 109
  host-parasite relationship, 86-88
  macrophages and, 107-108
  PHA and, 112, 113
  to pre-erythrocytic infection, 110-
    112
  protective responses to erythro-
    cytic infections, 88-108
  regulatory responses, 112-121
Mansonella ozzardi, 237
Mansonelliasis, 237
Meriones unguiculatus, 231, 259-260
Merozoites, 86-87, 101
Microfilaremia, immunity to, 266-
    267
Mononuclear phagocytic system (MPS),
    107, 209
  African trypanosomiasis and, 171,
    173, 174, 186, 187, 198-
    199
  schistosomules and, 16-18
Mucocutaneous *Leishmania* infections,
    293-301

N

Natural killer (NK) cell system, 88,
    89, 105-107, 112
Neutrophils, schistosomules and, 16
Nippostrongylus brasiliensis, 193
Nonspecific immunity:
    activation of, 103-105
    eggs of schistosomes and, 50-51
    mediators of, 105-108

O

Ocular disease, 240-241
Onchocerca armillata, 252
Onchocerca cervicalis, 252
Onchocerca gibsoni, 252
Onchoserca gutturosa, 146-147,
    252
Onchocerca volvulus, 228, 231, 235,
    237-252, 257, 259, 269,
    270, 271, 273
Onchocerciasis, 237-252
    biology of, 237-238
    clinical characteristics, 239-241
    geographical considerations, 241-
    243
    immune responses, 246-247
    immunopathology of, 249-251
    protective responses, 247-249
    reactions to DEC, 243-245
Opsonic antibodies, protective im-
    munologic responses in
    Chagas' disease, 146-147

P

Parasitized red blood cells (PRBC),
    91, 93-94, 96, 102, 105,
    107-109, 114

Phytohemagglutinin (PHA):
    African trypanosomiasis and, 196,
    197, 200, 202
    Chagas' disease and, 149, 150,
    154
    filarial nematodes and, 247, 262
    malaria and, 112, 113
    schistosomiasis and, 6, 8, 35, 48, 49,
    50
Plaque-forming cell (PFC) activity,
    114, 115, 117, 118, 175, 193,
    197, 201, 204
Plasmodium berghei, 87, 88-93, 95,
    96, 98, 100, 102, 103, 106-
    116, 118, 120, 121
Plasmodium chabaudi, 87, 98, 110
Plasmodium cynomolgi bastianelli,
    110
Plasmodium falciparum, 86, 88,
    97-98, 100, 101, 102, 117,
    152
Plasmodium gallinaceum, 98
Plasmodium inui, 121, 122
Plasmodium knowlesi, 87, 100, 101,
    102, 107, 109
Plasmodium lophurai, 98
Plasmodium malariae, 86
Plasmodium ovale, 86
Plasmodium vinchei, 87, 98, 103,
    110
Plasmodium vivax, 86, 98, 102
Plasmodium yoelii, 87, 88-100, 102,
    103, 105-109, 112-115, 118-
    122
Pre-erythrocytic infection, immune re-
    sponse to, 110-112
Purified protein derivative (PPD),
    48, 154, 196, 197

R

Red blood cells (RBC):
    African trypanosomiasis and, 193
    Chagas' disease and, 150
    host-parasite relationship, 86-87
    hypergammaglobulinemia and,
        118
    parasitized, 91, 93-94, 96, 102,
        105, 107-109, 114
    protective responses to erythro-
        cytic infections and, 88, 90,
        99, 102, 105, 107, 108
Ribonucleic acid (RNA):
    Chagas' disease and, 148
    eggs of schistosomes and, 38

S

Schistosoma bovis, 7
Schistosoma haematobium, 2, 30, 31
    eggs of, 37, 40, 41, 42, 46
Schistosoma japonicum, 2, 7, 28, 29,
        30, 35
    eggs of, 37, 38, 40, 41, 42, 46, 49
Schistosoma mansoni, 2, 4-8, 10, 12,
        15, 17-21, 26-31, 34, 35
    eggs of, 37-44, 46, 47, 49, 50
    immunogenetics of, 51
Schistosoma mattheei, 7
Schistosoma rodhani, 7
Schistosomes, eggs of, 37-52
    antibodies and, 44-45
    antigens and, 38, 43-44
    cell-mediated responses, 44-45
    consequences and conjecture, 50-
        52
    granulomatous response, 40-42
    host-parasite relationship, 39-45

[Schistosomes, eggs of]
    induced granulomas, 42-43
    nonspecific immunity, 50-51
    pathogenesis of, 39-40
    regulation of responsiveness, 46-50
Schistosomiasis:
    acute, 28-29
    chronic, 29-30
    immune responses and immunoregu-
        lation, 1-83
    adult worms, 24-37
    cercariae, 2-8
    eggs of schistosomes, 37-52
    schistosomules, 8-24
Schistosomules, 8-24
    acquisition of refractoriness to im-
        mune attack, 21-23
    antigens and, 9
    antischistosomular effector mechan-
        isms and, 12-18
    eosinophils, 13-16
    lethal antibodies, 13
    mononuclear phagocytes, 16-18
    neutrophils, 16
    normal serum, 12-13
    host-parasite relationship, 9-18
    immune responses, 8-24
    lymphocyte stimulation, 12
    passive transfer, 19-20
    regulation of responsiveness, 18-
        23
    resistance of, 19-20
Setaria digitata, 233
Simulium damnosum, 238
Simulium naevei, 238
Simulium ochraceum, 238
Simulium spp., 238, 242, 251
Soluble egg antigens (SEA), 38, 44,
        45, 47-51
    reactions to, 43-44, 45

Staphylococcal protein A (SPA), 14
Streptokinase-streptodornase (SKSD),
    6
SWAP-induced responsiveness, 35

                        T

Trichinella spiralis, 15, 45, 232, 244,
    248
Tropical eosinophilic lung, 257-259
Trypanosoma brucei, 115-117, 168,
    171-173, 180-186, 188,
    189, 190, 192-196, 199-
    200, 202-204, 208
Trypanosoma congolense, 168, 169,
    173, 175, 176, 180, 183,
    185, 186, 188, 190, 191,
    194-197, 204, 205
Trypanosoma cruzi, 302, 304
    B cell responses to, 143-144
    detection and destruction of in-
        fected host cells, 151-152
    immunology of, 137-161
Trypanosoma dionisii, 147-148
Trypanosoma equiperdum, 180, 185,
    193, 196
Trypanosoma evansi, 180
Trypanosoma gambiense, 168, 169,
    173, 176, 177, 183-187,
    193, 194, 196, 197, 200
Trypanosoma lewisi, 143
Trypanosoma rhodesiense, 152, 168,
    169, 172, 173, 174, 176,
    177, 183-186, 188, 190,
    191, 197, 198, 200, 204, 205

Trypanosoma simiae, 168
Trypanosoma vivax, 168, 195
Trypanosomiasis, African, see African
    trypanosomiasis

                        V

Variant-specific surface coat antigens
    (VSSA), 170-173, 177-
    185
    African trypanosomiasis and, 177-
        185, 188, 189, 190, 192,
        194, 195, 199, 206, 207,
        208
Visceral Leishmania infections, 301-
    304

                        W

Worms, adult, 24-37
    adaptation of, 267
    antigens and, 25-27
    host-parasite relationship, 27-33
    regulation of responses, 33-36
Wuchereria bancrofti, 229, 230, 231,
    233, 234, 235, 243, 252-259,
    267, 270, 271, 273

                        X

X-linked B-cell defect, 99